MW00612084

The Gods, Gemini, and the Great Pyramid

Written by JBowles
Gemini Books

The last clue came from 370 million year old coral of the Devonian period

The Twin Embryo
of Gemini

Gemini, *The Twins*, Not as we know it
today, but as it was when time began!

About the cover
Design layout and filming by
Blue Pencil Creative Group, Ltd., Mason, Michigan
The cover photograph is entitled
Allegory of Earth and Moon
Images copyright © 1997 PhotoDisc, Inc.

The author gratefully acknowledges the assistance provided by the "Asociación Maria Reiche," Nasca, Peru, in providing the photographs of the figures on the Nascan Plateau that are used herein. Without the photographic detail it may not have been possible to have solved the question of their origin!

Copyright © 1998 by JBowles

For information about permission to reproduce selections from this book, write to
Gemini, Permissions
P.O. Box 648
Grass Lake, Michigan 49240-0648

The Gods, Gemini, and the Great Pyramid
Published by James Bowles
Printed by Thomson-Shore, Inc.
Dexter, Michigan

Includes Bibliographical references.
1. Natural Catastrophe — 2. Great Pyramid —Giza, Egypt
Nasca, Peru — Alaska — Ancient Gods — Constellations of the Zodiac
3. Earthquake

ISBN 0-9666371-1-9

Table of Contents

Table of Contents (continued)

List of Illustrations

Chapter 13, *Thoth*

Chapter 14, *In the Land of Spreading Darkness*

Chapter 15, *The Whole of Manifestation*

Chapter 16, *The Lineage is Broken*

Chapter 22, *Means to Ends*

Appendix I, *Dr Yen's Centroid Analysis & The Author's Bending Moment Analysis*

Appendix II, *Spherical Trigonometry*

Appendix III, *Solution to the Nasca, Giza, Alaska relationship*

Appendix IV, *The Thickness of the Crust has no Bearing on the Final Outcome*

Appendix V, *The 11.5° Offset of the Geo-magnetic Axis.*

Photographs

List of Tables

1. The bracketed paragraph reference used here and other places throughout the book refer to numbered Articles quoted from R. O. Faulkner's *The Ancient Egyptian Pyramid Texts*.

Dedication and Prolog

This book is dedicated to my family, my wife Patty, and our four sons, David, Doug, Dana, and Duane, and to my faithful canine companion, The Moke, who spent many long hours beside my chair keeping me company while I was at the computer keyboard. They have all felt the pressures of its research and writing. I'm not sure that I'd ever do it again.

*****

There is no corner on the market of discovery. It is a field that is as open as all of outdoors, and it is not just for the scientist or the funded investigator, it is open to everyone. In fact, and in many ways, there are greater opportunities for discovery by the uninhibited individual, who knows his field, than there are for the tenured investigators who must toe the established line. Charles Hapgood, who we will quote many times in the upcoming chapters, wrote that it was his thought that "A scientist must know his field...and they must not be afraid of the imagination, but to let it lead them into new fields of thought."[1] Intuition, and that is what the imagination is all about, is a wonderful guide. It gets you started and it keeps you going, but it helps to have a friend along. In my case my friend is my dear wife and our adventure of discovery is going to take us to many parts of the world, Egypt, Peru, Alaska, Antarctica, Hudson Bay and beyond. My wife is with me on a trip that we take from Egypt to Peru in Chapter 11, *Alone on the Equator*...

> We are going to take an adventurous journey to Nasca. It will be an unusual journey through time and space...I have chosen my wife to be my traveling companion. I've not chosen her just because she is convenient, though of course she is, but because she is the type of person that you want at your side when your intuition is your only guide.

I'd started the research for this book with the intention of developing a workable explanation for those processes that, as Charles Hapgood expressed it, "...have been responsible for not only the ice ages, not only for the mountain ranges, but possibly for the very history of the continents and for all the principle features of the face of the earth,"[2] and I had as a further purpose the desire to find a new truth, a new set of authorities that would shed a brighter light on this very time worn subject. I was indeed fortunate to have been able to accomplish both goals. For not only, with the help of many, were we able to solve "...the mechanics of the ice ages, the mountain ranges, and the history of the continents..." but we discovered in ancient text, in terrestrial monuments, in sculptured landscape figures, and in the Constellations of the Zodiac, a chronicle so rich that it challenged our imagination. The chronicles took us back to a time when the North Geographic Pole was in Alaska...Egypt and Peru were both on the equator, and the Sphinx, for the only time in its aged history, faced due East.

We've been led to believe that the Constellations of the Zodiac are celestial conveniences used by astrologers for fortune telling. But nothing could be further from the truth. The twelve Zodiacal Constellations that lie on the orbital plane of the planets, are the extant evidence of a master plan that is as old as time itself. To the Ancients the orbital plane of the planets, ie., the ecliptic, was more than a celestial dimension, to them it was a *place*, they called it Ōn! And on Ōn is stored the sciences of the Ancients!

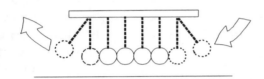

The concept of angular momentum and the Principle of Impulse and Momentum, is demonstrated by a toy that we can buy in a store.

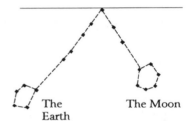

The Earth   The Moon

The Constellation of Pisces, depicts the age old agreement of Conservation of Angular Momentum between the earth and the moon.

The Gods, Gemini, and the Great Pyramid is about many things. It describes the formidable forces that shape earth's destiny.

We rotate, tilted at an angle of 23° 27', while the moon, pulling relentlessly at us, circles. With no change in time we orbit the sun and again we experience the relentless pull of gravity. The combined gravitational effects from the sun and the moon, and to a lesser extent that of the planets, pull at the crust from this oblique angle, relentlessly wearing the crust down until it is wrested from its moorings and fails from fatigue.

It sees in some ancient Peruvian sculptured figures the pictorial graphics that match in content some hieroglyphic text that was found inscribed on the walls of an ancient Egypt pyramid.

> (§ 1248) Atum is he who (once) came into being, (The primeval god who evolved from the Chaos.) who masturbated in Ōn.[1] He took his phallus in his grasp that he might create orgasm by means of it, and so...[1] (§1249) ...were born the twins Shu and Tefēnet!

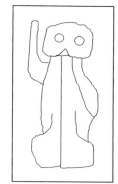

Atum Rēʕ. The ithyphallic Ghost of the Nasca Plateau

The Constellations of the Zodiac have been altered.

So who are *The Siamese Twins*? If you have begun to suspect that the *Twin Embryos*, the ever encircling twin sixes of Gemini, are the Twins Shu and Tefēnet then you have done extremely well! And if you further suspect that Shu and Tefēnet bestow their glory as the celestial twins, the Ecliptic, which spreads across the Heavens, and the Equator, which encircles the Earth, whose conjugation with the Sun, ie., with the Sun God **Atum Rēʕ**, ie., the Father, ie., the ithyphallic ghost, and that this conjunction chronicles the first day of Spring and the birth of a new year on earth...and the birth of man from Heaven at the vernal equinox, than...

In Chapter 14, we'll be discussing a most unusual concept. We are going to be looking at the Great Pyramid of Giza portrayed, not as a pyramid, but as a *triangle*. It will be from this perspective that many of the Pyramid's secrets will be revealed, and it will be from this perspective that we'll get corroboration of the ancient association between Giza, Nasca and the ancient Pole in Alaska. In Chapter 18 we'll be examining many more of the Pyramid's secrets, but for now lets just carry this image of a triangle in our mind as we explore the first of the wondrous secrets of the Great Pyramid of Giza. We're going to see why

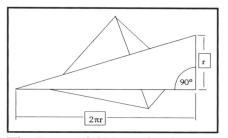

The Pyramidal Triangle, the Great Pyramid of Giza, and the Pi relationship.

---

[1] The term "on Ōn," as in "on-and-on," is made in reference to the everlasting Plane of the Ecliptic where the Constellations of the Zodiac encircle the sun and the earth. They are visible as stars at the distant borders of the ecliptic and they live Ōn and Ōn as the Imperishable Stars!

the Pi relationship was incorporated in the Pyramid's construction, and what substantiating proof exists. But first, turn to page 168 and read the middle paragraph and examine the accompanying *Symbol* of Cancer, there's a surprise in store for you there!

You will find the Ancients to be an amazing people. Who they were, where they came from, or whether they were Gods, near gods, or mere mortals such as we, we may never learn. But, there is no doubt, that they were something else! Lets look at the Constellation of Aquarius for a minute. Later we'll see that it illustrates a fight between Horus and Seth, but for now it will tell us where lightning comes from. Aquarius, *The Water Bearer,* carries ion saturated evaporates in sheets from the ocean waters where they collect in the clouds and burst in thunderous displays of lightning between the clouds. On other occasions the ion charges, in search of a discharge path from the clouds, or on occasion from the ground, send out leaders, called scouts, and when they find their target they discharge in a 50,000 degree fury of heat and destruction.

The Constellations of the Zodiac are a treasure of the sciences of the earth!

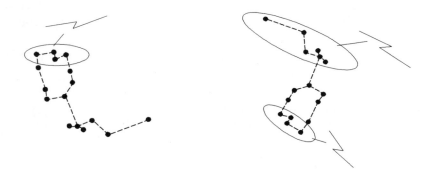

The Gods, Gemini, and the Great Pyramid, will take you to all these places and more!

1. Published by Savitria Press at AUM 2405 Ruscomb Lane, Baltimore. Md

2. Charles H. Hapgood, *Earth's Shifting Crust*, Pantheon Books, 1958. Pg. 314

Acknowledgments

Had it not been that my dad had urged me to find a solution to some of the unanswered questions left by Charles Hapgood in his book, *Earth's Shifting Crust*, I would never have thought the subject important, but I'd promised him I'd try. So in the early 1960's I took on the project. It was a fun project with one major disappointment. I was never to meet Charles Hapgood as he had died before I'd made enough progress to share my findings. In compensation perhaps, I decided to visit his home and the campus of Keene State College in New Hampshire where he taught. It was a fun visit that Beth was to call our nostalgia tour. Afterward she gave me her reflections of Charles...she titled them, *Some personal reflections on my cousin, collaborator, and friend Charles H. Hapgood.*

Charles (Charlie to me) never lost that childlike open eyed sense of wonder and curiosity about the world, a world he loved and enjoyed his whole lifetime. My favorite picture is of him leaning on his rake beside his great flower garden, where he did much of his private pondering while tending his many plants. He was interested and curious about rocks and plants, in oceans and creatures of all kinds, in people, and what it would be like to be anything any where. Always he felt that he had much to explore and discover and write about. There were many unanswered questions about life and this world, its many places and experiences to enjoy and savor ~~ To know Charles was to remember how his eyebrows shot up at a new idea, a new perspective, a new mystery. Always he listened intently, with an open mind and real interest, sometimes with a deep chuckle of amusement. He would use all of the available tools in his training to search out underlying truth, or something new and as yet unknown ~~ Always the sociable loner, he loved people but never really fit in or passively conformed to entrenched patterns of thought or behavior ~~ Always a pioneer on the frontiers of human thought and knowledge, he was not understood by many. He was a maverick in the college classroom. He included his students in seeking out the answers to certain mysteries or questions, not necessarily following a prepared curriculum. His students loved him, and were inspired by his way of challenging them and sharing with them ~~ Charles was never one to just piggyback on the work of others, though he always listened and studied their writings and thoughts. He was rather one to leapfrog and go a step beyond. And he never thought of his own discoveries as the final answers, but hoped others would share the adventure of his explorations and would leapfrog far beyond what he had discovered...He was my cousin, a collaborator, and a dear friend, with whom I shared many ideas, questions, life situations, and much more.

Benie to him, Beth, to everyone else.

xv

I want to extend a special thanks to Beth Hapgood because she helped me in a very meaningful way. When it came time to sit down and actually start writing, I discovered that I didn't know where or how to start. Some of the subject items that I'd wanted to include were even a little intimidating. But in June of 1996 Beth came to Michigan and we talked at length. "Jim", she said, "You are the only one who knows what you want to say, so sit down and say it. Be yourself. Tell your readers who you are and take them along on your adventure. But keep in mind that everyone has ideas of their own and you want to be sure to include even the most skeptical of your critics. So give them something to think about. Don't try to tell them how things are, they won't buy it, just tell them what you have discovered and let them make up their own minds." "One last thing," she said, "You want this to be a book that people will buy to put on their book shelf, not one that will end up in a garage sale, so write it with that in mind." So I must acknowledge Beth's support with the deepest of affection. But I want to leave it at that because I've said all that needs to be said.

My Beloved Wife Patty, Beth Hapgood, and Me!

My wife Patty, bless her heart, listened to my endless discussions about shifting crusts and Nascan figures, about Egyptian Hieroglyphics, and telepathic communication, about earthquakes, and isostasy, and ancient coral until her eyes glazed. But through it all she listened intently, read chapter after chapter, edited letter after letter, while never, as in never ever, complaining. While acknowledging her constant support, I want to leave it at that, because it says all that I need to say.

I also want to acknowledge the help given to me by a friend, Phil Troyer. When I met him he was working at a computer store, and he sold me my first computer, a toy now, but it was what I needed at the time. It was a first edition IBM 286, and it got me started. Phil and I spent many mornings and late nights talking. I wasn't working on this book at the time, but our conversations were enlightening, even though he kept telling me that he was not a scientist. No matter, he had common sense and he'd guide the conversations around to the pertinent issues each time. So to Phil, a special thanks!

As I wanted aerial photographs of the figures on the *pampa*, I contacted the Consulate General of Peru in Chicago. Their reply, dated August 21, 1996, directed me to an organization in Peru called Promperu which, they said..."...is the institution in charge of promoting abroad the image of Peru." From there it was a small step to the Asociación Maria Reiche in Nazca, Peru, and a young worker by the name of Mariana Navarro-Grav with whom I had many pleasant exchanges and obtained the photographs that I sought. My association with Mariana was very brief, but her enthusiasm over the figures on the Nascan plateau equaled mine, and her concerns for their preservation is a voice that is seldom heard. So not only do I acknowledge her help, but I acknowledge her concerns as well, and hope that this book brings a better understanding for the historical value of this most remarkable monument and moves us all to preserve it.

She wrote regarding the Nazca figures...

Jim, ... This past weekend I was in Nazca. I am not sure if you told me that you have seen the figures in the pampa.[1] Well anything that I could tell you is little, or nothing. The landscape of the figures, lines & geometric drawings is indescribable, or I do not know the words to tell you. It is magical, surreal but real, I don't know. This was my first time there & the impression that the 'pampa' has landed on me is indescribably deep & strong. Since I came back, on Sunday, I haven't been able to sleep well. I think that I am fascinated & obsessed at the same time. Also it hurts me to think that destruction of the figures goes on & not enough is being done to stop

---

[1] I have not.

it. I hope people are sensitive enough to respond. There are <u>so</u> many unknown drawings, small, hidden, here & there. There is so much to study & know yet. ... I am so grateful to be close to this monument. Regards, *Mariana*

So to her too, a special thanks.

Mariana Navarro-Grav in Sapa, Vietnam
with a woman from the H'mone Tribe

INTRODUCTION, Part 1.   From Apollo to Monadnock!

Part One of *The Gods, Gemini, and the Great Pyramid,* is an excursion into the process of discovery. It will take you from a time when radio played upon our imagination, a time when we all thought that breakfast food was something that we had to eat before we could go outdoors and become a hero.[A] It will take you from there to the discovery of the processes that officiate over the catastrophic episodes of rejuvenation that visit upon the earth with shattering magnitude and unrecorded regularity. We will introduce you to the principle actor in these processes. We call it Rotational-Bending, not a memorable name to be sure, but I don't know what else to call it because Rotational-Bending is what it is. Here is an explanation:

Rotational-Bending is the physical process imposed on an object, in this case the earth, by the combination of the effects of a force which causes the object to bend while it is simultaneously in rotational motion. A good example can be made in reference to a rotisserie spit. As you can imagine, if we were to cook something that is too heavy for the spit, the spit will break. It breaks because the internal stresses induced by the bending are being chased around by the rotation. From tension to compression and back again in a destructive fatiguing manner. That is the situation in the case of the earth's crust as well, except rather than the crust failing because it is "too heavy", it is instead a matter of dealing with **time**. Time is the controlling factor here because the earth rotates on its axis 24 hours a day, year after year, millennium after millennium, endlessly – and where such repeated cycling exists, objects, in this case the earth, can fail from fatigue at very low stress levels. The crust simply wears out over time, and fails!

We rotate, tilted at an angle of 23° 27', while the moon, pulling relentlessly at us, circles. With no change in time we orbit the sun and again we experience the relentless pull of gravity. The combined gravitational effects from the sun and the moon, and to a lesser extent that of the planets, pull at the crust from this oblique angle, relentlessly wearing the crust down until it is wrested from its moorings and fails from fatigue. We're being torn apart. It is from the effects of Rotational-Bending that a weakening bond in a zone

---

[A]The idea of a breakfast food "being something that we had to eat before we could go outdoors and become a hero" was broadcast in a 1941 radio program written by Norman Corwin, called *Radio Primer*.

1

just below the crust called the "plastic zone"[1] forms and allows the crust to separate from the inner mantle. Once the inner ties between the crust and the inner mantle are broken, centrifugal forces acting on the great masses of ice at the poles move the crust in a crashing search for equilibrium. Eventually stability is found and the event comes to a halt, but the effects are devastating. The most devastating are the waters. Hundred mile an hour walls of ocean water sweep the latitudes killing everything in their wake. The destruction is beyond our imagination, but there have been survivors.

A different characterization of the same event, sees celestial gravitational sources at work preparing the crust, and controlling earth's processes until at last the relentless forces prevail and the crust moves. The fatiguing preparations put into the crust and its eventual failure, culminated by a catastrophic shift goes on with a conspicuous measure of regularity. It will repeat as long as we are in orbit, and for as long as we are able to see the sun and the moon in the sky. So by the very nature of our circumstance, the cyclic process of regeneration is built-in. The process creates new mountains, new rivers, new fertilizing volcanic dusts for the fields and prairies, and, unfortunately, new people. Rotational-Bending is a built-in process for earth's regeneration. Without this frequent upheaval the mountains would have been worn down to so much rubble and the waters would have taken over the landscape.

Richard Noone has written a captivating book called *5/5/2000, Ice: The Ultimate Disaster,*[2] wherein he suggests that the conjunction of the earth with the sun, the moon, and the planets on May 5, 2000 (5/5/2000), was going to bring about another catastrophic movement of the earth's crust. This one unfortunately in our life time. I called him after reading the book, feeling free to do so because we had a mutual friend in the co-conspirator of this book, Beth Hapgood, and I conveyed my feelings, basically that I agreed in principle with his theory, but that I hoped that he was wrong about the date. He gave me no assurances one way or the other, so we'll just have to wait and see.

I hope that you enjoy the adventures of discovery that you are about to embark upon and do not come to think that our casualness in its presentation weighs heavy on our credibility. For it is our belief, both Beth Hapgood's and mine, that discovery is in part a function of our frame of mind. That the capacity to approach a new challenge and develop new ideas stems from the values that we were taught as children when we were allowed to discover freely for ourselves. So we will present what we have discovered with that same feeling of enjoyment that we bore as we sought the answers when we were younger. With that we will proceed!

Chapter 1

Living and Non-Living Creatures

I grew up in urban Detroit in the '30's and '40's. It was quite an adventure. The city was still in a "pre-modern" growing stage and there was an abundance of vacant lots on which to build forts and tree houses, and there were new houses under construction every where, or so it seemed, so it was easy to get good scrap wood and nails and stuff. The workmen knew the value of scrap wood for building forts and tree houses and so they'd set what they had in a pile separated from the good stuff each night so we'd know what was ours to get. There was an unwritten code of honor that we all obeyed which read that we weren't to touch the good wood. But that was fine, because you can't make a decent fort out of "good wood" anyway. Besides, honoring this code led to a kind of kinship between the neighborhood kids and the workmen so that when we needed something special, like a certain piece of wood, or more nails, or something, we could go to the "new house" and one of the workers would take time out and look around and try to get what we needed. Sometimes they'd even cut a board "to length" for us.

The forts were generally made in the ground by digging several holes, usually 3 to 4 feet across and 3 feet deep, and connecting them with narrow trenches, then we'd cover everything over with boards and conceal the maze with dirt and weeds. We went to great pain to conceal the fort opening with brush and other invisible making material so that even a woodchuck couldn't find it. The test came when we would get some grown-up, usually someone's mom, to go out into the field and challenge them to find the fort. In retrospect, I can see that a fort would have been visible from 500 feet away, but I don't remember anyone's mom being able to find one.

You could put all kinds of things in a fort, and make all kinds of conveniences. They all had periscopes, and floor and wall coverings made of cardboard. Secret compartments were everywhere to store supplies. But the real genius was displayed in the armaments and the provisions made for defense of the fort. In this department the advantage clearly went to those whose dads had workshops. I was fortunate, my dad had a workshop in the

3

basement so I was able to make all sorts of good things. The major item of defense was a Roman style shield that we made from a garbage can cover. They were best when we removed the handle from the top surface and attached it on the underside. This let the edge of the shield curve around toward us the way they were supposed to.

The periscopes were used to spy on the "enemy" as they approached. This so that we, "The Defenders of Right and Justice for All," were ready when they got there. If we weren't ready we had to let them know and they were supposed to stop their advance. Usually they did, and there was no problem and the war was re-scheduled. Sometimes they were impatient and that situation usually ended up with the war being called off and the offended side going home. You weren't supposed to cheat, and having war before the other side was ready was clearly cheating.

The offensive weapons, although they weren't called that, in fact I don't remember that they even had a name, were usually rubber band guns. The best of course were those that shot rubber bands cut from inner tubes. Best that is in appearance, in performance they were terrible because inner tube rubber didn't stretch very well and they didn't go very far. But they looked formidable. Besides, in those days all gas stations had piles of used inner tubes so getting ammunition was no problem. The next best thing to a rubber band gun was a sling shot, particularly in late summer when the crab apple's were plentiful. A good crab apple was red and about half an inch in diameter and would go clear across the street when fired from a good sling shot. Sling shots had their down side though because if anyone in the neighborhood got hurt from one it would be the end of the sling shots for the season. Parents ruled with a heavy hand in those days and we had to be careful. The first line of punishment was not being allowed to go out and play. The second was being sent to your room. Third, and this was worse than anything, was not being allowed to listen to the radio. Forth was being taken out behind the wood shed as it was called. So it was smart not to hurt anyone with those sling shots.

People today cannot imagine how powerful radio was. Programs like the Lone Ranger, Jack Armstrong, and I Love a Mystery, with Jack, Dock, and Regey, which started with a bell tolling the time of day in some remote region of Tibet, and others like Gang-Busters and The Shadow, were absolute musts. Missing one of those radio programs was a tragedy beyond description. Radio created its own reality by stimulating the imagination. It could take you into worlds that television can only think of. Even the message that radio conveyed to the audience was different. Jack Armstrong was "..the all American boy." Superman worked for "Truth, Justice, and the American way," and The Lone Ranger shot the gun out of the hand of the bad guy with silver bullets, and radio advertisers like Wonder Bread "...built strong bodies 12 ways." Radio was like that, it created morality, so it was no wonder that the mock wars that we staged in the neighborhood could end with the warring parties going home if the opposing party cheated, "... because you weren't supposed to cheat, and having war before the other side was ready was clearly cheating." Honor was important and it was never compromised for the sake of winning. It was a time when the day would start when we would go over to a friend's house, and while standing out on the sidewalk we'd holler out our friend's name. "Roy! Roy! Come out and play." It never occurred to anyone to go up to the door and knock. You only did that for grown-ups. If your friend couldn't come out they'd open a window and holler back. If they could come out, they'd still open a window and hollered back. We all had telephones, but that just wasn't the way it was done. Some things were sacred.

For instance, you never broke up anyone's fort. But somehow tree houses were different. They were demolished regularity and the only defense was to make them look unworthy of demolition. This wasn't easy because often as not a tree house was the center of all planning and it was difficult to hide its importance. Tree houses had two levels of activity. The highest perch was really a lookout and the lower level was the tree house itself where meetings and things were held. There were storage boxes for essential supplies like food, spying equipment, and the paper and pencils that were needed to take notes. Another thing, tree houses always had elaborate block and tackle systems for raising and lowering supplies, but for some reason they never seemed to work just right.

No one ever built a tree house in just any old tree. They were built in trees first that had bushes around them so they couldn't be found, and they had to have the right kind of branches, and the trunk had to be bare up to about 10 feet from the ground. At this 10 foot point there had to be at least two branches that spread out in a horizontal "V." This was for the platform to set on. Above this there had to be branches that grew from the trunk at regular intervals so that you could climb up to the lookout. It is clear that there could only be one tree in the whole world that had everything right. Houses built in other trees were clearly in violation of this "code of necessity" and they could be torn down by anyone who could find them. That's what made tree houses different from forts.

On really good days everybody got together and went on hikes. First you had to pack your supplies. These usually consisted of a sandwich of some sort, a canteen of water, a pocket knife and a compass. You could go anywhere on a hike. The favorites were to the gravel pit, the boulevard, or to the pond. The boulevard was the second best. It had rows of bush covered "islands" going down the middle of the road that had to be explored.

The uncontested favorite of all time, however, was the pond with its crawdads and cat tails, and other plants and small animal life. There was no end to the fascination of a pond, and there were hundreds of them around Detroit. Every neighborhood had at least one or two that needed exploring. Our hikes, regardless of the original destination, always ended up at a pond. Sometimes we'd take a crawdad home and set it up in an aquarium with a turtle, or any other good thing that we could find in the pond.

This fascination started a whole new adventure. My folks gave me a chemistry set, which seemed like the right thing to have but which I never learned to use for good purpose, and they gave me a microscope and a book called *Wonders of Living Things*. The book, which sits on the shelf in front of me even now, was published in 1945 by Metro Publications in New York. It doesn't seem to have an author at least none is listed anywhere in the book. The various sections are titled, Wonders of Life, Wonders of Plant Life, Wonders of Animal Life, etc.

The true wonder of the book is in the title of the first chapter, **LIVING AND NON-LIVING CREATURES** written in bold capitol print just as I have written it here. The portion of the title, "....NON-LIVING CREATURES" has held me captive for all the many years that I've had the book. The obvious question that it raises has never been satisfactorily answered, "What was meant by "non-living creatures?" The opening paragraphs read like this...

> All the objects in the world can be divided into two distinct and definite classes–the living and the non-living. The living vary enormously in shape, size and behavior, and though they are in their turn divided into two great classes, the plants and the animals, there are at certain points no clear distinctions between animals and plants. In other words there are lowly living creatures of which it is difficult to say definitely whether they should be classed as animals or plants.
>
> But the distinction between living and non-living objects is definite and distinct. A non-living object sometimes behaves as though it had life, but it is never mistaken by scientists for a living object.

My idea of a non-living creature at the time was like a whirlpool in a stream, or a dust devil in the barn yard. These give every indication of being alive, although I knew that they were not. But as a youngster it sufficed to think so and it turned into a game to find all the non-living creatures that I could find that looked alive. Strangely enough I found some really good ones. My favorite was what looked like water evaporating from the road on a hot summer day. It was particularly obvious on lightly rolling roads. What it really is, of course, is the heated air gyrating upward and distorting the image of the road. But that explanation wasn't near as much fun as saying that it was evaporating water. These special things always caused me to marvel at life and seek out neat answers to these "non-living creatures."

In 1969 I came across a small paperback written by Joseph V. Kopp entitled *Teilhard de Chardin, A new Synthesis of Evolution*. In this book Joseph V. Kopp explained how Chardin dealt with the topic of "non-living creatures." I was fascinated with his explanation as it contained a totally different point of view from anything I had thought of and I think it's worth a critique, so here, in paraphrase, are some of Chardin's thoughts as interpreted by J. V. Kopp...

> The whole world is continually changing. Everything in the world originated from an arrangement of a few elements and transforms itself according to a law of increasing "complexification." The material of the world has a propensity driving it from the simple to the complex.

> This cosmic phenomenon has only one sufficient, logical explanation, which Chardin calls the within of things, (this *within*, or *consciousness*) becomes visible, measurable, or capable of scientific confirmation only when (it reaches) a certain degree of intensity.

> In man... the evidence of a "within" or "consciousness" is immediately obvious and undisputed. Neither can we dispense with this "within" when considering the behavior of the vertebrates. Even the conduct of insects and coelenterates, (jellyfish, hydras, coral, etc.) cannot be explained without a "within." ...The further we go down the scale, the more difficult it becomes to establish the existence of this "within."

> Bacteriologists, physicists and chemists, only deal with the "without" of their subjects because, due to its low intensity, the "within" is no longer significant. ...the whole physical world contains a psyche...but in different concentrations.

> We have no right, therefore, to limit the origin of this "within" or consciousness to where we can first prove it. Accordingly, an intrinsic part of the "within" of cosmic matter is a force that drives the universe toward an ever more complex and centralized state...[1]

Accepting the thought of everything transforming to the more complex in accordance with Chardin's "...law of increasing complexification," is easy because that's what birth, and maturity, rust and erosion are all about, but I have to think a long time about inanimate objects having a "within" or a "consciousness." But who knows?[a]

KICK-THE-CAN AND QUEEN MU

Come late evening it was outside again for a local version of the game of "kick-the-can." Kick-the-can was a special version of "Hide-and-Seek." The game involved an "evil-one" who would cover their eyes and count to ten while everyone else went and hid. Then the evil-one would go around trying to find everyone to disclose their hiding place.

The object for those in hiding was to stay hidden until they could run in and "kick the can." This act got them in "free" and kept there hiding place secret. If we didn't have a can to kick we'd play regular "Hide-and-Seek" using a tree as "home" and, instead of kicking a can, we'd run in yelling "Olly Olly Oxen Cart" and touch the tree before we were caught. One evening after a late game of Hide-and-Seek my dad showed me a book that he had entitled, *Queen Moo and the Egyptian Sphinx*,[2] which was written in 1896 by Augustus Le Plongeon. In it my dad had discovered that Hide-and-Seek had been played by the ancient Mayans in the Yucatan thousands of years ago. The Mayans, however, would run in saying "Ilil ilil xaxbe." "Make room for one to pass...evil one," instead of, "Olly Olly Oxen Cart" as we did. Well after discovering this neat bit of history I started saying, admittedly to everyone's acute irritation, "Ilil ilil xaxbe," about everything, and to everybody. But soon everyone was saying it even if we weren't playing Hide-and-Seek...so it all ended well.

I don't know what ever happened to my dad's book, *Queen Moo and the Egyptian Sphinx*, I was never able to find it when I wanted it, but I always wondered how an ancient Mayan game like Hide-and-Seek managed to find its way to Detroit.

a. The grandest measure of Chardin's "...law of increasing complexification," is laid out in obvious form in the Periodic Chart where increasing numbers of electrons, protons, neutrons, etc., define the respective atoms. These in turn join to make molecules, which in turn join to make up everything that we know to exist!

Chapter 2

The Book!

We had some huge rocks in the back yard. The biggest ones were three to four feet across. They just lay there on top of the ground. One thing about them was clearly noticeable, they attracted lightning. It was a place you wanted to steer clear of during a thunder storm. I never knew why they attracted lightning like they did, and asking my folks or the teachers at school never produced any kind of an answer. Another question about them that always nagged at me was why they stayed on top of the ground when all the other stones around seemed to sink. *Wonders of Living Things* did offer an explanation on page 95 for why other stones would sink.

> (Charles) Darwin covered part of a field near his house with broken pieces of chalk and with infinite patience left this undisturbed for years. At the end of his study period Darwin examined the field, and found that a layer of chalk existed seven inches below the surface. This he attributed to the excavating work of worms.

> The work of the earthworm in burying stones and other objects that lie on the surface of the ground is almost incredible. Some of the great monoliths or upright stones at Stonehenge which had fallen to the ground had through the ages been partially buried by the work of earthworms. The creatures burrow underneath, and the ground sinks, taking the stone with it.

It bothered me at the time that the explanation that *"Wonders"* gave, which accounted for chalk and the monolithic stones of Stonehenge didn't recognize that other objects, like the boulders in my backyard, would stay on top of the ground. Why didn't they sink? The only thing that I could figure was that perhaps the lightning that these stones seemed to attract killed all the worms! But why didn't gravel and other pebble sized objects sink? It seemed to me that we really had a selective mechanism here. Stones got

9

partially buried by the work of earthworms only when the stones weren't influenced in a stronger way by something else. But what was that something else? I am going to come back to what I think that *something else* is later, but at the time that I was pondering the question of the stones my attention shifted to a tree in our back yard. It was an oak, and it had a long limb that hung 30 feet horizontally out across the yard. My dad always said that it bothered him to mow the grass under that limb, what with all the lightning that occurred in the yard because he was afraid that sometime it would be weakened and it would come tumbling down on him. So he had it cut off. I had a different perspective on that particular 30 foot limb. When I had nothing else to do I'd go out to the very end of it and take hold of the smallest part of the branch I could find, I'd hold it between two fingers and lift it. It would flex upward under this light force to a point as high as I was able to reach. One day I got a ladder and I climbed up and took hold of one of those slender branches and lifted it up several feet. The absolutely amazing part of it was that this limb, which at the trunk end was almost a foot and a half in diameter, bent upward, starting from the trunk, all the way out to where I was holding it. It didn't bend just at the end where I was holding it mind you, but it would bend all the way back to the trunk. Try it yourself some time it's amazing, the whole limb will lift with the greatest of ease! Hey! You talk about Superman!

But the day that limb was cut and it came thundering to the ground things changed for me, forever. I told the tree cutter that I was so strong that I could lift that whole limb with one hand and if he'd come around to the small end I'd show him. I flexed my muscles to show off a little and pretended to brace myself and went to lift the tree limb. But devastation of all devastations, the small branch responded as before but the main part of the limb wouldn't budge. He acknowledge my effort with a smile and said, "That's pretty good," but I was stunned. Why didn't that limb lift as easily while on the ground as it did when it was on the tree? As usual asking at home or at school didn't produce an answer, I just got muttering's about live and dead weight. About this time I noticed that it was getting increasingly more common that the "authorities" had no answers for all my discoveries, and I was coming to figure that I was discovering things that no one else knew about and so now each new discovery became pretty important. But things change, and now there was something that I'd found that was a lot more important than lifting that dumb limb.

Trees and other plants did a truly amazing thing. When ever a new tree or flower, or anything else would start to grow, the sprout would always grow upward while the roots would grow down. I never understood how they knew which way to grow so I was anxious to see what The Book had to say about it. I knew that I was going to be greatly disappointed if The Book gave me one explanation for what made roots of a plant grow down, and another, unaffiliated reason, for why stems grew up! But I wasn't to be disappointed because The Book said...

> The interesting and fascinating fact is that the root never grows upward and the stem never grows downward. If they come out of the seed pointing in the wrong direction they turn around and take the right course. Why? Scientists tell us that the plant has a sense of direction just as we ourselves have. We always know which end of us is up. We feel the pull of the Earth, and the growing seedling is the same. The tiny cells in the growing tips of the plant contain loose granules of starch and these always lie on the side of the cell which is toward the Earth. The plant only grows normally when the starch grains lie on the proper side of the cell.

Then The Book added...

> When growing seedlings are rotated on a disc in an experiment the resultant centrifugal force, (which creates an outward directed force...opposite to that of gravity, but sufficient for this experiment) pulls them continually in one direction just as gravity would have pulled at them in the ground...after several hours of rotation the roots will have grown away from the center of the disc, (ie., they are pulled toward the centrifugal force), while the stems turn toward the center...

> It is not the force or the pull of gravity which acts directly on the plant and causes the roots to grow in a downward direction...or the stem to grow upwards. Instead it is a property called geotropism, which means "earth turning." Gravity merely initiates a stimulus in the plant, it is acting on the granules of starch to tell the plant what to do.

Great! This explanation of gravity merely initiating a stimulus in the plant to grow the roots and the stems in their respective and proper directions made sense to me, and it meant that both the roots and the stem responded to the same stimulus.

Now, it seemed The Book was psychic, because it answered a question that I hadn't asked yet. "Why do the branches of a tree grow uniformly in all directions?" In school I was told that plants grew upward to seek the sun. But that answer would suggest that trees were sensitive to latitude, such that the branches would have a tendency to grow toward the South in the Northern hemisphere, and toward the North in the Southern hemisphere...that would give the greatest exposure to the sun it would seem. But it was clear to me that trees didn't grow that way. Instead, I knew them to grow symmetrically regardless of sun, latitude, or climate. But now, with this stimulus explanation, I could see that branches grew outward away from the trunk in a symmetrical pattern because of the centralizing influence of gravity. So the sun, unless the tree was shaded, didn't have anything to do with it. The equal distribution of the limbs was just a natural consequence of the uniform nature of gravity. Good for The Book! But there was still something that puzzled me. I knew that plants that are set in the sun in an orientation different from their previous setting will turn toward the sun...so I wondered whether we were looking at something different here? Again The Book.

Green leaves turn toward the light as we may prove by placing pots of growing plants near a window. In a very short time the leaves will be found to have turned into such positions as to enable them to receive the greatest sunshine...on the same tree the leaves are very often arranged differently on different branches in order that the maximum of light and air may be obtained.

Many of the leaves have the power of changing their position at different times of the day and night in order to accommodate themselves to varying conditions of light and temperature. It is by the oxidation of food materials within the plant that the energy used in growth and movement is released. The food is the product of the sun's rays which provides the energy for the manufacture of starch from water and carbon dioxide which is used in turn to build the plant. The process is called photosynthesis.

So when the leaves turn toward the light of the sun they are actually responding to a stimulus. In this case initiated by the sun. So things were still not "different" as I was hoping. They were the same! Good! The growth of the roots and stems, and the trunks and limbs, were stimulated by gravity, and the leaves grew in response to sun light. So, if I wanted to, I could test to see how many different stimuli might exist that the plant would respond to. I knew about gravity and sunlight now, but...

Some leaves which receive only a scanty supply of water often preserve it by rolling up so that the evaporating surface is on the inside of the roll. In some cases like the cowberry, the roll is permanent; in other cases, such as in maize (ie., corn) the leaf rolls up only when the weather is dry and unrolls again later when water is more plentiful.

So a shortage of water could stimulate the plant to respond too! These were all important

12

discoveries, and the single explanation, that plants were responding to an external stimuli in all cases, as they grew up, or down, or acted to acquire or conserve moisture, made all the sense in the world and I didn't have to be a genius to understand it. But while this was all pretty interesting, my all time greatest discovery was waiting to be made at our summer place on the lake.

There were a lot of power boats on this particular lake and during the course of a few hours they would rile the water so much that it would be murky for days, but if there should be a thunder storm with a lot of lightning, the lake would turn crystal clear. This was really pretty amazing because during a storm the wind would churn the waters up far more than the boats would have ever thought of doing. I recall watching a thunder storm through the protection of a window in our cottage one time when the wind came across the lake in gusts so strong that the waves would break from the water and be mixed with the rain in sheets a dozen feet high. I was able to see the bottom of the lake in the depression behind the gusting wind. But after the storm the water was so clear it would make a person thirsty. Now why all that storm generated turmoil wouldn't have left the waters as opaque as mud I never figured out as a kid, but I suspected that the lightning, or the accompanying ground currents must have had something to do with it.

It wasn't until May of 1995 that I was to find out why lightning cleared the waters. The answer appeared in the May 6, 1995 issue of Science News.

> Researchers at the Massachusetts Institute of Technology's Plasma Fusion Center are now testing a novel furnace in which a huge high-voltage electric spark between graphic electrodes creates a high-temperature plasma of ions and electrons. The intense heat in the vicinity of this arc melts the waste material and destroys organic molecules.[1]

Well! A high-temperature plasma of ions and electrons is exactly what lightning is all about. Voltages get up to thousands of volts, no problem, and temperatures within the sheath surrounding the lightening bolt itself are easily in excess of 50,000 degrees F. It was nice to have that problem solved! But as explained by Stuart A. Hoenig, an electrical engineer at the University of Arizona, Tucson, the most ingenious use of this electrical phenomenon was demonstrated by the Germans during World War II.

> The German Navy sought to garage some U-boats along the French coastline. But first it had to drain small portions of the wetlands long enough to sink the concrete footings needed to support the submarine pens...they did this by sinking

metal rods into the soil and applying small electric currents to them. The currents effectively drove the water out of the area where footings were to be laid.[2]

German Engineers told him that this use of electro-osmosis was fairly common. Indeed, he recalls their telling him that Hitler's army applied currents to the tracks of tanks in its Eastern campaign so that the vehicles could maneuver through the normally untraversable muck that characterizes Russia's spring thaw.

GROWING AMBITION

My life's ambition now after all these adventures was to become an engineer. As a 12 year old, I envisioned this to mean that I would be designing things like bridges and cars and I would be learning how everything worked. I imagined that I would be able to make or fix anything. That idea was pretty exciting and I really wanted to become an engineer. That ambition came closer to reality when my family moved from Detroit to East Lansing, Michigan in 1945. Michigan State University, or Michigan State College as it was called then, was in East Lansing and the campus was going to be just across the street. But I hadn't started high school yet, so I had a long time to go.

Chapter 3

From Apollo to Monadnock!

I entered High School in the fall of 1945. The school offered two general lines of study, one was 'general academics' which prepared the student for work right out of high school and the other was a 'college prep' program which was geared more toward college academics and contained more science and math courses. The college prep program was clearly what I needed if I was to follow an engineering career. I would like to say that I was an excellent student graduating at the head of my class with all A's, but that would be too far from the truth. I can say this though, the school had no quarrel with parents if they held a student back from moving on to the next grade, or holding them back from graduating for that matter if the student hadn't genuinely met the academic standards set by the school. But I graduated on schedule in June of 1951, and entered Michigan State College as a freshman that Fall so that must say something.

Unfortunately, the first year of college wasn't any easier for me than high school was. Course study at MSU was structured on a term basis with four terms per academic year and it was typical for a first term freshman to take 16 hours of class study, with an additional 2 hours of physical fitness, and an hour of Army Reserve Officer Training, (ROTC.[1]) An engineering student would therefore be taking anywhere between five to eight different classes per term of pre-scheduled course study. This was a lot of diversity and required real concentration...something that I was not prepared for at this time.

The obstacle that really kept me stumbling my freshmen year was my old nemeses, "The need to know the real reason why things were the way they were." I would spend far too much time solving problems because I kept looking for that unifying principle so that I could catagorize the specifics of the material, but there was just too much and I was lost from the start. The courses I was taking weren't taught in a fashion that would get to the point quickly and simply like I was needing them to, and worse, the books weren't written that way either. Frankly I was having a terrible time. What I needed was a method to over come my self imposed obstacle course. Unfortunately the answer wasn't

15

to come to me for a while. Besides, the Korean War had been going on for a few years by this time, and since I wasn't doing very well in college, and since I was getting restless and irritated anyway, I enlisted in the army, got married, got assigned to a unit in Korea, and went overseas, in that order.

If nothing else the army experience had a settling effect, or maybe it was that I was married, in any case, after I returned I re-entered the School of Engineering at Michigan State and this time it was a good deal easier. MSU was an excellent school. Not overly large, it had a rigorous program, a beautiful campus, and an excellent staff. It was almost fun, but as favorable as it was, by the time that forth year rolled around I was needing to start something new.

After graduation I went to work as a design engineer for a company that manufactured fuel and hydraulic system components for aerospace and the civilian industrial markets. The space program was in full swing and America was looking to go to the moon and Apollo and Saturn-5 were going to take her there. Apollo was the multi-sectioned manned spacecraft that went to the moon, and Saturn-5 was the multi-engined first stage launch vehicle. It took seven and a half million pounds of thrust to lift Apollo off the ground, so five Saturn-C3 engines, each producing a million and a half pounds of thrust, were cluster in a single functional unit as the first stage to accomplish the task.

This company was bidding on some NASA contracts for fuel and hydraulic components to be used on the C3 engine and they needed engineers. So my first assignment after joining them was to "work up" a proposal to include the design and development of a series of fluid components. This required that I create detail and assembly drawings of the parts involved, make a prototype, and write-up test procedures and test the prototype. Throughout this proposal development time I would be preparing estimates on schedules for the manufacture, test, and delivery of the production parts.

The procedure that a company went through to obtain a NASA contract in the first place had an appeal all to itself. Here's what we had to do. First NASA would provide a description of what they needed in a public bulletin called a "Request-to-Bid." I only saw the *Request-to-Bid* for the small components that we produced, but I imagine there was one out for the entire spacecraft. If it was within a company's interest to bid, they would send representatives from sales and engineering to a bidding conference to hear a detailed presentation of the system requirements. The next step was to go back to the company, and in our case because the parts we bid on were small, we would design the parts, make detail drawings, develop a test program, and price and submit the proposal all within a two week period, 14 days! Not a lot of time, but that was all we had so we had to think clear and fast. That was one of the things that made the moon program so exciting. There was a lot of hype associated with the Apollo program and everybody was enthusiastic. I had the fortunate opportunity to examine one of the C3 engines up close when I was in California for a design review meeting with the prime engine contractor. The engine was standing alone in a large room with a stair that went up to a catwalk that surrounded it. It's insufficient to say that the engine was impressive, but how else do you describe a single engine capable of producing a million and a half pounds of thrust all by itself? It's just as difficult to describe the emotion that is felt...because it's a mixture of many things. Awe, humility, pride, excitement, but perhaps more than anything...it's sobering! It is easy to describe the sobering part. I was on the catwalk that surrounded the engine, and right there at eye level were two Champion spark plugs. Henry Ford would have loved that moment, sobering as it was, because here as the source of ignition for the engine that was parent to the highest level of hype since bubble gum, were two spark plugs. You have to love the thought. It took a spark plug to ignite the engine that was going to the moon. You can't get any more basic than that.

I never saw a launch myself other than on television, so my enthusiasm for seeing what seven and a half million pounds of thrust looked like was never satisfied. But those that I know that did get up close told me that it was not the towering size of the vehicle, or the power that was being unleashed that impressed them, instead they said, the awesome presence of Apollo came from the thunder of the engines that immersed the scene during the launch and for many long minutes after it was out of sight.

It was just a fun program to work on. But as much fun as it was, and as much influence as this experience was to have on everything else I did throughout my engineering career, it was going to be the gift that my father gave me on the day that I graduated from college that was going to have the greatest impact on my life.

My father was a dentist in Detroit, as was his father before him. My grandfather had served as President of the Michigan Dental Association for a number of years and had been quite active socially and professionally. My father on the other hand tended to be more studious and sedate and he spent a lot of time just developing his dental practice. In his spare time he would work on new products for use in dentistry. He was particularly proud of three products that he had developed and introduced. One was a compound of bee's wax that was used in the molding process that made gold fillings. It melted and reformed at temperatures well suited for the dental office. Another was an articulating "jaw" mechanism that was used to align dentures for evaluating "fit." The

17

third item was a packet of X-ray film. The packets were small and easily handled. They were about an inch and a half on a side and a sixteenth of an inch thick. Their advantage was that they replaced a bulkier, more difficult to handle, film pack.

Dad loved to read. So it was that he happened in a book store one afternoon and picked up a book that, as he told me later, had some new and interesting ideas. "Besides," he said, "The forward is written by Albert Einstein." My father had always admired Albert Einstein and had wanted to meet him someday. In his younger years he had worked on one of Henry Ford II's farms, and it happen one day that one of "Henry's" horses became mired, so the two of them, my dad and Henry, worked for several hours, or so the story is told, and finally freed the horse. It was my dad's hope that this association, brief as it was, would lead in some way to an introduction to Einstein since the two were acquainted, but that never happened. Fortunately that didn't do anything to diminish my dad's interest in this new book.

This is what Albert Einstein wrote as the forward material for Hapgood's book...

> I frequently receive communications from people who wish to consult me concerning their unpublished ideas. It goes without saying that these ideas are seldom possessed of scientific validity. The very first communication, however that I received from Mr. Hapgood electrified me. His idea is original, of great simplicity, and–if it continues to prove itself–of great importance to everything that is related to the history of the earth's surface.

> A great many empirical data indicate that at each point on the earth's surface that has been carefully studied, many climatic changes have taken place, apparently quite suddenly. This, according to Hapgood, is explicable if the virtually rigid outer crust of the earth undergoes, from time to time, extensive displacement over the viscus, plastic, possibly fluid inner layers. Such displacements may take place as the consequence of comparatively slight forces exerted on the crust, derived from the earth's momentum of rotation, which in turn will tend to alter the axis of rotation of the earth's crust.

> In a polar region there is continual deposition of ice, which is not symmetrically distributed about the pole. The earth's rotation acts on these unsymmetrically deposited masses, and produces centrifugal momentum that is transmitted to the rigid crust of the earth. The constantly increasing centrifugal momentum that was produced, will, when it has reached a certain point, produce a movement of the

earth's crust over the rest of the earth's body, and this will displace the polar regions toward the equator.

Without a doubt the earth's crust is strong enough not to give way proportionately as the ice is deposited. The only doubtful assumption is that the earth's crust can be moved easily enough over the inner layers.

The author has not confined himself to a simple presentation of this data. He has also set forth, cautiously and comprehensively, the extraordinary rich material that supports his displacement theory. I think that this rather astonishing, even fascinating, idea deserves the serious attention of anyone who concerns himself with the theory of the earth's development.

To close with an observation that has occurred to me while writing these lines: If the earth's crust is really so easily displaced over its substratum as this theory requires, then the rigid masses near the earth's surface must be distributed in such a way that they give rise to no other considerable centrifugal momentum, which would displace the crust by centrifugal effect. I think that this deduction might be capable of verification, at least approximately. This centrifugal momentum should in any case be smaller than that produced by the masses of deposited ice."

Albert Einstein

GRADUATION

President Truman was the commencement speaker at the graduation ceremony the year I graduated, and my father sat and listened in rapt silence as the President spoke. In a way I think that he felt that being at this ceremony and hearing Mr. Truman was more compensation for his not meeting Dr. Einstein than he could have hoped for. We were still seated in the MSU's Spartan Football Stadium, where the ceremony was held, it was hot, and noisy, and people were pushing past us to get out when he turned to me and said, "Here I've got something that I want to give you." and my father handed me Charles Hapgood's book *Earth's Shifting Crust,*[2] and then he added "I want you to read the forward."

"OK," I said, "But let's get home first."

"No! Read it here," he said "I won't have time later." It was almost a command, although not entirely unlike my dad. When I finished reading, he said, "I've marked out two sections that I want you to read, see what you think of them."

The first page that he had marked was page 97.

> The time element is essential to visualizing the general process of a displacement. Some concept of the probable speed of the displacement is required. A basis for such an estimate is provided by evidence that will be fully considered later, but I may here anticipate by saying that displacement may have required periods of 10,000 to 20,000 years. This means that this amount of time would be available for the creation of the system of fractures we are considering.

The second was page 210,

> The crust would now start to move, and it would continue to move easily to the distance permitted by the extent of the fractures so far created. The movement might then come to a halt, and the accompanying volcanism would tend then to subside. Meanwhile, on the poleward side of the ice cap the ice still would be building up, and the bursting stress resulting from it would again be on the increase. New fracturing would eventually occur, with a new outburst of volcanism, and the movement would be renewed.

> Finally a time would come when the rising temperatures of the lower latitudes and the accumulating of carbon dioxide would so far exceed the refrigerating effects of volcanic outbursts that the latter would become impotent to maintain the icecap.

I must have given him a quizzical look afterward that told him that I wasn't sure where all of this was leading because he quickly injected, "So what do you think?"

"Well, first of all," I said, "There are a lot of specifics there and I haven't seen or heard tell of any of it before, so I don't really know what to think."

My dad stood up, which was a signal for me to get up too, and I noticed that my wife and family were getting impatient and I wanted to hurry before I got yelled at, but it was clear that my dad had something more to say.

"So! What do you think? Is there any chance that Hapgood could be right?" Then he added, "Wouldn't that be something if the earth's crust really could move?"

"I really don't know." I said, "I suppose he could be, Einstein thought so!"

I still wasn't sure where this was all going and this hardly seemed the place to be talking of displacements of the earth's crust. But somehow he'd gotten the book back, I don't remember how, but he handed it back to me in a gesture that didn't include an option for me to hesitate, and he said, "I think that he's on the right track but as you can see Hapgood doesn't know what could trigger the crust to start moving, or what would stop it, or how fast it could move or really how far." "Find out," he said, "And give Hapgood a call."

I knew my dad too well to be flabbergasted at that suggestion. I don't think it ever occurred to him that something couldn't be done. To him, getting something accomplished was not a matter for discussion, it was just a matter of time. But that didn't do anything for me at the moment, and all I can remember saying for sure was, "Are you kidding?"

"Call him!" he said. And he followed it up with a look that told me that this was really important to him. So I agreed, but I had no idea at the time what I was going to do, or what I could possibly say to Charles Hapgood, and I was absolutely positive that I didn't know what I could say that I would have wanted Hapgood to pass on to Albert Einstein, should such an event occur. I didn't know a thing about the earth's crust or glacial ice for that matter. But I agreed.

That was June 1960. I joined my wife and family, who were all but ready to tell me, "What for," and we went home.

MY PROMISE TO CALL CHARLES HAPGOOD!

"Call him!" he'd said, and that is exactly what I did late in the Summer of 1993. That is I tried. It took me 33 years, mixed in with four children, a full time engineering career, a masters degree, and 30 years of teaching physics, hydraulics, and various levels of math part time at the local community college, but I called. At first I didn't know where to start looking. But then I remembered that he had written in one of his books that he could see Mount Monadnock[3] from the window of his home in New Hampshire. So I got out a map and I quickly found Mount Monadnock. With that I called the information operator in New Hampshire and in a few minutes I had the phone number of every Hapgood that could see the mountain from their window. It was a Saturday, and I thought with all the numbers that I had I would find someone home. But all I got were two answering machines. So I left a message on both machines to have someone call me, and I waited. My disappointment upon receiving a call from Charles Hapgood's grandson must have been as great as my father's disappointment when he'd not been able to meet Albert Einstein. Charles Hapgood had died some years earlier.

My favorite picture is of him leaning on his rake
(From: *Some personal reflections on my cousin, collaborator, and friend Charles H. Hapgood. By Beth Hapgood, pg. xv*)

Chapter 4

Rivers of Molten Rock

Engineering was everything that I'd envisioned it to be, although describing it as designing and testing doesn't capture much of its character, or say anything of what it demands. It is better to say that engineering is about meeting challenges. It is about addressing a challenge with an intuitive sense that begins to provide answers before you know all of the detail. That may sound pretty nebulous and impossible to teach at an engineering school, and if that is your thought then I would agree with you. But that is exactly what engineering is all about, and if a person doesn't have that "sixth sense," that intuitive feeling that senses purpose and order, natural or otherwise, they would not be happy in this field. That's not to reduce the importance of schooling in mathematics and mechanics, and physics, and chemistry. These in fact make up the knowledge base upon which solid intuitive judgements are made.

Engineers are not able to bring everything that they need to the job. So what their education and experience lacks was ably supplied in multi-volume publications like those put out by the SAE, Society of Automotive Engineers, or ASTM, the American Society for Testing and Materials, or in thick bound handbooks like the Machinery's Handbook, or the Metallurgy, or Chemistry, and Physics Handbooks, or the Handbook for Electrical Engineers. It was all there. The experience and the knowledge, the formulas and the procedures.

A DAY IN THE LIFE OF AN ENGINEER

NASA has to service the launch vehicle during countdown from ground facilities. In part this requires that hoses to carry air and fluids for cooling the electronics have to be connected. These connections are to be made between the gantry and the vehicle, and they must breakaway as the gantry swings clear prior to launch. The hose-end-connections want to be something special. They weren't to have a locking mechanism, ie., no mechanical device to hold them together. So push them together and they stay.

Pressurize them and they stay. But pull on them and they separate. Garden variety hoses have to be threaded onto the faucet, but not at NASA. The contract to supply these connections went to another bidder, but we submitted a design that worked.

A manufacturer that injection molded precision plastic parts for the electronics industry was having quality problems. The parts were coming out of the mold showing thin lines where the mold parts, a condition like having a fine fold on a new piece of paper. A quick study showed that a very brief, but high amplitude shock occurred as the die halves made initial contact on closing. It was just enough, despite the restraints provided by the guide pins and the mass of the die halves, to shift the mold ever so much. The fix, which was incorporated in the hydraulic system that controlled the machine, was to allow the mold to close at normal speed up to the last eighth of an inch, then it was slowed to a crawl so that it closed without producing so much as a quiver.[1]

The wing mounted connection between the outboard drop tank on the swept-wing F-111 is best constructed from parts made by a composite of processes. The base should be cast because of its multiple contours and overall complexity, but spin-form the spherical housings because this gives you the best control of weight and quality. Machine the hose connections from wrought aluminum and then weld these pieces together. Test for cracks with a flourescent penetrant and seal the assembly with a liquid plastic that is pressure induced into the pores after a vacuum is drawn over the part to remove the air. Use silicone lip seals between the drop-tank's delivery tubes and this in-wing-fixture to meet the demands of the minus 65 degree Fahrenheit high altitude environment, and you have yourself a fuel-connection system. Now run shock and vibration tests, then simulate the conditions of connecting the drop tank to the wing ten thousand times, and finally run flexure tests on a mounted specimen for 1200 hours to confirm that this composite assembly will not crack under stress. When you're done and everything works you can say, "Now I have a product."

There is one thing that is learned quickly when you are working in industry and there are production deadlines and warrantee obligations. You don't want to be making many mistakes. I retired from an auto manufacturer, but when I hired in, my boss who must have done this a hundred times before, said, "Look! We manufacture 4 million vehicles a year, and if there is just one mistake that costs us a nickel...that's four million vehicles times one nickel and that's two hundred thousand dollars! I can hire a lot of engineers for two hundred thousand dollars. So don't make any nickel mistakes!" He had a point, and he made it in a way that left a lasting impression. So I tried not to make any "nickel" mistakes!

SOLVING THE MATTER OF EARTH'S SHIFTING CRUST!

The first thing I did after retirement was to get a computer with word processing software for writing, a spread sheet program for mathematical computations, a modem and some communications software to peruse the library index files, and a database program to store and sort my research data. I wasn't sure that I could make any substantial contribution toward solving the mechanics of the motions of the crust, but I was going to try. On the surface, the project looked immense, but it became a little better focused by Hapgood's words...

> The prospect that unfolds before us, as we contemplate the possibility that total displacements of the earth's crust have been a feature of geological history since the formation of the crust itself, is nothing less than the discovery of the formative force, of the shaping factor, that has been responsible not only for ice ages, not only for the mountain ranges, but possibly for the very history of the continents and for all the principle features of the face of the earth.[2]

That passage had immense appeal. As a youngster, I had developed the sense that the world was not really very complicated, and thirty years in the field of engineering did nothing to change that. For instance, it is a fundamental truth, without compromise, that a force, and only a force can produce motion. Energy can't do it, neither can momentum or inertia, or any hidden characteristic that might be buried deep in the heart of the earth, or the moon, or the sun for that matter! And it doesn't matter what form or color the influence comes in. It can be thermal, or chemical, or electrical, or both, it doesn't matter. Nature *must* convert the influence to a force before there can be any motion or work performed. So it really isn't all that hard to figure out what is happening in nature, or what is causing it. If there is motion, ie., if the wind is blowing, or the clouds are moving, whether the Himalayan mountains are rising, or we see a streak of lightning, we know a force has caused it. This principle is so fundamental, so straight forward in its implications, that it is a pure waste of a person's time and energy to worry about any of it until the forces involved have been identified. It is fundamental! So what is all this malarkey about thermal currents moving continents around the earth and have them bang into one another to form mountains? Plain and simple it can't happen. Hapgood understood this principle and that's what makes his work so appealing.

> The prospect that unfolds before us is nothing less than the discovery of the *formative force*...that has been responsible not only for *ice ages*...but for all the principle *features of the face of the earth*.   C. H. Hapgood

Hapgood, who was one of the most astute researchers of recent time, recognized that even the ice ages were brought on by a *force*. So why is it that modern day scientists are still in the dark about the origin of the ice ages? I think the answer to that question is that they are too busy denying and haven't been looking for that *formative force*, and until they do, they'll never know!

It is said that the precepts of plate tectonics are well established, but that understanding this geo-physical phenomenon remains difficult because the forces are hidden from view, and hence beyond understanding.

Hidden from view? Yes! But than all forces are hidden from view. It is their nature. But they are never so totally hidden as to defy diagnosis. Some scientists would say that my "hidden from view," statement does not represent the views of researchers as a whole. Perhaps! But the truth of the matter is that there is not a researcher in the world that actually knows what moves the crustal plates, or what process causes earthquakes, or volcanos, or how surface rock forms into those familiar serpentine structures which geologists call synclines and anticlines,[3] and are so visible along the nation's highways. They plain and simple don't know!

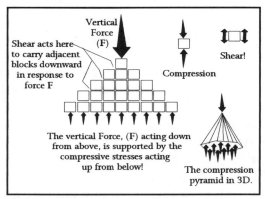

Figure 1 Compressive forces are dissipated rapidly through shear. The ever growing "pyramid" of blocks dissipate the original force to nothing!

Speaking of serpentining rock formations, it is unexplained why the established position regarding the formation of these structures is that some gigantic horizontal force has somehow compressed and folded the rock. For short distances we can see how that might happen. But many of these formations cover great distances. They serpentine above and below the ground for hundreds of miles, and for them, that explanation cannot hold. Compressive forces, those forces which act to squeeze an object, and hence the compressive stresses that they create, are in fact so efficiently dissipated through another stress called shear, that it would be a miracle of chance to ripple a mile of rock into any form, to say nothing of rippling it across half a continent.[4]

It is fortunate, in fact, that compressive forces are dissipated so efficiently because every building in the world, every road and every highway, and our very lives in the event of an accident, depends upon this efficient dissipation of compressive forces through shear. The bulk weight of a building, for example, is dissipated through the footings enlarged for that purpose. The weight of a vehicle on the road is dissipated first through the tires which carries the load via air pressure to the pavement, and the pavement dissipates it from there to the soil below, all through shear. Shear is an action like that exerted by scissors, or a chisel, or a punch that pushes sideways into a material. The forces that are involved create stress in the material that accounts for the cutting action. Your experience with using scissors or a chisel tells you that the force that you must exert goes up as the thickness of the material increases. This is because your efforts are being dissipated inside the material and you have to overcome this resistance with greater force. It is a concept that can be illustrated very well with a diagram, (See Figure 1). This same kind of diagram can be found in most civil engineering texts and handbooks.

Some readers, remembering how the pavement on some expressways will buckle in the heat of Summer, might say "But I have seen concrete buckle and twist into a serpentine structure, so I know it happens." Of course, and you will be right! But that condition is caused by another factor entirely. The expansion of the road, and consequentially the buckling of the concrete, is caused by forces generated by thermal expansion. These are forces from within which are acting against secure end restraints. It is not being man-handled by some gigantic unknown force from outside! When the Summer sun heats the road it must expand, it is one of those underlining principles, and the road simply has no other place to go but up. Every molecule in the road is pushing to get more room, and it's happening from the inside out, not the outside in.

Another case in point that explains why tent stakes are so difficult to drive, and why they crumple only at the point of contact with the sledge hammer or the ground, is that the forces created by the hammer blows cause internal stresses that exceed the strength of the material and the stake fractures, or splits. But in the middle of the stake the stresses of the impact are dissipated across the full cross section and this larger area can handle the forces well, so no damage is incurred in this area. The reason they drive so hard, however, is that friction between the stake and the soil acts to collect soil around the stake and makes it as fat as a barrel, and the compression pyramid that forms in front of the stake, which is very similar to the sonic wave that forms in front of a jet aircraft, is simply very difficult to overcome. This same rational can be used to describe what happens to the structure of an automobile in an accident situation. The impact forces are dissipated as they pyramid out picking up structure as they go. This pyramiding action, which crumples a lot of sheet metal, frame, and engine parts, in an energy consuming life saving manner, is an overt demonstration of the dissipation of compressive forces through shear. As a general rule the ability to transfer compressive stress is proportional to the strength of the material and certain frictional and column-cross-sectional characteristics. Steel is better than rock, and rock is better than soil. But even than soil is pretty good at it. These examples, going back to our story, relate directly to the theory of plate tectonics and cause us to wonder whether horizontal forces, as we are told, can really serpentine a rock formation.

In general plate tectonic theory holds also that the continents and oceanic crust form parts of a fractured plate system that move about the earth's surface under the influence of circulating thermal currents,[5] and that oceanic crust subducts at the continental margins, i.e., they move to bury themselves in the dense rock below. These plates according to theorists, are thousands of miles long and 5 to 20 miles thick, and move at speeds measured in inch(s) per year. The idea of thermal currents, or rivers of molten rock as some have called them, moving the oceanic crust anywhere is a rather puzzling notion because it is not as though these currents have hooks that lock into the crust to move it along, or that there is a hole up ahead for the crust to move into. There are no hooks – and there are no holes. So the only way the plate is going to move, by this means anyway, is through the friction established between the underside of the crust and the flowing rock. But can this happen? Friction has never been a very reliable agent to accomplish anything except for brake applications which work by dissipating energy through friction generated heat.

THERMAL SYSTEMS MUST BE ORDERLY

To work as a propulsion engine, a thermal system would have to be world wide with the underside of every square inch of crustal material in contact with the flowing magmas. The flow would have to be orderly across the entire globe and over great spans of time in order to establish sustainable movements of the continents without producing chaos at the surface. These simply are not the characteristics of open, uncontrolled, thermal systems. Another thing that we should take into account if we are thinking of accepting the thermal solution is that thermal systems, by their very nature, are not very efficient and we should expect that they would lose heat to the cooler underside of the crust. The most significant consequence of this is that this loss of heat would cause the flowing magma to crust over creating a thermal barrier which would isolate the crust from further disturbance and bring the process to a halt.

Another speculation offered by theorists as a mechanism for moving the planet's crust,

28

is one that suggests that molten lava wells up at mid-ocean ridges, i.e., ridges associated with cracks that follow a mid-ocean course around the world. This up-welling magma is said to push the crust aside as it rises and cools. But there again we have a rather puzzling notion. How is this sustainable? An explanation goes like this...

> A simple view of sea-floor spreading has up welling magma and sea-floor volcanism filling the crack between two plates which are separating at rates of tens of millimeters a year (about three quarters of an inch). Thus the creation of new sea floor mimics a giant conveyor belt.[6]

These widely accepted tenets of plate tectonic theory are not commonly disputed, but a geologist wrote me not long ago and said, in contrast to the spreading sea-floor and subducting crust theory...

> In Northern California we find a mass of sea floor sediments thrust upon the continent,[7] they are a jumbled, faulted mess.[8] Then he added...I too have a problem with the concept of up-welling magma at the (sea-floor) "spreading zone" pushing even a thin slice of ocean floor some 3000 miles wide anywhere!

There are other scientists who agree as well that nothing as bulky as oceanic crust could move anywhere without digging a hole first. For instance, an article review in the *News and Views* section of the February 1, 1990 issue of the scientific journal *Nature*, though not speaking specifically of oceanic crust burrowing into the earth, but looking instead for a hole in the outer crust for up-flowing magma to break out into the open air, asks a very searching question...

> Where does the space in the Earth's crust that intrusive granite (solidified magma) bodies, occupy come from?" This problem has long puzzled geologists. Evidence that the intrusions push aside the intruded rocks is usually absent or feeble; flexuring is rarely adequate to provide the space required.[9]

That's a good question! Where does the space come from? But if we have to ask this question of up-flowing magma, doesn't it seem reasonable that we should be asking it of the rock that is trying to go down, ie., subduct, into solid earth as well?

SUBDUCTION

As far as the "hole" up ahead for the crust to enter is concerned, there is no answer. So

29

here again we have a conundrum. How can subduction happen? Scientists tell us that increasing hydrostatic forces with depth, i.e., the affect of increasing pressure from over-burdening rock, has an increasing influence on the density of the earth's structure. So the earth inside is getting denser and denser. This is hardly an inviting environment for intruding rock! Particularly the low density surface basalts. As further testimony, the pressure created by the overburdening rock at the depth of the core is thought by some, to be so great as to render the core molten. A slightly different, yet corroborating view, suggests that the core is made up of two parts, a solid iron inner core made solid by the extreme pressures, surrounded by a molten iron layer. So where, if density increases with depth, does subducting crust find room, or opportunity, to submerge?

It isn't sufficient to say that there are no hooks and there are no holes, and that subduction, at least by the mechanism that is being advanced, is impossible, unless we're are also ready to offer a more viable alternative. There is no question that the earth's crust is broken into sections that can be call plates, and that the plates move. And there is no question that the interfaces between oceanic-plate and the continental margins look like a subduction process is going on. This is not in dispute. I'm just not ready to accept the premise that thermal energies are doing any of the work! Thermal energy, as a physical concept, could not move out of its own way. Energy must be converted to a force first in order to do any work. So the mechanics that should be used to describe earth's processes should be force systems, not energy systems. The rest of this book is going to be dedicated to demonstrating for the reader that there are real forces at work, and we'll be seeing where these forces of change come from. But we'll not leave the subject of subduction without asking at least one more question, and that should be in regard to the amount of rock that would be entering the earth at any given moment from subduction. We know, for instance, that the crust can be 5-20 miles thick and have a globe girdling breath of over a 100,000 miles, so our question is this, "How can that much material enter the earth without dire consequence being evident at the surface?" I thought it simple geometry that surface volumes are larger than underlying volumes... so it seems that proponents are trying to put two pounds of rock in a one pound pail, almost like sticking your finger in a grapefruit!

THE EARTH AS A MECHANISM TO SUSTAIN LIFE

As we progress, it would help to look at the earth, not as something so mysterious and hidden from view that we can't possibly understand it, but as a mechanical structure with components controlled by forces. As a beginning, imagine the outside surface of the earth as being crust like, and below that imagine a zone where the material gets more like soft plastic than anything else, and think of the crust as being loosely attached to the rest of the earth because of this plastic layer. Now think of the crust, because of the plastic layer, as having some freedom for independent motion if acted upon by external gravitational forces. Below the plastic layer is fractured rock that goes down to where pressure solidifies everything. At the outer core, pressures have brought the temperature up to a point that things get molten, and finally we're down to an inner core of solid iron that is known to be rotating at a speed different from the speed of rotation of the rest of the planet.[10] This gives us a simple picture from which we can begin to structure the earth as a mechanism, rather than a passive rock orbiting in space.

Although there are opposing views, the seismic data that has been gathered since the early 1920's is solidifying the views of scientists around the composite structure of the core. All proponents, molten vs the composite structure theorists, however, would accept the discovery from seismic data of an outer shell casing around the core called the Dee Double Prime layer, or simply the D″ layer. Jeanloz and Lay discuss this subject in depth (no pun intended!) in an easily read 1993 *Scientific American* article entitled, "The Core-Mantle Boundary."[11] The point of interest here being that we will be offering a new theory on the nature and origin of earthquakes in a later chapter and it will be important at that time to be able to envision the core as a functional part of the earth system having separate discernable parts with the D″ layer being one of those parts.

ROCK IS ROCK

Rock is rock...what more can we say! But rock is not really all that different from other solid substances. It responds to forces in exactly the same way as common metallurgical materials do. It follows the same rules. The problems arise when we begin to think that because the earth is bigger, and because we can't see any deeper than we're able to dig, that all of a sudden the rules change. They don't change! What happens in the machine shop, and what happens on the construction site, and what happens in the process of mountain building are all the same stuff. Only the size and the cost of the operation changes. So what we're looking for in our quest for "...that formative force...that shaping factor," that Hapgood was talking about earlier, is not a new set of rules, or new laws, or new principles. The ones we have right now will work just fine. So what we are looking for is a new way to apply what we already know, and this requires that we shed ourselves of this stigma...we need to stop saying that the solution to deep earth processes defies analysis because we can't see what's going on at depth!

Chapter 5

The R. R. Moore Machine

The first real breakthrough in solving the quandary of the motions of the earth's crust came during an all night pig roast. As it turned out, this wasn't going to be any ordinary pig roast, but it started out innocently enough. It came about because some family friends, a couple named Terry and Bonny, met us for a drink after work one evening and suggested that we all get together and do something exciting. So after some discussion it was agreed that a pig roast was more exciting than anything else that we could think of. So the plan that we devised would have the women buy the pig and line up the guests, and the men would put the meal together and roast the pig. Well there are all kinds of ways to roast a pig, but we decided to do it on a revolving spit over a bed of coals. The mechanism that we came up with is not easily described so rather than trying I'll just illustrate it, except to say, and this is important to the overall story, the spit that we designed to mount the pig on, is better portrayed as a one and a half inch diameter galvanized water pipe rather than a proper spit. See Figure 1.

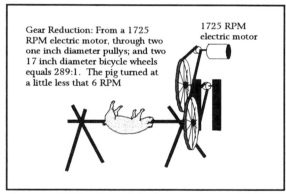

Gear Reduction: From a 1725 RPM electric motor, through two one inch diameter pullys; and two 17 inch diameter bicycle wheels equals 289:1. The pig turned at a little less that 6 RPM

1725 RPM electric motor

Figure 1 The Spit Mechanism.

On the day of the pig roast everything was ready. The spit mechanism was in place, the pit had been dug, there was all kinds of charcoal, and all the guests were milling about. All we needed to start the festivities was the pig and a match. So my dear wife, along with Bonny, led us into the bathroom where the pig was laying covered with ice in the bathtub. But one look at that pig and I knew we were in trouble! My first thought was that this pig was a monster. I'd figured on a fifty pound pig, because that's what we'd talked about, but this one had to be a 100 pounds if it was an ounce. Well after learning that the farmer was going to charge the girls the same amount whether it was 50 pounds or a 100, and that it was ever so much more logical, (Thank you Spock!), to get the 100 pound pig that...and so on and on, and on, so here it was!

Well now that one and a half inch galvanized water pipe looked like a tooth pick next to the pig, but it was too late to do anything about it at this point, besides somebody had lit the charcoal. So we proceeded, thinking that we'd make the best-of-it if anything dire happened. Well "dire" doesn't describe it! Half way through the night, the pipe broke, and the pig fell in the fire. Actually it was pretty funny. We'd been sitting around the fire, talking, drinking beer, telling lies, and having an overall good time, when this pig decides to change the subject! It must have been in the fire for fifteen minutes while we discussed what we were going to do about it, when several guests figured that they'd better save it before it went up in smoke, and they fished it out of the pit. Well to make a long story short, a friend of mine and I went into town and got a bigger pipe from behind the garage, and put everything back together again. We had other pig roasts in later years, but the spontaneity of that mid-night adventure made all the rest seem like a walk in the park.

THE PROJECT

I was now spending a lot of time on "The Project," as my wife called it. I'd bought a world globe that I set up beside my computer, and I had books stacked everywhere. I'd added a couple of Meg's of Ram memory to my computer and a 200MB IDE hard drive to handle the new software. It was the second morning anniversary of the first pig roast and I was looking at the globe and thinking about our adventure, when I was struck with the sudden realization that the pig had solved my dilemma. There it was, the answer, right there in front of me! It was what I'd been looking for. When that pig fell into the fire, it wasn't *just* because the pipe broke, although that is certainly what it did, rather it fell into the fire because the pipe broke from fatigue. Let me explain with an example:

When we try to break off a piece of wire from a coat hanger we bend it back and forth wanting to fatigue the wire so it will break, wear it out as it were. It doesn't work very well, not because that isn't a good way to go about it, but because bending the wire back and forth changes the structure of the metal, it work hardens it. The hardening comes about because the internal friction from the bending heats the wire and hardens it in the process. We should keep this idea of frictionally induced heat from bending in mind because it applies to the earth as well. Anyway, so now with this hardened spot in the wire it won't bend in that same spot when we go to bend it in the other direction. If we really want to make the wire break in a particular place we can force it by getting some pliers and holding the section tight so that now it has to bend in the same place each time, and with that it will very obligingly break for us. The process by which we exhaust an objects resistance to failure is called fatigue, and associated with fatigue is heat, and when there are two or more pieces associated with the process, such as in a "machine" of some sort, there is another nemesis to a machines mechanical life which we call fretting. We'll be introducing you to fretting later on in this story because it is actively responsible for much of Nature's wonders.

Let's go back now to that sudden realization which Beth Hapgood, who I have introduced earlier, calls an "Ah Ha!" What I'd realized was that my hapless spit, which was bending under the weight of that 100 pound pig, had been constantly rotating and the combination, the bending under the weight of the pig and the rotating, was doing a fatigue number on the pipe. In itself not any big surprise, the spit was small and we were really expecting it if you'll remember the episode beside the bathtub. No! The surprise came in the realization that the crust of the earth was going through the same process.

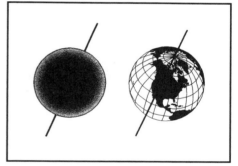

In the case of the spit, the bending was creating internal tension and compression stresses, and the rotation was continually walking these stresses around and around inside the pipe and heating it and wearing it out as it went. The direction of these internal stresses changed from tension to compression continuously around the pipe as it rotated at nearly 6 times a minute. The speed being determined by the gear ratio of my bicycle tire system which drove the spit.

Figure 2 The earth pictured as consisting of two parts. A solid inner sphere, and an outer oblate crust.

So the on-going stress reversals, plus the heat from the bending induced friction, plus the heat from the charcoal, plus the time factor, plus a slight out of balance condition, plain and simple wore the pipe out. The exact same thing can be shown to happen to the crust of the earth. In a simplified fashion, and liken it to the adventure with the pig, this is what takes place...First! Think of the crust as having some independent freedom to move as we described in the previous chapter. It would be a little like loose cargo moving about on the deck of a ship. And accept for now that the crust is about a hundred miles thick.

35

Later we will be saying more about this working upper-crustal-layer. Now, to continue, imagine the inner portion of the inner earth just below the plastic layer to be in passive orbit around the sun. We want to imagine it, for the moment anyway, as though it doesn't do anything but spin on its axis and go around the sun. In reality it is very dynamic as is the core, but for now the inner earth is passive!

Now here is what happens to the earth's crust that makes its eventual failure so similar to the failure of the pig spit, and keep in mind that it is the bending action along with continuous rotation that causes failure. The upper crust is caused to bend along the plane of the ecliptic by the gravitational pull of the sun and the moon, while it is in a state of simultaneous rotation. It rotates at a thousand miles an hour at the equator, 24 hours a day, 365 days a year, on and on for all eternity. The rotation and simultaneous bending has the consequence of fatiguing the crust and eventually exhausting the plastic layer's resilience. The crust's ties to the inner earth will eventually break and everything will be set to fail. It plain out-and-out fails from fatigue!

Once the inner ties are broken other factors are permitted to enter the fray. As Hapgood theorized, and as Einstein wrote...

> In a polar region there is continual deposition of ice, which is not symmetrically distributed about the pole. The earth's rotation acts on these unsymmetrical... masses, and produces (a) centrifugal momentum that is transmitted to the rigid crust of the earth. The constantly increasing centrifugal momentum produced in this way will, when it has reached a certain point, produce a movement of the earth's crust over the rest of the earth's body, and this will displace the polar regions toward the equator.

That certain point at which the ice would "...produce a movement of the earth's crust over the rest of the earth's body..." as Einstein wrote, is actually the concurrence of two conditions. The polar ice accumulations must be of such mass as to generate sufficient "centrifugal momentum," and the ties between the crust and the inner earth must be at the breaking point to allow the crust to move. These two conditions are mutually dependent, that is to say that one cannot occur until the other is ready.

THE MECHANISM: Rotational–Bending.

Rotational-Bending, or the RB-Effect, as a cause for fatigue failure has been around since time began. A machine that is used to simulate the condition in metallurgical labs, and the procedures for its use are described in the Metals Handbook. It is referred to as the Rotating-Beam-Fatigue-Testing-Machine, or as it is more commonly called in the metals industry, the R. R. Moore Machine.[1]

To understand why such a machine was invented, and why it is now in use, we have to learn something about stress and fatigue. Stress is a term that describes "something like pressure" that is being applied inside of a material as a result of the application of a force. While fatigue is the wearing out of a material by stresses that break down the inner strengths of the material. We'll be discussing this further as we go along, but what we want to introduce now is the fact that an object subjected to fatigue producing stresses can fail from fatigue at very low stress levels, far lower than the yield strength of the material. Particularly when there is repeated cycling. A case in point is the repeated cycling that is associated with the RB-Effect. If you eliminate the factors that produce fatigue, an object such as a machine part, or the crust of the earth or its crustal ties, will support high stress levels forever and ever without failure. But if you wear the object down with constant cycling it will fail at low stress levels. It is a trade-off. So the R. R. Moore machine was a product of the need to know how the cycling of stresses...brought by constant bending under conditions of continuous rotation...related to fatigue.

The **inner** earth, as a whole, is too massive to be affected to any great extent by the Rotational-Bending phenomenon. But the inner earth plays a very important role. The crust cannot bend, for instance, unless there is some substantial support holding it firmly enough to provide a reaction surface. We can go back to the wire to provide an example. The wire must be held firmly while the attempts to bend it are being made. If it is not held firmly the forces that you exert to bend it will simply result in the wire twisting around aimlessly. The outer crust must have a similar system of support in order for it to bend. That support is provided by the inner earth which, for this purpose, is held tightly in orbit by the gravitational attraction of the sun. The crust uses the inner earth as one might use their knee to support a board that they were wishing to bend or break.

What we are speaking about in describing the failure of the crustal ties and the subsequent slipping of the crust over the inner mantle from the forces produced by the polar ice's accumulated centrifugal momentum, is that the catastrophic shifts of the earth's crust, far from being mysterious or un-natural, are occasioned instead by the all-familiar gravitational influence of the sun and the moon. In order for the gravitational influence to be significant in producing the preempting conditions the crust as we stated above, must to be able to act independent of the inner earth. It must act like loose cargo on the deck of a ship. If the crust was secure in its moorings it would ride undisturbed with mother earth throughout all eternity. But such is not the case, the crust is free to move and the crustal ties are vulnerable. The point that we are addressing here is a concern that was raised by Einstein...

> Without a doubt the earth's crust is strong enough not to give way proportionately as the ice is deposited. The only doubtful assumption is that the earth's crust can be moved easily enough over the inner layers.

Our answer is that when the deck-cargo is tied securely, it will ride with the ship. But when the ties loosen, the cargo is free to move. So when the inner ties break the crust can be moved easily enough over the inner layers. There are at least two levels below the immediate surface of the earth that show evidence of sufficient plasticity. The first is the Mohorovičic discontinuity,[2] or Moho, which is a thin layer which tends to follow the earth's surface configuration and is known to affect the speed of seismic waves. The other is known as the plastic layer. This latter, more geo-active layer, was first suggested by Beno Gutenberg in 1926 as a zone that also affected the velocity of seismic waves and is now referred to by seismologists as a zone of "low seismic velocity" or "The Plastic Layer of the Earth's Crust."[3] as Don L. Anderson called it in a 1962 article. Actually both of these "zones" are areas where the earth's ties to the crust have been weakened. So to the extent that the crust is able to move because of these zones, and to the extent that the centrifugal force has influence to act strongly, we are going to have motion of the crust.

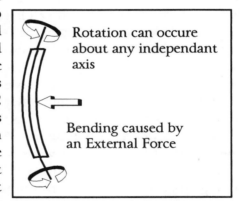

Rotation can occure about any independant axis

Bending caused by an External Force

Figure 3. A simple beam in Rotational-Bending.

NOT READY TO CALL

I wasn't ready to call Charles Hapgood with this discovery yet, because there was more to do. But I was beginning to feel that chance had looked my way, or maybe, the pig that we roasted that night wasn't just any old pig, perhaps it was my Angel from Serendipity in pig skin.

My "Angel from Serendipity" needs some explanation. Many of us feel that we have an Angel somewhere behind us that looks after us and makes a suggestion now and again.

Mine acts from just behind and above the left shoulder. Serendipity, is synonymous with chance, coincidence, luck, and providence. I could say my "Angel from Providence," but as you can see that just doesn't have the same ring to it!

THE CYCLE IS CONTINUOUS

Figures 3 and 4, illustrate the concepts of the RB-Effect. The simple beam in Figure 3, is shown to be rotating and bending at the same time, it will fail eventually under these combined affects...just as the crust of the earth in Figure 4 will fail. But note the angle of the earth's axis of rotation in this illustration. It is tilted at the very destructive angle of 23° 27' relative to the direction of the gravitational forces. Earth's crust is going through a very severe loading condition. Not only is it bending, but it is bending in a severely oblique direction relative to its rotation. This condition is going to lead to catastrophic failure in time! But what of the other factor, the accumulation of the ice at the poles? Hapgood discusses this in great detail in his book *Earth's Shifting Crust*, as I mentioned earlier. In this book Hapgood suggests that the accumulation mechanism is associated with long periods of warm global weather. NASA, has written on this subject and concurs with his assessment, as we'll see later. We tend not to associate warm weather with major ice accumulations

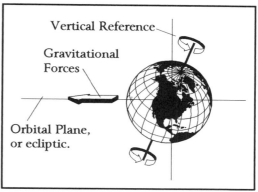

Figure 4 The Earth in Rotational-Bending!

at the poles, rather, we're inclined to think that the opposite is true...that we need extended periods of cold weather. But lets give this another thought. Warm weather means greater quantities of evaporation from the ocean, and warm weather also means greater plant and animal activity, both of which contribute to the atmosphere's reserve of evaporative waters. Warm weather also creates stronger circulative activities in the earth's atmosphere...circulation that moves the moisture from the lower latitudes of the equatorial and temperate zones to the higher latitudes of the polar regions where it condenses out as snow. Cold world temperatures, on the other hand, reduce evaporation, and attenuates the power of the circulative character of the atmosphere. We'll learn more of what NASA has to say about the accumulation of polar ice in the next chapter.

Chapter 6

A Continent Without A Home

How can anything be so extraordinary that every culture, ancient and new, has found a need to immortalize it? The full answer is the subject of our continuing story. It will unfold in the following pages and it will bring to light many interacting processes, which, if we are extraordinarily fortunate, will not play out in our lifetime. The main actors are the Rotational-Bending effect, fatigue, and the accumulation of ice at the poles. As our story develops we will watch the continent of Antarctica switch oceans from the Pacific to the Atlantic. It will be the continent of Mu in the Pacific, and the continent of Atlantis in the Atlantic. It will be getting a new home and a new name with each shift of the earth's crust. How these processes interact to bring these events about will become more familiar as we introduce the mechanism that engages the actions of vibration, fretting, isostasy and earth's own gravitational system.

Our task at this point is one of sorting out from all of the possible deep earth processes, those that affect us the most, and then to weave the details into a comprehensive narrative of temporary chaos where continents are shifted around like so many ships on a turbulent sea. Some of the events began thousands of years ago when warm climates came upon the scene. These climates, with their wide spread wind patterns and high levels of evaporation brought rainfall to all parts of the global system, some forming as snow and ice in the polar regions. But this is really NASA's story, so lets see what they wrote in a July 1993 report, *Modeling the Earth System in the Mission to Planet Earth Era...*

> The importance of major ice sheets in the global climate is rapidly becoming recognized. No longer are the ice sheets seen solely as a passive reservoir of the Earth's water supply. In either hemisphere, the ice sheets and their connected ice shelves have experienced variations in volume and extent that far exceed the seasonal variations of sea ice. These variations must have affected weather patterns, ocean currents, and, by changing sea level, the entire global climate.[1] It is not inconceivable that an initial warming trend leading to an acceleration of the

hydrological cycle...would transport more moisture from tropical to middle and higher latitudes, thus causing (even)more snow cover.[2]

NASA in another statement recognizes a recent ten fold change in the characteristics governing the accumulation of the ice cover at the poles.

A major issue yet unresolved is the time scales of these large variations of the ice sheets. Response times for Greenland and Antarctica are usually quoted as thousands to tens of thousands of years, yet data on sea level suggest the possibility of more rapid changes in ice volume and (evidence showing) fluctuating oxygen isotope values in an ice core (taken) from central Greenland have been used to detect a major transition that occurred in less than 100 years.[3]

In addressing this changing pattern in the Polar ice sheets, and in suggesting a mechanism for growth, NASA is contributing to the beginning of our account. Conditions at Antarctica apparently are not stable. If the conditions of accumulation were balanced, as we would hope them to be, we'd have no cause for concern, but they are not. The influx of moisture is causing the glaciers to change far faster than expected. It is extremely important in considering this that the data that brought NASA to these conclusions is based on very recent research which is without historical support. So it would be prudent for us to look for corroborating evidences. Fortunately support in quite a different form does exist. It comes to us in the form of ancient cultural leftovers!

There is evidence that Antarctica, though closely centered at the South Pole and covered with over two miles of ice today, has not always been centered at the South Pole nor covered with ice as we might have supposed. The evidence of this is in the form of maps drawn by cartographers from an earlier age showing a surprisingly un-glaciated Antarctica and an accurately portrayed shoreline. I can't do the subject justice by reproducing the maps here because there is a whole other story to be told. So let me direct you to another book written by Charles Hapgood entitled, *Maps of the Ancient Sea Kings*,[4] whose full subject concerns the story of an un-glaciated Antarctica. The hard cover version was first published in 1966, but it is now available in a beautifully illustrated paperback. Figure 18, on page 37, and Figure 50, on page 82 of this book, illustrate respectively, the Piri Re'is Map of 1513 A.D., and the Oronteus Finaeus World Map of 1532 A.D., as excellent examples of cultural artifacts that boast of a continental shoreline free of ice and open for trade. Hapgood was convinced that this coastal detail was not the work of cartographers of the 16th century but from a generation of map makers that lived many thousands of years earlier. There are a number of conclusions that we might draw from this ancient geographical knowledge. One scenario might be that the world was warmer in recent times, and these maps came into being because Antarctica was not glaciated and adventuresome maritime interests were lured south in search of new markets. Or, and this is our conclusion of choice, as it was Hapgood's, Antarctica was not glaciated because it wasn't at the pole. It was significantly further north. It was within the normal trade routes of ancient civilizations, and mapping grew out of the normal course of conducting commercial and private business.

SUMMARIZING...ICE RESERVES ARE NOT A CASUAL CONCERN

Let's look at the three most compelling pieces of evidence that give us cause to be concerned about the menace brought on by the polar ice caps. In part, this concern originates from the evidence given us by the Peri Re'is and Oronteus Finaeus maps that detail an ice free Antarctica. These are our concerns...

Warming climates, as we've been experiencing, transport more moisture than usual from tropical to middle and higher latitudes, thus causing more snow cover.

Historical leftovers from cartographers of an earlier maritime civilization showing open shore lines on Antarctica have given us a startling incite on how fast the change in the size of the polar ice caps really is.

... constantly increasing centrifugal momentum will produce, when it has reached a certain point, a movement of the Earth's crust over the rest of the Earth's body, and this will displace the polar regions toward the equator. (*Einstein*)

IT IS TIME TO GET TO WORK

The earth is a mysterious place, not just because it is large in comparison to everything else we know, but it is mysterious because we haven't had the means to probe its depths. We've had no learning tools, and we've been afraid to apply the familiar laws of physics and mechanics that we were taught in school because we think somehow that the earth must have its own laws. Not true! Sure the earth is large and unfamiliar, but it is also a tangible object with all the properties of a machine, and fortunately we are very familiar with machines. So size and unfamiliarity, in my opinion, gives us no cause to abandon familiar analytical tools. So this was my premise as I prepared to approach my analysis of the gravitational influences on earth's shifting crust. The equations for determining the forces between two mutually attracting bodies, like the earth, the sun and the moon,

43

have been around since the mid-eighteenth century and they represent one of the most universally applied principles in all of physics. The equation takes into account three factors... The vigor of the gravitational attraction, the mass of the objects under consideration, and the distance that separates them.

THE LAWS OF GRAVITATION

Newton's Law of Gravitation[A] states that two celestial bodies of mass m_1 and m_2 are mutually attracted by a force, F, given by the formula...

1. $F=G(m_1 m_2)/r^2$ Where:[5]

> F = The gravitational attractive force.
> G = Universal constant of gravitation.
> r = Distance between the mass centers of the two bodies.
> m_1 = The mass of celestial body number 1.
> m_2 = The mass of celestial body number 2.

As a start in my investigation, I had to determine the character and magnitude of the variables that could reasonably define a crustal shape that would move easily around the earth in some inestimable fashion in the future. The variables had to include a definition for the specific contours of the crust, and the determination of its volume and center of mass. The other factors, the acceleration of gravity, and the distances between the earth and the sun, and the distance to the moon, are well known quantities so there was no discovery required here. Determining the actual contour and mass distribution of the crust, however, was going to be a monumental task. But after some extended thought, and hours of discussion with others, including the mathematician who was to eventually solve the problem for me, I settled upon the decision that I wouldn't be introducing a significant error if I simply thought of the crust as having a somewhat uniform shape with a somewhat smooth spherical inner surface and an ellipsoidal outer surface. I was later to come to suspect that the inner surface was probably not uniformly spherical, but the initial choice provided me with a starting point. It might seem to the reader that the problems are so numerous that there is no solution, but actually it got easier as we went.

[A] Newton's Principles of the Law of Gravitation are based on experimental evidence and cannot be derived mathematically. Their universality has been challenged by Einstein's theory of relativity, but in applications where system velocities are small compared to the speed of light, they have yet to be disproved.

The oblate gradient, or the pear shape character of the outer crust,[B] is well known, and is published as 298.24 to 1. We used this figure in establishing the specific contour of the outer crust and hence were able to calculate the volume and the mass center. But at the same time I felt that I could ignore any elevational influences from mountains and oceans, for instance. The authority for this decision is well established in the Principles of Isostasy,[6] which we'll address in detail in the concluding chapter, *Means to Ends*, but for now let it be said that the principle states that features such as oceans and mountains are "hydrostatically balanced" and become an almost indistinguishable part of the landscape. This means that we can see them visually but if we were to look for them by the gravitational influences that their mass would exert upon our instruments, they would be pretty much invisible.

The shape of the crust that I arrived at, and the coordinates that were calculated from it, are illustrated in Figure 1. But one aspect of this mathematical investigation that was going to stymie me for a while was how to determine the thickness of the moving crust. I didn't know whether I should figure on perhaps five miles or twenty. Or even a hundred! Actually it turned out that the thickness was not a factor, it had nothing to do with anything! It could shift at what ever depth the plastic layer developed without consequence to either the end result or to any of the postulates we developed. We'll see why in Chapter 8, *Thirty Degrees, No More, No Less*. But again, we had to get started somewhere, and not knowing in the beginning that thickness was not a factor, we made some guesses and the mathematician who I was working with, Dr. David Yen, wrote a general equation to cover all possible thickness opportunities, and then he solved the equations for those specific conditions that I chose. The data that we were interested in was the volume and the center of mass for each of the trial crustal thicknesses.

I owe a great deal to this mathematician. At the time that we worked together Dr. David Yen was a Professor in the math department of Michigan State University and was a world renown figure in his field having given many seminars in advanced mathematics in seven countries around the world, and he gave unselfishly to this project. I made an initial contact by phone and was pleased by his cordiality. When my wife, Patty, and I walked into his office in the math building at MSU he treated me as though I was a fellow colleague of long standing, and when I handed him the sketch of the crust he took an immediate interest. We discussed the subject for several hours, afterwards taking time

---

[B]The ellipsoidal gradient, 298.24:1, refers to the transitioning of the shape of the surface of the earth from the lesser radial dimension at the poles of 3949.92 miles, to the greater radial dimension at the equator of 3963.21 miles.

for coffee at the Student Union. The conversations that we had led to a few corrections and clarifications and afterward he said that he'd see what he could do. He said that he would like us to communicate through the Internet via e-mail, but since I didn't have e-mail at the time I had to do something to set it up. Fortune was looking my way this time as I taught math and physics in the evening at the local community college and as it turned out the school provided e-mail services for instructors. So having it set up at home was not the problem that I'd anticipated. From there on out it was just a matter of time.

Besides the physical aspects of the crust, I was also concerned about the actual dynamics of its motion. I spent a lot of time on this question and my many discussions were extended because there was absolutely no scientific precedence for a conclusion, and the combined experiences of those that I conferred with offered no incites. The lack of scientific research in this area and the corresponding lack of data was clearly the problem, but there was nothing that we could do about that so we just had to pioneer the research. The pioneering aspect of this project was going to lead

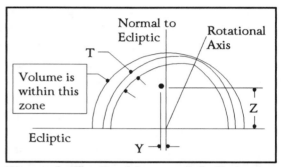

Figure 1. The Earth's crustal shell above the Ecliptic.
@T=7 miles
  Y=304.4., Z=1763.9, V=1.5E9 cu mi
@T=37 miles
  Y=106.1., Z=1894.3, V=4.5E9 cu mi
@T=87 miles
  Y= 51.4., Z=1919.9, V=9.2E9 cu mi
@T=155 miles
  Y= 30.6., Z=1917.8, V=15E9 cu mi

to our making some basic assumptions that had only circumstantial support. But we felt that if we were prudent, and if subsequent results were supporting, we were probably safe. It was this or nothing. Another problem that we encountered was that the general public maintains an *equatorial* orientation with regard to the land masses, and I include myself in this category. This gives us the perspective of an up-right-world with the pole areas at the top and bottom as illustrated in Figure 2. This upright-orientation is gravely misleading because it causes us to ignore the highly influencing fields of gravity from the sun and the moon, and it gives us a poor picture of the effect of the sun's radiant energies on weather and climate. These two environmentally important factors actually act upon the earth at a 23.5 degree angle...and they influence our weather patterns in a manner totally different than we think. It would help us, it would seem, if the weather maps were to look more like a globe than a road map so that we could get a truer picture.

The dynamics of the crust's motion were eventually solved and led us to compute the volume and the coordinates with a very specific perspective in mind. The configuration is so important to the central idea of the theory that I must lay it out for you in detail.

THE CASE GOES LIKE THIS

It is not in dispute that all influences from gravity and light that act upon the planetary bodies in the solar system interact along the plane of the ecliptic. In consequence, neither gravity nor light are oriented in any influential way with either the equator, or in relation to the earth's axis of rotation. We had to take this into account as we were developing our analysis techniques because it is a very important point to take into consideration. Figures 1 and 4, illustrate this point well! The location for the center of mass of the crust, which are directly affected by the lunar and solar gravitational forces, and which encouraged the development of our equations and guided the countless calculations, is correspondingly associated with a vertical profile of the crust relative to the **ecliptic**, and specifically not to the equator. This consideration, to my knowledge, is unique to our research and is thus unlike any analytical solution that has ever been published on the subject.

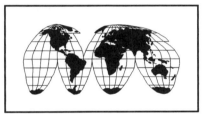

Figure 2. This type of map is somewhat illusionary because it puts no emphasis at all on solar radiation, or the highly influential fields of solar and lunar gravity.

As another factor for consideration, we wanted to be able to address the question of mountain building directly, but a computerized model cannot be channeled towards this query without a huge suppositional base, and that didn't seem appropriate here. Our questions would have been, "Did mountain building occur because the crust encountered some local resistance during movement which bloomed into a temporary traffic jam that wrinkled some fenders? Or, "Was the crust elevated as it moved...and did earth's gravity bring it down as things settled out, thus serpenting the surface and forming mountains in the process?" We accepted the latter view of an elevated crust bring brought down by gravity as our scenario of choice. Hapgood who devoted an extensive part of his books to addressing this very problem accepted this view as well. I should note, however, that our initial thoughts were that it would be impossible to move something as large as the crust part way around the world without something happening locally to slow it down. But in retrospect we realized that a local event would be over whelmed by the immensity of the crust's momentum and it would be unnoticed in the final analysis. This reasoning was in full accord with Hapgood's analysis so we decided to leave it at that.

In a subsequent meeting with Dr. Yen he informed me that he would need a special computer program to solve the equations that he wrote, and that getting the program and setting it up was going to take some time. Well, I'd been working on this project since I graduated from Michigan State University in 1960, and I was thrilled at the prospect of getting some finite answers after all this time and a little wait wasn't going to bother me any. So as soon as I had e-mail in place I sent him my address and agreed that we could start our investigations whenever he was ready, and that we should get data for the effective thickness of the moving portion of the crust beginning with thicknesses of 37, 87, and 155 miles. In November I got this reply...

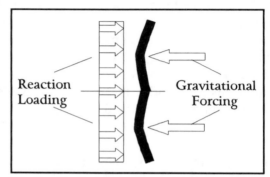

> 19 Nov 1993. Jim: Thank you for sending me your e-mail address. I hope to find some time next week to do some computations. Regards, David Yen.

This was followed shortly by another message...

> 14 Dec 93. Jim: I was able to do some computations (learning the software Mathematica). Here are the results: Regards, David Yen.

Figure 3. A simple bar in bending with a shape developed as though it was acted upon by gravity at two centroidal locations, and supported by a material like soft, freshly laid concrete!

He sent me a table of values for the three starting thicknesses, which I have reproduced in Figure 1 above, and I immediately started working out the criteria and the equations necessary to compute the bending moments from the gravitational influences. The basis for the equations that we used to evaluate the bending influences followed conventional practices, and except for the hollow-shell cross section of the earth, they are essentially as illustrated by the rod which I've shown in simple bending in Figure 3. The next task was to take the data and put it into an analytical model that would allow me to evaluate the Rotational-Bending Effect. That done, it became suspect that any value over 30 miles for the thickness of the moving portion of the crust was going to be far too great. I was learned later, as I developed better analytical techniques, that thickness was really not a significant factor, but these were my thoughts at the time as I mentioned earlier. So I wired Dr. Yen and asked him for data that would correspond to a thickness of 7 miles. Here's his reply...

16 Dec 1993. Jim: Here are the results for T=7 Regards, David

I noticed as I examined Dr. Yen's data that the "Z" coordinate, the distance from the ecliptic vertically to the mass center of the crust, increased from 1763.99 for a crustal thickness of 7 miles, to 1919.9 for a thickness of 37 miles, and then it dropped off to 1917.9 miles when the thickness was calculated for 155 miles. I didn't know if this change in character was due to the ellipsoidal shape of the crust or if it was an error, but I needed to know. I also wondered whether his computer program could give me a crustal thickness if I gave him a volumetric input. So I e-mailed my questions...

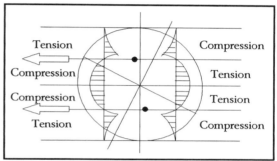

Figure 4. The earth, under the loading conditions that I have illustrated in Figure 3 above, would bend in a similar way and would create the tension-compression zones that I have illustrated here.

21 Dec 1993. Jim: It appears that as T increases, Z increases at first and then decreases. My program cannot handle a V input for an Y output. Regards David.

OK! So apparently there was no error, the vertical coordinate "Z" simply changed as a characteristic of the ellipsoidal shape of the crust. Not surprising! It was going to be a little inconvenient, however, not being able to get additional coordinate data based upon a volumetric input. That would have been handy because it would have allowed me to match the magnitude of the driving forces with those of the restraining forces, but I could work around it. Besides, just being able to get this information was such a big help that I was delighted beyond mention, and to have someone as capable as Dr. Yen performing the mathematical analysis was extraordinarily good fortune. My job now was to calculate the bending moments that were brought about by the gravitational forces.

PROBLEMS ASSOCIATED WITH THE ANALYSIS!

A hard question had to be answered at this point...what were the supporting reactions opposite the gravitational forces going to look like? My decision, after another long period of debate, was that I was going to assume that the plastic layer below the crust would react like soft freshly poured concrete. This would mean, for analysis purposes anyway, that it could support a load in compression, which would result in some form of uniform loading of varying magnitudes, but it would have insufficient strength, or body, to support any type of load in tension. Hence we concluded that no significant reaction load could develop in tension on the gravitational side of the earth. This rational led to the discovery of the loading pattern that is illustrated in Figure 4. It was obvious too that this alternating pattern of compression and tension would "walk" around the **ecliptic** every 24 hours with the rotation of the earth. The stresses would go from tension to compression, and compression back to tension again...over and over again. There simply can be no question that this constant cycling, day after day, year after year, millennium after millennium would have a wearying affect on the crust.

I don't know what I would have done without a computer and a spreadsheet program to handle all of the mathematical computations. There were a million of them and each revelation led to even more. The principle discovery that the analysis revealed was that the crust of the earth would bend under the gravitational loads in a fashion very similar to the way a simple bar would bend. The associated stresses that developed are similarity conventional in character. There was nothing mysterious at all about them. They are totally familiar and not unlike the stresses in the structural beams that are used to support the roof in the downtown shopping mall. See Figure 3.

But in one sense these stresses are different. These walk around the earth changing in direction and magnitude in a manner similar to the way the stresses varied within the pig-spit that caused our pig of Chapter 5 to drop into the fire. Is it any wonder that after tens of thousands of years of this endless flexural-conditioning, accompanied as it is by the continual build up of the ice at the Pole with all of its associated force producing stresses, that one day the system would let go and the crust would slip? One might get a better perspective for the character of these cycling stresses by recalling how we "knead" a fresh orange by working the orange over and over, rotating and squeezing it to break down the inner fibers. If we were to do this for a while and if we were then able to look inside, we'd find that we had broken the skin from its internal moorings so that if we could give it a nudge, it would slip over the inner segments. It's not much different than the processes that go on within the earth! For instance, imagine the following, on the gravitational side of the earth, the individual influences of the sun and the moon, acting from their respective positions, flexes the crust outward in compliance with the forces, while on the lee side, where the crust is supported by the inner earth, it is caused to flex inward. The crust flexes inward as it enters the shadow of gravitational darkness and it waits there passively for daylight to come and for its turn to be distended. The instrumental aspect of this process is that it's this act that destroys the crustal ties, and until this stage is complete the crust can not move despite what ever ice masses might have accumulated at the poles.

It might be appropriate, in order to enhance our perspective at this point, to ask whether there is any additional proof of this cycling stress phenomenon other than our mathematical model or the experiences cited from the metals industry. The best way that I can see to address this question is to access the geological evidences, particularly those that I believe to be intuitively obvious. For instance, let me simply ask, "If the earth's mountainous heights were not refreshed periodically, why wouldn't they have been worn down to nothingness by now?" "And why do the rivers still have some elevation at their head waters?" "And why haven't all the waterfalls around the world eroded away their escarpments?" "Why is coal and oil found so shallow and fresh in their beds, and in such unlikely places as the North-Shore-Fields of Alaska, and in the North Atlantic off the shore of England?" Could it be that the surface is renewed on occasion and nothing is very old? The answers to these questions, when rendered intuitively, suggest that the geological evidences are not the work of processes from 65 million years ago, or even 30 million years ago, but rather from processes far more recent. Mountainous heights look closer to thirty or a hundred thousand years old! They look young. They are worn and wearing, but they look young! They haven't had time to wear down to the nothingness that years of grueling exposure would bring. And let us not ignore the presence of animal fossils and the many mineral deposits that are found in strangely shallow locations around the world. These too suggest the action of some recent, yet very powerful, influence that goes beyond that possessed by a drifting continent!

A CHANGING WORLD SCENE

As our adventure of discovery continues we will be watching the world change as it goes through two shifts of the earth's crust. Our story will start at a time when the land in the extreme southeastern corner of Alaska, near the modern town of Juneau, was situated at the North geographic pole. The South Pole will be homesteading the waters off the Southern tip of Africa. This global scene places Antarctica, the land without a home, in the South Pacific Ocean at 45 degrees South latitude, and close to the legendary lost continent of Moo. It will be enjoying a climate similar to that of modern day Chile and Argentina. It's shores, as evidenced by the ancient maritime maps, will be free of ice and

51

its harbors will be the stopping point for merchant ships of the day.

NOW THE CRUST WILL SHIFT, AND SHIFT AGAIN

At some point, after thousands of years of development, the conditions will be right for the crust to shift. The ice, which will have grown to over burden Alaska, Canada, and Eastern Siberia will provide the force to cause the crust to shift. The lands will move taking Alaska southward and moving Hudson Bay northward. The North Pole star will now brighten the area currently occupied by the town of Povungnituk in Northern Quebec just inside the Eastern shore line of Hudson Bay. Antarctica will move into the latitude of the ancient land of Atlantis in the South Atlantic Ocean where it will enjoy the mild climates of the lower latitudes.

Then, still many more thousands of years later, the crust will shift a second time, Hudson Bay will move southward, and the Arctic Ocean will move northward giving us the world picture that we are accustomed to. The move will put Antarctica at the geographic South Pole where its drastically changed climate will put it into the throes of the *accumulation stage* of an Ice Age to come! One day, yet in our future, Antarctica's ice will cause the lands to shift again. The shift will follow a line of movement that will take Siberia to the Pole position, India will follow along the same path only to end up in the less hospitable climates of 50 degrees North latitude. Canada and the Americas will move southward, and Antarctica, which will follow along the path laid down by northward movements of Siberia, will move into the Indian Ocean where it will undergo the only ice age that this world has ever experienced...an ice age brought about as the ice sheets that formed when Antarctica was at the Pole, melt in the warmer weather of the lower latitudes.

You can experience these most startling historical events for yourself by picking up a World Globe and placing your fingers antipodal, one opposite the other, at each of the respective pole positions that I have diagramed. You can observe, with each shift of the earth's crust, the continent of Antarctica switching oceans. It will move from the Pacific to the Atlantic. Antarctica will be the continent of Mu in the Pacific, and the continent of Atlantis, in the Atlantic. It will be getting a new home and a new name with each shift.

> We are to examine the construction of the present earth, in order to understand the natural operations of times past.[7]
>
> *James Hutton*, 1788

INTRODUCTION, Part 2.   Evidences of Catastrophe

The most compelling piece of evidence that we can find that supports the enigmatic view of geologic events growing out of world wide catastrophe, are the cultural records left by the Ancients. These past generations experienced it, they lived through it, and they left us their records. And of all the records that exist, none capture the imagination more than do the giant figures on the plateau, Pampa Jumana-Colorada, above Nasca, Peru. Here we find the history of man from time immemorial. Immemorial? Well not really, because they were careful to leave us two dates, one from around 10,500 BC, and the other from around 103,000 BC. But that is a separate story in itself that we'll get to in Part 3, *The Pampa Jumana-Colorada*. In the mean time we will look at the more prosaic evidences that lie in the geologic and fossil records.

Everywhere about us are the evidences of catastrophe. Every where we look we encounter the inexplicable evidences of a world thrown into temporary chaos. How many, and what and where are they? The simplest example, and the most pervasive, are the pebbles. We know that pebbles were once larger rock, and that rock was once mountain, and strangely, that mountain was once ocean bottom. And we know that the pebbles got their size and roundness from erosive weathering and the action of water. They are everywhere, small rounded examples of the rock from which they came...some with imbedded fossils. We know too that a single quarry will yield examples of almost every type of rock that ever was. But interestingly, doesn't it also follow that each unique pebble must also represent a unique place of origin? And how many different types of pebbles did we say we could find in one quarry? So how did they all get mixed up and delivered to the same rock quarry, or delivered to any of the hundred hill sides that we know of within walking distance?

William Buckland, a geologist, born in Trusham in Devon, England on March 12, 1784, a Fellow of his college and Reader in Mineralogy, was a lecturer and somewhat of a humorist. Buckland's particular interest, and the one which probably best captured the imagination of his pupils, was in the fossil skeletons of awesome monsters like the ichthyosaurus or pterodactyl, as well as the more recent animal remains which were being unearthed in cave deposits (of the time)."[1]

Buckland was also fascinated by the pebbles that he, like ourselves, found every where. In 1820 he authored a book titled, *Vindiciae Geologicae,* wherein he wrote of the "pebbles" as his proof to the recent action of deluging waters...[2]

> There are immense deposits of gravel that occur occasionally on the summits of hills, and almost universally in valleys over the whole world; in situations to which no torrents or rivers such as are now in action could ever have drifted them. The nature of this gravel, being in part composed of the wreck of the neighboring hills, and partly of fragments and blocks that have been transported from very distant regions.

> (I recognize) ...the total impossibility of referring to any one of these appearances to the action of ancient or modern rivers, or any other causes, that are now, or appear ever to have been in action since the last retreat of the diluvian waters.

No one should ever believe, is his comment, that the processes that produce and distribute pebbles is under any local influence. Eroded to pebble size and rounded by the tumbling action of water, and dispersed world wide, pebbles are proof in themselves of chaos, un-needing of verification. But unfortunately, though valid as this argument is, it is insufficient in itself to sway the misanthrope. So for them, and for the rest of us too, we need to see what else there is to be said. So let's go about this business and move on to Part Two, *Evidences of Catastrophe*.

Chapter 7

Fire, Water, Earth, and Air

The mysteries of the earth have always been the subject of controversy and debate. It is a circumstance wherein each new researcher, author, and debater has enhanced our understanding and added to our pool of knowledge, but it is also the circumstance where among the proponents of these issues, neither side, and sometimes the many sides, have been unwilling, or unable, to narrow the issues of debate. Thomas Kuhn has pointed out that it is the accumulation of anomalies that eventually forces the abandonment of old scientific paradigms and the installation of new ones. And so it happens that the many debates have come down to the modern generations essentially unresolved.

Lao-tze, (c., 604 BC)

> ...everything in existence is composed of – water, fire, wood, metal, soil, and Yin and Yang.[1]

Paracelsus, (c., 500 BC)

> ...everything in existence is composed of – mercury, sulfur, and salt.[2]

Empedocles, (c., 490 BC)

> ...everything in existence is composed of – fire, water, earth, and air.[3]

Henry Wadsworth Longfellow, (c., 1857)

> ... let me add that I believe the Laws of Nature are just, but terrible. There is no weak mercy in them. Cause and consequence are inseparable and inevitable. The elements have no forbearance. The fire burns, the water drowns, the air consumes, and the earth buries.[4]

Plato, (c., 427-347 B.C.)

> Poets utter great and wise things which they do not themselves understand. But who am I to say, for to learn is why I am here.[5]

Richard Heinberg, Author of *Memories and Visions of Paradise*...

> In archaeology and anthropology, the current paradigm— which has ruled for more than a century— is that human culture has evolved unidirectionally from the primitive to the advanced. Any evidence that contradicts this view is, by definition, an anomaly. In this instance the anomalies are legend. On every continent there are earthworks, artifacts, and human remains that do not fit the current paradigm because they are too old, too "advanced," or simply in the wrong place. For example, artifacts, and human remains have been found in America that are tens of thousands of years too old to fit present theories of how and when the New World was first inhabited. Objects obviously made by humans have been found in solid lumps of coal or in stone. ...[6]

Heinberg reminds us too that there is a story of a deluge...a history of sacredness...in virtually all cultures...

> According to Greek myth, Deucalion was the son of Prometheus; he married his cousin Pyrrha, the daughter of Epimetheus and Pandora. When Zeus decided to destroy the human race (Hesoid's Bronze Race, who were violent and vicious), Prometheus advised Deucalion to build a box and furnish it with the necessities of life. In it, Deucalion and Pyrrha survived while the rest of mankind perished.

While the Deluge is the most widely and vividly remembered catastrophe of ancient times, most cultures retain traditions of other world-destructions as well. Of these perhaps the most widely read version of the Deucalion floods is Ovid's.[7]

> At His command the mouths of fountains opened
> racing their mountain waters to the sea.
> Under the blow of Neptune's fork earth trembled,
> And a way was opened for a sea of water:
> Where the land was the great rivers toppled orchards,
> Uncut corn, cottages, sheep, men, and cattle
> Into the flood. Even stone shrines and temples

Were washed away, and if farmhouse or barn
Or palace still stood its ground, the waves
Climbed over door and lintel, up roof and tower.
All vanished as though lost in glassy waters,
Road, highway, valley, and hill swept into ocean,
All was a moving sea without a shore.[8]

In his *Theogony*, Hesoid described the end of one of the ages thus,

The life-giving Earth crashed around in burning...all the land seethed...It seemed
even as if Earth and wide Heaven above came together; for such a mighty crash
would have arisen Earth (as if it) were being hurled to ruin, and Heaven from on
high were hurtling her down."[9]

There are endless accounts, ancient in origin, modeled to fit cultural molds, and for the
most part un-corrupted which we may call upon to add substance to these debates. The
Hopi Indians of Arizona, and the Mayans of the Yucatan represent the best of these and
are well known for the similarities of their accounts of Creation and Catastrophe. The
Mayan tradition has come to us through the Mayan bible, the *Popol Vuh,* and the Hopi
Indian rendering through the telling...

The first three worlds ended in destruction. When the First world is about to be
destroyed, Sótuknang says to the people...You will go to a certain place. Your
Kopave (vibratory center on top of the head) will lead you. This inner wisdom will
give you the sight to see a certain cloud, which you will follow by day, and a
certain star, which you will follow by night. Take nothing with you. When (they)
were all safe and settled...Sótuknang opened up the volcanos. Fire came from
above and below and all around until the earth, the waters, the air, all was one
element, *fire,* and there was nothing left except the people safe inside the womb
of the earth.[10]

And so it has come down to us through the ages, each account relating stories where the
sea is carried out of its bed, mountains spring out of the ground, and rivers change their
course, and human beings and everything are ruined by conflagration, floods, and
hurricane.[11] It was part of their culture, it is our heritage, though we lay no claim to it.
The western mind seems to have abandoned the past and has gone on blind as though
modern history only started yesterday. I heard Graham Hancock, author of *Fingerprints
of the Gods,*[12] say in interview that he thought that we were a people with amnesia, "We

57

have become a people," he said "who have forgotten our past." Now into this fray steps Berry Fell, a Harvard professor and author of two books on early American history, *America B.C.* (1976) and *Saga America* (1983). Both of these books give us a marvelously contrasting picture to the Columbus chronologies...

> There is more to America's past than appears upon the surface. A strange unrest is apparent among many of the younger historians and archeologists of the colleges and universities, a sense that somehow a very large slice of America's past has mysteriously vanished from our public records. For how else can we explain the ever-swelling tally of puzzling ancient inscriptions now being reported from nearly all parts of the United States, Canada, and Latin America?
>
> The inscriptions are written in various European and Mediterranean languages in alphabets that date from 2500 years ago, and they speak not only of visits by ancient ships, but also of permanent colonies of Celts, Basques, Libyans, and even Egyptians. They occur on buried temples, on tablets and on gravestones and on cliff faces. From some of them we infer that the colonists intermarried with the Amerindians, and so their descendants still live here today.[13]

Barry Fell, almost in apology for public actions in matters foreign, relates to us a story of a wayward meteor that had this country in "quite a stir."

> On December 14, 1807 in the township of Weston, in western Connecticut a meteor was seen to fall out of the sky and subsequently raised quite a stir. Rumors spread. In New Haven, the press spoke of the event as a public occurrence worthy of note. Yale University was induced to dispatch two reluctant and skeptical professors to investigate the situation. In due course the professors returned to announce to an astonished faculty that in fact a stone had fallen out of the sky.
>
> ...asked for comment, (Thomas) Jefferson's reply was to the effect "...that he could more easily believe that two Yankee professors (would) lie than accept the notion that stones can fall from the sky. (But in) sequel to the Weston controversy, like all true investigators, Thomas Jefferson soon amended his oversight, and we hear no more of lying Yankee professors. Meteorites were granted recognition and henceforth might land on American soil without hindrance, and with full approval from Washington.[14]

Again it was a case of a few wayward meteors when in early-nineteenth-century Europe, the scientific authorities of the day held fast to the belief that meteors cannot fall from the sky because there are no stones in the sky to begin with but after enough stones had fallen and had been seen by thousands of people, scientists included, the authorities's bulwark of denial simply collapsed.[15]

THERE WERE OTHER CONTROVERSIES

James Hutton, author of *Theory of the Earth*, (1788) was a Scottish geologist, and the first great prophet of fluvial erosion[16] at the dawning of the modern age of geology. He was well known for his dogged stand against any suggestion of catastrophe.

> As it was in the beginning, is now, and ever shall be, world without end.[17] Not only are no powers to be employed that are not natural to the globe, no action to be admitted of except those of which we know the principle, and no extraordinary events to be alleged in order to explain a common appearance, the powers of nature are not to be employed in order to destroy the very object of those powers;...Chaos and confusion are not to be introduced into the order of nature, because certain things appear to our partial views as being in some disorder. Nor are we to proceed in feigning causes when those seem insufficient which occur in our experience.[18]

> A theory of the earth, which has for object truth, can have no retrospect to that which had preceded the present order of this world![19]

Though not identified as such in James Hutton's time, this view is what came to be known as the Uniformitarianism view. Hutton continues:

> We are to examine the construction of the present earth, in order to understand the natural operations of times past; to acquire principles, by which we may conclude with regard to the future course of things, or judge of those operations, by which a world, so wisely ordered, goes into decay; and to learn, by what means such a decayed world may be renovated, or the waste of habitable land upon the globe repaired.[20]

Charles Lyell, fondly referred to in Britain as the Napoleon of the geological world, was author of the bulwark of all geologic study, *The Principles of Geology*, in 1833.

> ....We hear of sudden and violent revolutions of the globe, of the instantaneous

elevation of mountain chains, of paroxysms of volcanic energy, declining according to some, and according to others increasing in violence, from the earliest to the latest stages. We are also told of general catastrophes and a succession of deluges, of the alteration of periods of repose and disorder, of the refrigeration of the globe, of the sudden annihilation of the whole races of animals and plants, and the hypotheses, in which we see the ancient spirit of speculation revived, and a desire manifested to cut, rather than patiently to untie, the Gordian knot.[21, A] In our attempt to unravel these difficult questions, we shall adopt a different course, restricting ourselves to the known or possible operations of existing causes; feeling assured that we have not yet exhausted the resources which the study of the present course of nature may provide, and therefore that we are not authorized, in the infancy of our science to recur to extraordinary agents.[22]

Conybeare, an English Geologist known for his synthesis of catastrophism, wrote a scorching letter in regards to Mr. Lyell's book, *Principles of Geology*.

I hope that it will not be considered as an invidious remark, but merely as expressing the general impression which your book has left on my mind, that it is an expanded commentary on the celebrated Huttonian axiom, that "in the economy of the world no traces of a beginning or prospect of an end can be discerned." Now I would not doubt for a moment on the unfounded (as I am most willing to own) moral objections which have been urged against this axiom; but I continue to regard it, as one of the most gratuitous and unsupported assertions ever hazarded.[23]

And the debates go on!

[A] An intricate knot tied by King Gordius of Phrygia and cut by Alexander the Great with his sword after hearing an oracle promise that whoever undid it would be the next ruler of Asia. Per The American Heritage®Dictionary of the English Language. Third Edition copyright©1992 By Houghton Mifflin Company

Chapter 8

Thirty Degrees, No More–No Less!

In Chapter 6 we were looking at evidence of two shifts of the earth's crust. We started with Alaska at the Pole, then the first shift moved Alaska south bringing the town of Povungnituk in Northern Quebec to the northern pole position. The second move brought the Arctic Ocean to the Pole and gave us the world as we know it today. There was a unique occurrence associated with each of these displacements which is not outwardly apparent. It is a curiosity whose interest almost goes beyond the discovery of the movements themselves. The crust moves through thirty degrees of arc with each shift. No more, no less! With a little measuring of the distance between the North Geographic Pole and each of the ancient pole locations, you can confirm it for yourself.

In terms of miles, each shift moved the land 2000 miles. I observed this in my early research and then I recalled that Hapgood had come to a similar conclusion forty years earlier. He characterized the movements as being unusually regular in terms of both frequency and distance of movement, and he demonstrated it through the presentation of extensive geologic evidences. One such piece of evidence came from cores of glacial sediment pulled from the bottom of the Ross Sea off the Pacific coast of Antarctica. Hapgood said that these cores... No wait! Let me have him tell you this part of the story.

Charles Hapgood...

> I am suggesting three displacements of the crust in the last 130,000 years, the intervals between being of the order of 30,000 or 40,000 years.[1] ...we consider the displacements (themselves) to have taken place in short periods of the order of 10 or 20 thousand years...(And) core evidence (from the Ross Sea bottom) may be used to support the thesis that the crust displacement that brought the Hudson Bay region to the pole started about 50,000 years ago.[2]

Periods of geological change in the order of thousands of years, as Hapgood is suggesting, is short indeed. But if memory serves us right, we can recall from our school days that native Americans drew pictures of mastodons, saber tooth tigers, and woolly mammoths and giant sloths on cave walls in fairly recent times.[3] So perhaps his conclusion isn't as implausible as it might appear at first, although I think that we'd find few historians who would agree. However, we should say in recognition of the many authors who have come out on this subject that we are beginning to see more and more discovery appearing in print that supports the catastrophic view point. One of the most recent of these is Graham Hancock's *Finger Prints of the Gods*.[4] He devotes the first chapters to Hapgood's work in apparent support. We'll find another example, though put in a different time frame, in a report, *Modeling the Earth System in the Mission to Planet Earth Era*, prepared by NASA, for presentation, according to the authors, Unninayar and Bergman, "...to a multi-disciplinary audience of the Global Change Research Program (GCRP)."[5] Therein the authors say that...

> Fossil and paleo-climatic records point to catastrophic changes approximately every 25 to 30 million years that were involved with the mass extinction of entire species on the earth...

We can accept NASA's premise of catastrophe here without accepting their time-table, as we've pointed to an abundance of evidence that suggests that the time table may have been much shorter. But even than, NASA has broken the waters for us in addressing the subject of catastrophe at all. Interestingly enough, even NASA gets a bit miffed with some of the scientific denouncements in regard to the demise of the dinosaurs, as you'll see from this next item from their "GCRP" report.

> ...for example, the dinosaurs that dominated the world for over 100 million years were rather abruptly terminated; a lack of intelligence for survival is an unacceptable and somewhat arrogant concoction....Several theories exist, most refer to impacts by large comets or asteroids...Some evidence (e.g. mammoths that were instantly frozen and recently excavated in a frozen, not fossilized, state) points to abrupt shifts of the earth's axis. A third scenario refers to the large rise and fall of sea level (along with changes in ice cover/extent), which is supported by evidence of extensive black shale deposits made possible through the extinction of biota by anoxia, (ie., extinction through suffocation).[6]

They don't suggest a program of investigation but they clearly acknowledge that there is an issue here! A group of researchers led by Christian Jeanthon of the Centre National de la Recherche Scientifique, and we're speaking now of evidences of catastrophe, have reported in an article titled, "Some Like it Hot," the discovery of "...bacteria thriving as deep as 1,670 meters (5,480 feet) in an oil reservoir." "Subterranean bacteria," they say, "may be able to survive by breaking down available materials, such as crude oil, into energy."[7] But doesn't the discovery of bacteria thriving deep within the earth cause us to wonder how they might have gotten there? After all 5,480 feet is well over a mile! Certainly no recognized geologic process has the character to do that! But as we can easily imagine, a crust that shifts, and buckles, and buries, has in it not only the character but the opportunity. These French authors, while side stepping the catastrophe issue just a little, go on to say...

Whether these bacteria were buried by some catastrophic event along with the fossil ingredients of the reserve, or were introduced as contaminants during some phase of the drilling and sampling processes, has yet to be proven. (But they are quick to add.)...they have proof that the bacteria are indigenous to the reservoir and were not introduced to the well by the drill bit itself. (And the article goes on to state...) "We didn't contaminate the well!"[8]

...In 1989, on the occasion of the boring of an artesian well at Nampa, Idaho, on the Columbia plateau near the Snake River, and having just pierced a sheet of basalt lava fifteen feet thick, a small figurine of baked clay was extracted from a depth of 320 feet. G. F. Wright wrote in describing the find...

The well was tubed with heavy iron tubing six inches in diameter, so that there could be no mistake about the occurrence (of the small figurine of baked clay) at the depth stated.[9]

In Sioux County, Nebraska, on the south side of the Niobrara River, in Agate Spring Quarry, is an example of a fossil-bearing deposit that is up to twenty inches thick. R. S. Lull, Director of the Peabody Museum at Yale, in his book *Fossils,* as told to us by Velikovsky in his book *Earth in Upheaval,* speaks of the profusion of bones in the Quarry relating...

The state of the bones indicate a long and violent transportation before they reached their final resting place. The fossils are in such remarkable profusion in places as to form a veritable pavement of interlacing bones, very few of which are in their natural articulation with one another. The profusion of bones may be judged by a single block now in the American Museum of Natural History in New York. This block contains about 100 bones to the square foot. The animals found there were mammals. The most numerous was the small twin-horned rhinoceros ...and bones of a giant swine that stood six feet high.[10]

Clearly catastrophe on a world wide front has been a fact of life since time began, and yet for some reason we have excluded it from our cultural psyche. Perhaps because it is too horrible to contemplate. I don't know. But let's be reminded that there is nothing in, on, or around the globe that has not been churned up and reconstituted. Everything is new and different, the animals, the plants, the soil, the rivers, the hills, even the people, everything. It's all new...its just the way nature is. Even the mountains are fairly new. For certainly we cannot believe them to be millions of years old...erosion would have made them so much rubble in the vast time spans assigned by geologists! No! We know from the drawings of mastodons and saber tooth tigers that they are fairly recent!

We need to get back to where we left off in our explanation of the title subject, Thirty Degrees, No More, No Less! We were saying that the work of establishing a measure in the movements of the crust was done almost forty years ago by Hapgood. He'd done an extensive amount of work in documenting the shifts of the earth's crust in citing enormous amounts of evidence. He laid the evidences out in a form that was almost encyclopedic in its completeness. He'd laid it out in his book, *Earth's Shifting Crust*, with the hopes that the work would be accepted by the scientific community in general and in the form of a Thesis for a Doctoral Degree, but neither, according to family members, was to happen. When he applied for a Ph.D., based on this work,[11] he was requested to change the tone of the material to better reflect the opinions of the day. But Charles, and I call him Charles out of total respect, held such a strong conviction regarding his discoveries that he declined. So he lost the acceptance that he desired, as well as the opportunity for the peer reviews that he had so strongly sought. So as we proceed, and as I quote Charles Hapgood, please keep in mind that this was no light matter with him. It was total dedication.

Let's see how Hapgood envisioned the crust to move...

The crust would now start to move, and it would continue to move easily to the distance permitted by the extent of the fractures so far created. The movement might then come to a halt, and the accompanying volcanism would tend then to subside. Meanwhile, on the poleward side of the ice cap the ice still would be building up, and the bursting stress resulting from it would again be on the increase. New fracturing would eventually occur, with a new outburst of volcanism, and the movement would be renewed."[12]

I'd like to add comment here relative to the event that would initiate the polar ice cap's movement and the sequence that it would follow. It will probably be obvious to the reader by now that the initial movements of the crust are not signaled by an event so much as by a condition. That condition being the break down of the crustal ties. I don't want to speculate on the specific processes and movements that would follow the initial movements of the crust as they are beyond the scope of this book. But since I have no argument with Hapgood's accounting, let me simply refer you to his works. In regard to the second item of difference, ie., the sequence, I'd like to suggest that there appears to be a possibility that the crust does not shift from one pole position to another, as say from Alaska to Hudson Bay. Rather there is some evidence that suggests, to the contrary, that the crust shifts toward a new pole position, then shifts back to its original position. Then shifts to another pole position and then shifts back again. For instance, it would shift from the Arctic to Alaska, then back to the Arctic. Then it would shift to Hudson Bay and then back to the Arctic. There is a very strong possibility that this is so, but there is little proof, so while I believe it to be true, we'll only mention here in passing and go back to Hapgood's displacement analysis as a starting point for our own. He came up with a distance of 2000 miles per shift.[13]

> According to the evidence...the Hudson Bay region lay at the North Pole during the period of the Wisconsin ice sheet. It is not possible (with evidence now at hand) to define the geographical position of the pole more exactly; it may have been located in Hudson Bay itself, somewhat to the west in Keewatin, or somewhere to the east in the province of Quebec.

> Now it follows logically that if the Wisconsin ice sheet (which covered Canada as well as Michigan, Ohio, Wisconsin and other Northeastern states) existed because the Hudson Bay region lay at the pole, and it disappeared because of a displacement of the crust that moved North America away from the pole, then the Wisconsin ice sheet must have been brought into existence as the result of an earlier displacement. The question, therefore now arises, Where was the pole situated previous to its location in or near Hudson Bay?

> The method of locating a previous polar position is simple in principle, but very complicated in practice. The principle is to find a point on a circle drawn about the last established polar position with a radius of the same order of magnitude as the distance between the present pole and the last position. The assumption underlying this is that while one displacement may move the crust farther than another, the chances are against any very great differences.[14]

65

I concur with Hapgood's belief that the displacement of the crust is the same with each shift. Our analysis showed that while most of the governing parameters remain the same between shifts, a few change. For instance, those that remain the same are the nature of the mooring ties, the character of their breakdown, and the amount of ice required to break the last links to free the crust to move. Those that change relate to the geographics of the land at the Pole following a shift. For instance, the greater the land mass at the Pole, the easier it is for anchoring ice to accumulate. Hapgood goes on to describe the process of picking a pole location from the geological data.

> Our first step is to draw a circle around a hypothetical polar position in Hudson Bay, with a radius of 2000 miles. Now with a very liberal margin of error, we can assume that the previous pole lay somewhere near that circle. Our second step is to check the field evidence for past climates for the whole earth to see what position on or near that circle will explain the most facts.

> The difficulties encountered in assembling the evidence for a pole in Hudson Bay were very great, but they did not compare with the difficulties of establishing a reasonable case for the position of the previous pole. For this earlier period, embracing about 40,000 years, the evidence was much scantier. The margins of error on all climatic determinations had to be much greater.

> The method used was that of trial and error, I selected a possible location, and then searched the available evidence to see whether that location was reasonable. I tried many locations, giving up one after another as facts turned out to conflict with each of them. (From the Hudson Bay location) The previous position of the pole was, I concluded, in or near Greenland, or between Greenland and Iceland...I repeated the process, with this polar position as the center of my circle, and with a rather flexible radius, and came up, to my considerable surprise, with a pole somewhere in or near Alaska, perhaps in the Alaska Peninsula or in the Aleutian Islands. This third pole takes us back to about 130,000 years ago.[15]

A glimpse at the globe and a little measuring will show the reader that the Alaska Peninsula is right at the 2000 mile radius from Hudson Bay, and since this was one of Hapgood's criteria for establishing a previous pole position, I don't understand the rational in rejecting the Alaska position as the one immediately prior to Hudson Bay. In fact I don't see how Greenland fits into the picture at all, unless we accept the "Bobbing Scenario." Even than, we didn't find any cultural evidence to support a pole position in Greenland...but who knows? Hapgood continues...

The difficulties encountered in assembling the evidence for a pole in Hudson Bay were very great, but they did not compare with the difficulties of establishing a reasonable case for the position of the previous pole.

The ancient cultural evidence that we'll be presenting to you in the succeeding chapters is exceedingly strong for a sequence of movement following this path... Alaska to Hudson Bay and Hudson Bay to the Arctic Ocean. This sequence involves two shifts of the crust rather than the three Hapgood suggested. Our time frame, starting with Alaska's initial movement to the Pole, until about 8000 B.C., is approximately 110,000 years. We'll develop additional rational for this timetable in Chapter 14, *In The Land of Spreading Darkness*, and in Chapter 15, *The Whole of manifestation*. The data is ancient and the study of the crust's movements is not a simple one, but we had one advantage...that of hindsight provided us by Hapgood's research.

THE STRENGTH AND CHARACTER OF THE FOUNDATION

As starters, we must agree that in order for the crust to move at all there must to be a force of sufficient magnitude to move it! In this regard we accepted Hapgood's thesis, supported by Einstein, that the Antarctic ice cap with its associated centrifugal momentum would produce such a force. Secondly, we had to have a condition at the lower crust/lithosphere interface that would embrace the crust's movements. A slippery zone, so to speak. In answer to this requirement we acknowledged the agents of the RB-Effect to perform the necessary work in preparing a "plastic zone."

Thirdly we had to have a condition develop such that on one side of time the crust would be stable, and on the other side, and just moments later, the crust would become unstable and it would begin to slip. Forth, we depended upon a shape of the inner lithospheric surface that would be neither encumbering nor totally passive. The earth was going to lose the stabilizing effect of the equatorial bulge during a shift and this had to be compensated for. Meeting this requirement was a little more difficult. Little is known about these processes, and answers were going be long in coming. So we put together a list of everything that we felt controlled the event and then we built a hypothesis around it. Our conclusions were derived from this analysis. (See also Figure 1.)

1. The item of greatest importance in any construction where ground movements are anticipated is the strength and character of the foundation. This is particularly true of traffic bearing constructions such as bridges, railroads, and highways, the rules had to be true of the crust as well. So in anticipation of this, we looked for

a condition wherein the crustal foundation, in order to *allow* movement, would be weak in areas where other traffic bearing constructions were strong.

2. The moment of inertia of the earth as a whole would change with a displacement of the crust, and this would cause the earth to lose rotational stability unless something intervened. So we asked ourselves, "What could intervene?"

3. The contour of the lower crust had to be influenced by the forces that shaped it, as we've said...nothing else works...so our anticipations were that the lithosphere would have an oblate character to it, much like the crust itself.

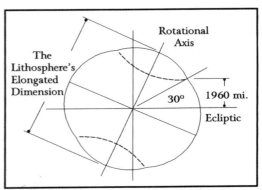

4. We believed too, since each crustal movement was similar in character, that there had to be some overall governing criteria that dictated the consistency...and since only forces can cause motion, it was obvious that the consistency had to be dictated by a confrontation between the driving and the restraining forces.

Figure 1. The inner crustal shell which is created by the bending actions of the RB Effect.

Another piece of evidence in support of the probable existence of a unique sub-crustal shape is evidenced by the fact that there is no earthquake activity in Antarctica, and virtually none in the Arctic, while in the lower latitudes, where the constant bending of the crust occurs, there is strong earthquake activity. It is not surprising, therefore, to discover that at the higher latitudes bending, via the incidence of Rotational-Bending, is totally absent. The crust at those latitudes, because the shaping scalpel of the RB-Effect is absent, must be significantly different from other zones around the world and would confirm that the lower boundary of the crust is shaped by bending action. From this analysis we envisioned a contoured inner surface that roughly paralleled the crust and modeled well with the forces that produced it. (See the bending stress diagram reproduced from Chapter 6, in Figure 2.)

It is not uncommon for initial engineering studies to draw heavily upon experience, and it was certainly necessary in this case because there was absolutely no scientific support for our conclusions. Theories that arise from studies such as these will eventually draw the power of research into the field if they have merit, so I will hope that this is the case. In the mean time we are going to stay with our analysis.

ROTATIONAL STABILITY

Hapgood was concerned about the earth's ability to maintain rotational stability during a shift...the problem being, of course, that there was going to be a colossal redistribution of mass and if something didn't step in quickly to correct it the earth's axis would gyrate out of control. On this point he sought the advice of Dr. Harlow Shapley, then Director of the Harvard Observatory.

I have concluded, Hapgood wrote, that the work that we are doing is dependent upon a clear answer to the question as to whether the geographical poles are stabilized by the momentum of rotation of the earth, or solely by that of the equatorial bulge...I am hoping that you can give me a steer in nontechnical terms on the general concepts.[16]

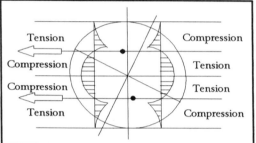

Figure 2. It is evident that the stresses due to bending are totally absent at latitudes between about 60° and 68°.

Dr. Shapley's reply to Hapgood, dated February 2, 1951, was, in part, as follows...

Dr. [Harold] Jeffreys was fortunately here at the Harvard Observatory and I could turn your inquiry to him. I now have his reply. He says in effect that the fullest discussion of the points mentioned by you is in Routh's Rigid Dynamics, probably in Volume I. Most textbooks of rigid dynamics will have something about it. The theory goes back to Euler. Really both the rotation and the equatorial bulge are needed to maintain stability. Without rotation the body could be at rest at any position; with rotation but without the equatorial bulge it could rotate permanently about an axis in any direction...[17]

Here again the "Bobbing Scenario" would answer a lot of questions. For instance under this scenario, the crust would be at the new pole location for a very brief period of time, say ten-twenty thousand years, during which time the ice would begin to melt and the rotational axis would be quite unstable, but then stability would be ushered in with a return shift, or a partial shift, to the permanent Pole. It is an intriguing thought, and more and more it is looking like the scenario of choice.

The lithosphere, as we envisioned it, was going to provide the major portion of the stabilizing inertia needed during a shift. But too, there had to be a system available, a governor of sorts, to smooth over the transient periods. There were two other areas of concern as well. The stabilizing control had to respond very quickly and the earth's rotational speed had to be maintained at a reasonably constant rate.

Without a speed control earth-time would change. Let me explain. A spinning object remains at a fixed rate of rotation, ignoring friction, just as long as the mass remains symmetrically distributed, ie., unchanging in configuration. If the mass is re-distributed to change the moment of inertia, the rate of rotation will change accordingly. The example which is quoted ad nauseam, is the one of the ice skaters who move their arms outward to slow their rate of rotation, or bring them in to the body to increase it. Mechanical governors do the same thing. So do the centrifugal switches on electric motor shafts that serve to switch field windings. In going through this "arm swinging" maneuver the skater is changing their moment of inertia. It is one of those things of nature that science accepts without fully understanding all the whys-and-where-fores. It just works that way!

In the earth-moon system, however, it is far more complicated. If the earth slows down because of a change in its moment of inertia, the moon is going to get upset, it will increase its speed and move away. It does this in accordance with the Law of Conservation of Angular Momentum. Meanwhile, back on earth, since we've slowed down, we'll no longer have a 24 hour day, it will have increased to 24.5 or 25 hours, or what ever, depending on how much things have changed. In reality the changes will be small, far too small for the moon to notice or care, but not so small that it can be ignored here on earth. There has to be a mechanism that is sensitive to small changes, a mechanism that will react with proper magnitude and in direct response, increasingly or decreasingly, to absorb and store the undistributed angular momentum, and we need that mechanism to react smoothly and without excessive duress.

We knew that a governor had to exist in some form within the earth, and we resolved to find it. Our conclusions were, as we're going to suggest to you, that it is earth's own inner core. The core is known to be rotating at a speed different from that of the crust, so apparently, at least from outward appearances, it has already absorbed some inertial responses and is holding them locked in the energy of its own distinct rotation in lieu of having distributed them to the moon.[18]

Some day we will see the re-distribution process occur. It will happen because the earth-moon-core is a system that is locked into a conservation of angular momentum agreement that cannot be broken. We discuss this in Chapter 20, *370 Million Year Old Coral,* as well, because it is important in regards to another body of evidence that suggests that there are other agents at work that are requiring the core's assistance in maintaining the 24 hour clock. But for now, if the crust should shift again, and if there is some change of inertia, we should expect the core to pick up the reserve, and either slow its rate of rotation, or speed up, depending upon the requirements foisted upon it.

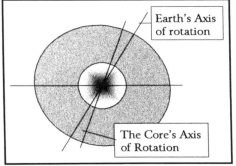

The knowledge that the core is rotating at a speed different than that of the crust opens the door for some interesting investigation. There is one item of particular interest. We know, for instance, that during a shift, the crust will be moving away from the pole at some speed. This imparts a component of momentum on the crust which is oblique to the earth's eastward directed momentum. If the core is required to pick up this oblique component, it would have

Figure 3. If the core picked up the southern component of the crust's momentum during a displacement, it would have to speed up and its rotational axis would move out of alignment with the earth's to absorb it

to shift ever so much and start rotating on an axis oblique to that of the earth's axis. If an angle of obliqueness, were somehow shown to exist, it would prove that its unique velocity was in response to the "conservation of angular momentum agreement with the moon."

It is impossible to estimate how long such an offset would be maintained, but the oblique component would have to be dissipated before the core's axis could shift back in alignment with the earth's again. The big question now is how fast and how smoothly does the system respond? If it is immediate then the earth's axis will remain stable, and the clocks will remain "on time." If the response time is slow then the earth may well go through a period of wobble and general instability. But the fact that the elements are in place for a smooth transition suggests that the smooth transition is the process of choice.

We still have two questions to answer with regard to how far the crust will move and what stops it. For these answers we want to refer to Figure 4, and to follow this scenario. When the Antarctic ice is forced toward the equator, the centroid of each of the crustal segments, above and below the ecliptic, are caused to move toward the advancing ice and away from the rotational axis. This is true because the ice is driving the equatorial mass to higher latitudes, and it is moving along the same line of movement followed by the ice, and the added weight of the ice attracts the centroids. It is like adding weight to one side of a teeter-totter. When you do this, you will notice that the pivot, or the balance point, has moved in the direction of the added weight. Balance a pencil on your finger and try it by adding a drop of water to one side or the other, and you'll notice that the added weight of the water "attracts" the balance point.

Once under motion, the status of the crust is one of severe lose of equilibrium. It is a time of temporary chaos when the laws of nature are being violated. The crust is cracking, the lands are undulating, and the ocean waters are being hurled across the land and washing away everything in their paths. Conditions are not going to change soon, because as the event progresses and the ice moves further from the pole, the forces grow and the moving ice is driven to new energy levels. The noise, chaotic and deafening, and perhaps even maddening, will dominate everything.

It is not in the scheme of things, however, for chaos to prevail for long, for far greater in their influence are the laws of nature. Restraining forces will take over and everything will come to a stop. It is a system temporarily out of control like a run-a-way freight train...100 tons of steel coming down the track at 40 MPH...but it will eventually run out of fuel and then it must stop. So the question really is, "How much fuel does the system have?"

Well the fuel is being supplied by the forces that convert to energy as the system gains momentum. Forces drive the ice, it has mass, and now it has velocity, and these are the ingredients of momentum, and until the forces finally disappear, or are counterbalanced by others, the event will continue out of control. But control is coming. The forces which gave the ice the potential to move in the first place, with the movement of the mass of the equatorial bulge into the higher latitudes of the Northern and Southern hemispheres, are now working on the crust to slow it down.

THE RETROGRADE FORCES.

Three couples, or three twisting actions would be another way of expressing it, are being created by the movement of the crust as the ice moves toward the equator. The first is created by the force of the ice relative to the center of the earth, and it is causing a clockwise torque. In Figure 5, this is represented by the force, F_3 and the distance "d." The ensuing motion of the crust, which moves the mass of the equatorial bulge into the higher latitudes, separates the centroids, this is distance "D" in Figure 5. With this movement, the gravitational influence on them from the sun and the moon, increases to produce a restraining motion. The third moment, or twisting motion, is created by the centrifugal forces acting on the displaced mass of the equatorial bulge to send it back to the equator. In the mean time ice is building up at the pole at ever increasing rates, and the centrifugal forces there are growing.

EVERYTHING IS IN A STATE OF CHANGE.

Everything is in a continual state of change during these events. Prior to a shift, when the earth is symmetrical about the rotational axis, the mass centers of the crust, relative to the ecliptic, remain fixed in the plane of the rotational axis and do not rotate with the earth. But when the crust shifts the mass centers move to oppose the oncoming ice and they become locked in the regulatory disciplines of planetary motion and are forced to rotate with the earth once every 24 hours. With this new rotational mode, the distance between the mass centers of the crust and the gravitational centers of the sun and the moon change continuously, hence the gravitational forces change continuously.

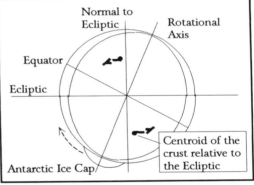

Figure 4. The centroids of the earth's crust, above and below the ecliptic, will move away from the vertical axis as the crust shifts.

They vary in magnitude on a minute to minute basis, they act always to restrain the ice, but they fluctuate from a maximum value as the sun or the moon passes through the plane of crustal movement, to a value of zero, when they are perpendicular to the plane of movement. It is a curious combination of push and pull, with the ice pushing its way toward the equator with ever increasing force, and the displaced crust, through the combined action of centrifugal force and gravity, is shoving it back with a pulsing restraining force.

IT MAKES NO DIFFERENCE

73

During our initial investigations we selected crustal thickness values of 7, 37, 87, and 155 miles and we were now trying to establish the magnitude of the forces that acted upon each unit. But much to our surprise, we discovered that it didn't matter how thick the crust was when the ice began its movements, because the differential forces acting to restrain the crust from above and below the ecliptic, were always going to be the same anyway. The crust could be 30 miles thick, or two hundred and thirty, it didn't matter.

A summary of the differential forces that act to restrain the crust once that it begins to move can be seen in Table AIV-1, on page 241. The important aspect of this data is that the restraining forces are identical for all thickness values of the crust for at least the first two or three decimal places, which for forces of this magnitude are the only ones of significance anyway. What this means overall is that the crust can shift

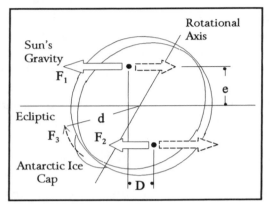

Figure 5. Two couples, or torques, are created by the movement of the crust. The first is a clockwise torque, caused by the motion of the crust. The second is caused as the centroids separate and the earth's gravitational pull produces a restraining torque.

across any surface where a plasticized condition develops regardless of the depth at which it forms. Crustal thickness is going to have a very marked consequence **during** a shift, however. It is a guess, but I would suspect thin crustal shells in motion would result in splintering, while thick shells would show less splintering and more mountain building.

In the upcoming chapters we are going to demonstrate that the Sphinx, which today gazes forlornly eastward from the West bank of the Nile was spawned from the bedrock when Giza lay on the equator. It took two, and perhaps three, 30 degree shifts of the earth's crust to move it from its original home on the equator to 30 degrees North latitude where it is today! And it took a most unusual set of circumstances, with a little help from man, to bring it around to face east again. It is the story of Part Three of this book. It is called The PAMPA JUMANA-COLORADA.

INTRODUCTION, Part 3.   The Pampa Jumana-Colorada

In his book, *The Migration of Symbols,* Count Goblet d' Alviella explains that in symbolic language the part is equal to the whole.

There is a tendency, he says, to reduce an abbreviated figure in order either to enclose it in a smaller space, or else to lessen the work of the artist, especially when it is a complicated image in frequent use. In all systems of writing where the characters first appeared under the form of hieroglyphs, the letter need only be glanced over in order to find the symbol. It is known, for instance, that our vowel "A" was originally a bull's head, a bucrane, and that the latter, in its turn, represented the whole animal, in conformity with the popular rule that the part is equal to the whole in the matter of symbols, as well as sacrifices. It is thus, again, that in the signs of the Zodiac the Lion is merely represented by its tail.[1]

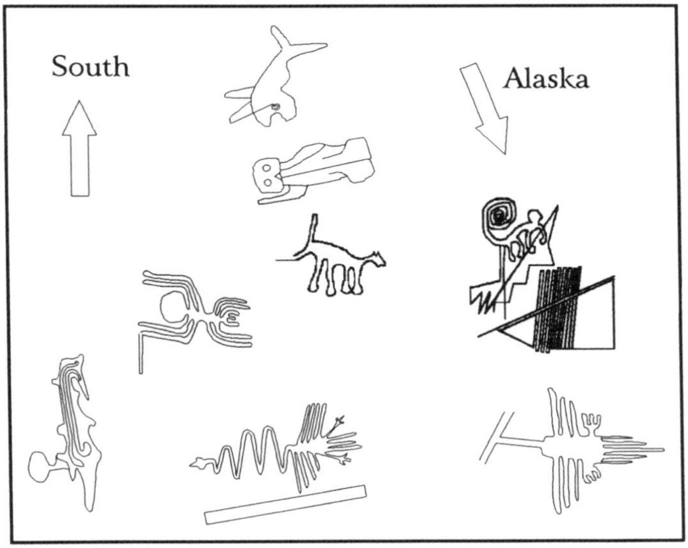

Figure 1 The Figures on the Nascan plateau shown right side up. They represent a time when Nasca and Egypt were both on the equator and Alaska was at the North Geographical Pole! It was a time that was far different than today!

READING THE GLYPHS

In the coming pages we'll be examining many of the figures on the plateau above Nasca, Peru and there we will see how the makers have interwoven many tales across the outlines. Which tale is being told, or what message is being relayed, depends upon which set of lines the inquirer has chosen to represent the image of interest. For instance, let's have the inquirer pick the spider in Figure 1., as their

75

subject. For this example we'll take the whole figure of the spider to investigate. Although we could have taken just the stringer that grows toward the right from the lower leg because it carries a message of its own as we'll see.

Before we go on we want to pick another figure as well. Let's say we pick the many-fingered Glyph from the lower right of Figure 1. We might say that it represents a tree, and from there go on to analyze the meaning of its branches. On the other hand it may be observed to resemble a "key" in which case it would lead the observer to examine some of the other figures to see what secret this "key" may unlock. This line of thinking would reveal the similarities between the key and the eight-legged spider-like figure. In what way are they similar?

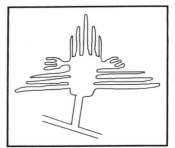

Figure 2 This figure from the upper right of Figure 1 may be thought of as a "tree" or a "key."

Envision the spider-like figure not as a spider, but as a plant that has been pulled up by its roots and is now laying atop the ground. In this characterization, it takes on several interpretations. One interpretation, which is depicted in Figure 4, takes the observer back to when the plant was alive with soil around its roots...now the bulbous projection which grows from the waistline of the figure transforms itself from the abdomen of a spider into the seed bulb from which this plant grew. So who knows whether it is a spider or a plant? Or maybe it is both! If we assume it is a plant we could conclude that this plant, because of the way that the bulb is caged by the roots, is a member of the rhizome family of plants, and reasonably therefore, it is a lotus. A distinguishing characteristic of a lotus, which may be important to us here, is that if a rhizome is split, it does not die but becomes several plants instead of one.[2] One plant creates its own double in this process and it administers upon itself a form of immortality. Another aspect of the rhizome family of plants is that they produce underground stems by means of which they propagate themselves.[3] So now the stringer that grows toward the right from the root, which we thought earlier to be a leg, is really a blossoming shoot of the root of the plant which is in a state of growth directed towards its own propagation.

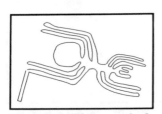

Figure 3 This symbol from Figure 1 may be envisioned as a spider

Now the theory that this figure is a plant, in addition to its claim to being a spider, and that it has grown from a bulb, and that it is a member of the rhizome family of plants, and that it has been pulled up by its roots, is corroborated by the presence of the underground stem. Without the stem it is a spider, with the stem it is a plant belonging to the rhizome family of plants, and as such, it is no doubt a lotus. In Greek mythology there were a people called the Lotus-Eaters...

...who lived on the North coast of Africa and subsisted on the fruit of the lotus tree. This made them forget the past and live in blissful indolence. In the Odyssey when ODYSSEUS landed on their coast, some of the scouts tasted the lotus fruit, forgot their homes and families, and had to be forcibly carried back to the ships by their companions.[4, 5]

From this, we may say that we have read 'a partial message' from the 'lotus figure' in that either the Ancient workers on the Nascan plateau were Lotus-Eaters too and lived 'in blissful indolence,' **or** the message reads, and this is my interpretation of choice, that mankind, like the scouts who tasted the lotus fruit, had tasted of the fruit and now live in blissful indolence. This conclusion would seem like a leap in the dark unless you were familiar with the sanctifications in the Brotherhood between man and the lotus which are found within virtually all ancient cultures. In *An Encyclopaedia of Traditional Symbols*, J. C. Cooper tells us that the lotus symbolizes the interaction between Purusha, the soul, and Prakriti, nature.[A]

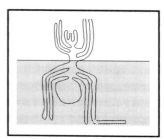

Figure 4 By imagining soil surrounding the "roots" of this figure it becomes a plant that grew from a "bulb."

It is 'the flower that was in the Beginning'...the source of all existence...Its root signifies an indissoluble union, the stem the umbilical cord attaching man to his origins...it depicts the live-giving, death-dealing powers of the Great Mother...in man it represents the skull...The lotus also represents the past, present and future since the same plant bears buds, flowers and seeds at the same time.[6]

The ways of Ancient cultures reaches us in the form of legend and myth which we are far too readily inclined to dismiss as simple mystic elements of the past. Nothing could be further from the truth. Let's look carefully at the flowering 'three-fingered-center' of the lotus plant while we remind ourselves that the lotus, because the same plant bears, buds, flowers, and seeds at the same time, represents...the past...the present...and the future. At the same time, let's envision the

---

[A] The modern English interpretation of "Purusha, the soul, and Prakriti, nature" interestingly enough, is Purusha, *pursue*, Prakriti, *procreation*. "Pursue procreation!"

amount of time taken up by man's past... how much time is consumed by his present existence... and how much time lays in his future. With this in mind, look carefully at the physical sizes of the flowering 'three-fingered-center' of the lotus. Wouldn't you say that the proportion of size to time are representative? There is a disturbing aspect to it, however, the representation of time is finite!

We will see that representing a thought or a message via the language of symbolic representation is not *just* to enclose a figure in a smaller space to lessen the work of the artist or the reader, although certainly that is true in many cases, but more than that, it is a language onto itself that has a thought, like a Rembrandt or a Picasso, born of every stroke. In this modern age, because our thoughts come to us one image onto another – one word, one sentence at a time, we must study each piece of art

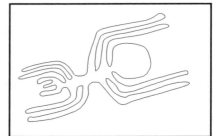

Figure 5 The Thunderbolt, The Language of the Ancients.

– piece by piece – one section at a time, hoping that at the end we have engage the emotion of the artist successfully. Our thoughts come to us in a different way than those of the Ancients, they saw what they wanted to see in a blinding flash of recognition. We ponder and dally, question and deny, and all too often forget to remember.

The figures on the plateau were the labor of a people who were telepathic, and who probably never vocalized their thoughts! Telepathy is a universal language, it is a language without alphabet or word, but it is also a language that must be "accepted" more than it is "learned" if we are to *speak* it. Telepathic exchanges are complete expressions of image and movement, of emotion and purpose all transmitted as a *thunderbolt* of expression. There is no other word to describe it. The Thunderbolt has been described as transcendental truth,[7] meaning, as we'll see in a later chapter, "Beyond thought or experience, an intuitive basis of knowledge independent of experience, even mystical or supernatural."[8] The thunderbolt, in other representations, symbolizes divine force, cosmic intelligence, and enlightenment,[9] and when it, or the trident which is used in its place in some instances, is seen in ancient encryptions, in the boldest of all ancient messages, it is telling us that the language in use is telepathy. It was the language of the ancient–Ancients, and if we as modern man who must use words and books to convey our thoughts, wish to understand these wondrous people, we must first accept their language. It is all too easy to dismiss these thoughts of "...divine force, cosmic intelligence, and enlightenment", as mysticisms or 'ramblings from the occult', but what we are witnessing in the discoveries being made from the ancient cultures is neither mysticism nor the occult, it was simply their way of living. It was their 'pebble', and they wrote their beliefs in every conceivable place and manner. Look at the Zodiacal

Constellation of Taurus, in Figure 7, and see if you agree with me that this Constellation looks like a symbol of "...divine force, and cosmic intelligence..." Or is it a Divining rod?

I spoke earlier of a second interpretation that we might put to the figure of the plant and its having been pulled out by its roots and laid upon the ground. That interpretation is derived from this. In a later chapter we will be looking upon "The primeval god who evolved from the Chaos, who... took his phallus in his grasp that he might create orgasm by means of it, and so...were born the twins..."[10] – One male, one female. That 'primeval god' had the power of procreation. Procreation as symbolized by the rhizome plant when it was alive and growing and sending out stems. But things have changed, the rhizome plant on this ancient plateau – this lotus, has been pulled up by its roots. That brings us, symbolically, to that point in history that followed the decision that man, in propagating the species, would forever more, dependent upon union.

Figure 6 The primeval God, **Atum Rēͼ.**

On the ground, its roots having been pulled, no longer capable of self-propagation, the lotus symbolizes *modern* man. Man who traverses upright across the ground, and having tasted of the fruit, like the Lotus-Eaters, has lost his memory. Having been pulled up from the sustaining soils, he has lost his memory of his God and his origins. He is without knowledge of his roots. But let's not forget the feature of the rhizome that so distinguished it in the first place, a feature which now is of extreme importance. If a rhizome is split, if the soul separates from the body, it does not die but becomes another plant instead! Or so the makers of the plateau tell us!

The skill portrayed by the artisans on the plateau in conveying their message can only be appreciated if you will walk with us as we stroll the desert of the Pampa Jumana-Colorada! We'll be visiting each figure one by one. But our stroll cannot be taken in this modern time, we must go to an ancient epoch, there we will find Nasca and Giza both on the equator, and we will find Alaska at the North geographic Pole. We will have two purposes in mind as we walk along. The first will be to demonstrate the existence of a cultural link between Nasca and Giza, and we will demonstrate for you that

Figure 7 Taurus, *The Bull*, **Atum Rēͼ**, or is it a Divining Rod?

their civilizations had a common origin. The second purpose in demonstrating the genesis of the figures is one of enlightenment. We hope by this to start a revival of spirit that will take us back to our real origins.

The Tree of Knowledge, The Cosmic Tree!
The Whole of Manifestation, by what ever name, a Tree.

The Language of the Ancients.
A spider? A rhizome? Or, is it The Thunderbolt?

Chapter 9

The Story Begins

As an engineer and a teacher I was always dealing with the physical laws...laws which for some inexplicable reason were changeless with time and always worked in accordance with the mathematical equations that were written for them as though they were ours to command. They worked yesterday, they work today, and they will work tomorrow. They work for water, and steel, for television, and airplanes, they work for people, and dogs, and birds, and anything else that you can name. I always thought of this truism as though somehow these laws had been given some binding sacramental character.

I got a clearer insight into sacramental character when I discovered, while researching this book, that the Sphinx which faces east today, and faced east when it was built, didn't always face east. It is an intriguing story, one that involves the sun, the moon, some ancient coral, and 10 Egyptian Gods... Atum, Shu, Tefēnet, Gēb, Nūt, Osiris, Isis, Seth, Nephthys, and an un-named god, perhaps Thoth maybe Horus. I'll introduce you to them as we go along but it is more important now, as we begin, for you to know that everything that we will be discussing here is true to the best of my knowledge. It will seem fantastic and unbelievable and you'll keep wondering how some of it came about. Well, I can't answer that question because I don't know. I only know that it did. Should you want, you can walk up and put your hands on many of the artifactual elements of our account because they are still there. They are lost as to purpose, but they are there, carved often from the very rock upon which they endure. One such lasting artifactual element is written in hieroglyphic form on the walls of an ancient Egyptian pyramid...

> (§ 35) Recite four times, A boon which the King grants to the double of the King. O Osiris the King, take the Eye of Horus, your pɘt-cake, that you may eat— a pɘt-cake of the offering.[1]

This artifactual text assures us, unlike what we've been otherwise lead to believe, that Yes! "You **can** have your cake -and eat it too!"[A]

We have to go to Egypt to begin the rest of this story.

On the West bank of the Nile, at what is the Southern boundary of the Nile Delta, and very near the border of the ancient Kingdoms of Upper and Lower Egypt, at a site called Giza, is a complex of pyramids. Three in particular stand out silhouetted against the Western sky, but only one has the stature to attract our attention and capture our imagination. It is the Great Pyramid of Giza. Covering 13 plus acres, and measuring 481 feet tall and more that 3000 feet around the base, it is one of the largest structures on earth. Speculation over the meaning or significance of this pyramid has occupied the attention of historians for centuries, and for little wonder, for despite its lack of ennobling features it is an incredible structure. Not just because of its size, though it is immense, and not just because of the superb craftsmanship, though each stone was cut and placed with a precision that might better be called exacting, but rather because built into every stone of this great pyramid, and built into every stone at the Giza complex as a whole, is a code, or to be more faithful to the intent of the builders, an encrypted message that all but cries out for a solution. It cries out for a conversion from the ancient ideologies of the past to something that reads meaningfully to the 20th century mind.

The true mystique of the Pyramid is hidden to all who fail to realize that the ancient plea for understanding is real. As a start, imagine, as perhaps you have, that we would find it a challenge to our skills and our technology should we attempt to build the Great Pyramid today. It may even be impossible. But should we succeed, would we have found it desirable to have build it with a meaningful message encrypted for others to find, and read, and interpret 10,000 years from now? That was the desire of the Ancients!

THE INCREDIBLE MYSTERY OF THE PYRAMID OF GIZA

Why was the Pyramid built? We may never know for sure. But it won't be for a lack of effort, and it won't be for a lack of interest. If it is for any reason at all...it will be because the clues are so skillfully embedded in the sole of the complex that the modern mind may never comprehend the extent of the encryption, and as much as it might injure our vanity, we may not possess the knowledge necessary to understand what we discover. We may not know enough to put it all together! Most historians are satisfied with the theory that suggests that the Great Pyramid is a mausoleum built in the 3rd millennium B.C. by Cheops, the second king of the IV Dynasty of Egypt.[2] If we accept this traditional interpretation, however, it will have to be on faith because no one has ever found any evidence to support it. No mummies, no jewels, no anything. The truth in fact is that since its abandonment the Pyramid has been empty, save for a single stone sarcophagus, a few tools, and some intriguing passages that angle up from the two main chambers. At least one of these having a door at the end that is too far away to reach or open.[3]

Others who have contested the supposition that the Pyramid is a mausoleum, see in the clues the suggestion of a much different meaning. Some see that it chronicles a record of catastrophe in earth's past and a prediction of catastrophe in earth's future. Some feel that the mathematically encrypted clues may lead to a trove of knowledge that was stored for posterity by the Ancients, perhaps even the fabled Tree of Knowledge. Although again, to entertain the notion of these deeper meanings, they too must be accepted on faith, at least at the start, for the clues are scant and they only suggest that there is something more to be found. But for those who have maintained a faith in their conviction there have been rewards. The proof of the reward has been in the discovery of further evidence, sometimes found in the architectural scheme of the Pyramid, or the Giza complex, or another part of the world entirely, and it leads the adventurer on.

So whether the Great Pyramid or the Giza complex as a whole, is an edifice to the Gods, or a mausoleum, or whether either conceal some yet to be resolved cipher remains to be determined. The Giza adventure, however, starts with a most improbable predicament, because embodied in the sole of any mystery is the implicit assumption that there is a mystery to be solved. But to many historians who see no mystery at all strongly repudiate all suggestions that the complex contains an encrypted message or a secret of any kind. So to those who would struggle to break this "Mysterious Code of Giza" goes the unusual task of having to write the mystery around the clues as they are revealed. But the lure remains as an enigma that has the drawing power of the boldest adventure.

The Ancients must have realized that time would eventually consume the record that they wanted to preserve and it would destroy the opportunity for their story to be told unless they cataloged it in such bold and anomalous expression that it would stand out in contrast to its surroundings and be found and recognized. So in the only way that would transcend time, they published their message-catalog in wondrous structures that employed astronomical and mathematical relationships anomalous to their character and spread them around the world. But more than that, since their sciences were developed to extraordinary levels, they employed a precision in the astronomical relationships that would require computers to replicate today. Millenniums ago they used a numerical system based on units of ten that would be classed as modern today, and they took their mathematical calculations out to 9 and often 10 decimal places. Not for accuracy, as accuracy does not lay in the use of endless decimal expression, but as a tool to convey their message. As we contemplate this, we should be reminded that our books tell us that the numerical system in use today, was "..discovered in India by natives counting on their fingers"[4] Makes you wonder!

THE SEARCH BEGINS: The terrestrial connection.

There are two major clues that are known to express the meaning of the Mysterious Code of Giza, one that involves the orientation of the pyramids and the Sphinx to the Cardinal points, North, East, South & West, and another that demonstrates an anomalous height to perimeter ratio in the structure of the Great Pyramid involving the value Pi,[5] which is a relationship found only in circles and related shapes. These two clues play a central part in our story. Pi, which is the verbal expression, or the Greek letter "π" which is the mathematical form, is a transcendental number.[6] It is derived experimentally by dividing the measured distance around a circle, ie., the circumference, by the greatest distance across the circle, ie., the diameter. The answer will always come out to be 3.14159, if we restrict our answer to 5 decimal places. This is true regardless of the size of the circle. The Ancients, as I mentioned, and as we'll see later, took Pi out to 9 decimal places in their mathematical expressions. They used algebra, geometry, trigonometry, and the exponential functions. They used astronomy, and they used a grid system of latitude and longitude to map the earth. All, just as we do today.

Many of the mathematical clues that have been found involve transcendental numbers. Transcendental meaning an entitlement wherein the final value is indeterminate, as all calculations go on past the decimal point unendingly and never repeat. Given this un-ending character of transcendental numbers, it causes me to wondered whether this is a clue in itself! What could they be trying to say to us? "That life goes on forever," like a transcendental number! Or, "That life does not repeat!" Or both? Or is it a clue at all? We might look at the term transcendental in the modern sense in an attempt to understand what they may have been trying to convey.

In Philosophy transcendental means "Beyond thought or experience, an intuitive basis of knowledge independent of experience, even mystical or supernatural."

In Mathematics it means "Not being capable of being determined by any combination of a finite number of equations with rational integral coefficients." What this means is that you can't derive the number using equations without experimental data.[7]

Transcendental is also used in describing a technique of meditation derived from

Hindu traditions that promotes deep relaxation through the use of a mantra. A mantra being a sacred verbal formula repeated in prayer, or meditation, such as an invocation of a God.[8]

A SPECIAL CODE

We'll see in later chapters that the Ancients used a special three ingredient foundation of encryption. The first ingredient is perhaps the most interesting. Every inch of every line they drew has a unique meaning that varies depending upon which set of lines the observer puts together to construct the image. The Ancients also made frequent use of redundancy, the repeating of clues, and they used anomalous, attention getting clues. Everything that they did was repeated over, and over again. Redundancy is found everywhere, and as an expression of this code they aligned everything with everything. Giza yesterday, as we'll soon discover, was at the same latitude as Nasca, Peru. We'll have to go there to understand how and why, but in the mean time, and as we follow the paths that were laid out for us to travel, we must be alert least we miss their meaning.

A QUESTIONABLE CLAIM

It has been observed that the ancient inhabitants of Egypt oriented themselves to the South. The rational being that the Nile, which afforded them their agricultural life's blood, flowed from the South. But therein lays a curiosity! The flooding waters of the Nile River are historically significant, but they are seasonal, they are local, and they afford the traveler no guidance. So why, from the latitude of Egypt, would anyone look south? The South polar region is void of stars. The Southern Cross, which only points south, cannot be seen readily from Giza, but the North Star is clearly visible. So why would they orient themselves in a direction from which they were unable to get their bearings? It makes no sense! Giza is situated at 30° North latitude within feet of the latitude of the oldest city in the United States, St Augustine, Florida. The people of St Augustine today, as with yesterday when it was inhabited by seven foot tall "giants" whose remains are currently on display at the museum of the Fountain of Youth, orient themselves to the North, and to the North star Polaris, not the South! Unless, the belief is a remnant from the ancient culture that thrived in the region when Giza lay on the equator! It would make sense under those circumstances!

THE CELESTIAL CONNECTION

The discovery of the second trail of clues can be attributed to a number of independent researchers. This time the clues orient us to the stars, and specifically to the stars in the constellation Orion.[9] These clues are worthy of note but they do not have a continuing bearing on this story, so I wish only to mention them in passing, and then only to say that the precision with which the Pyramid was built to align with the stars, and the constellation Orion, employs a knowledge of astronomy that few possess today.

There are six clues in this sequence, five are taken from Robert Bauval and Adrian Gilbert's book, *The Orion Mystery*. [10]

1. The Pyramids at Giza are oriented in relation to the stars in the belt of the constellation Orion.[11]

2. The shaft that bears South from the Queen's chamber aligns with the star Sirius.[12]

3. The Southern shaft from the King's Chamber is sighted on Al Nitak, the lowest of the three stars of Orion's belt.[13]

4. The shaft that bears North from the King's chamber aligns with the star Thuban in the constellation Draco.[14]

5. The shaft that bears North from the Queen's chamber aligns with "...the center of the four stars forming the head of Ursa Minor."[15]

6. The South side of the Great Pyramid aligns broadside with the sun, and the shaft that bears South from the Queen's chamber, referenced in the second clue above, aligns like a rifle bore, with the Sun at the Winter Solstice, the first day of Winter. (*Discovered during my own researching.*)

Much thought has to be given to this last clue, How is it possible for these ancient people to align the same passage, the one leading South from the Queen's chamber, to the star Sirius in the constellation Orion at one time of the year, and precisely to the sun at another time of the year? How did they do that, and why? While ending this, the beginning of our story, I'd like to add this. We know these people to be remarkable. The lasting impression that we get, and it is not without foundation, is that they were advanced beyond imagination. They were happy, and they were guided by an immense sense of purpose. I add this comment because I think that in the search for a meanings to the Great Pyramid, the Giza complex, and to the Egyptian mystery as a whole, that it would help if we were to broaden our view beyond what historians have centralized upon — their religious and funerary habits and beliefs.

If, in recognition of these extraordinary people, we were wanting to pay tribute to their sagacity, I can think of no better way than to repeat Edward Bacon's words about *"a love of an ideal beauty."* His words are uniquely appropriate because they speak to the fulfillment that experiencing the past provides.

> The instinct to find out the past has many sources: idle curiosity, and the stimulus of scholarship – which are similar in kind, though differing in intensity; a love of object truth, or a desire for romance; an escape from the squalor of present into the glories of long ago, or vice versa, a compulsive need to prove a point – or to disprove one; a love of an ideal beauty, or the need to find objects of beauty, new aspects of art or the material of magic, which amount perhaps to the same thing; or, most frequently, a lifelong love-affair, a which has started irrationally from the chance-found object, some accidental vision, and has become an obsession, a habit from which there is no escape.[16]

Our story continues!

A. This brief passage from the Egyptian *Text,* "A boon which the King grants to the double of the King. O Osiris the King, take the Eye of Horus, your pɘt-cake, that you may eat— a pɘt-cake of the offering," is a story in itself, it is a bit of history in the evolutionary drama of man. These texts are a unique record of our beginnings as envisioned by the Ancients.

"A boon which the King grants to the double of the King." is **Atum Rēᶜ**, the father, granting to his son, *O Osiris the King,* a special blessing, a boon as it is called!

"...take the Eye of Horus..." Horus is the allegorical God of fertility. A lose of vision in his right eye ensuing from a fight with Seth, marks the point in history when the gods will no longer be hermaphroditic, now they are "man-gods" and will henceforth unite with a partner in the act of procreation. *The Eye of Horus,* that *boon,* granted *Osiris the King,* the status of being the first man god. **Atum Rēᶜ** is giving *Osiris the King,* his son, a true gift, hence forth he will know a woman. (See Chapter 18, Page 174)

A similar recognition is made in the Old Testament. *That the sons of God saw the daughters of men that they were fair; and they took them of all which they chose.* Genesis 1:6

...in a state of growth directed toward
...propagation."

Chapter 10

A Rope of Many Hues

There have always been differing views about the origin of life and land. Some authors, following a course of evolution, have found evidence of slow movements of the continents and the gradual evolution of life forms. Others, differing from this course, formulated a role for catastrophic intervention that usurped the tranquility of the planet in brief episodes of chaos. Different as these views are we might conclude that they found their origins in worlds apart. But how could they? They all must have used the same data bank of geological and fossil evidences...after all there is but one! Than how did they separate in view and come to opposite conclusions?

R. J. Campbell suggests that...

> If the intellect were thoroughly reliable there ought to be no room for differences. But unfortunately it is not so, two individuals both intelligent and both conscientious, may form diametrically opposite judgements from exactly the same evidence.[1]

Is it possible that our intellect has a propensity toward deception? Might it set a trap that would lead us into the dilemma of contradiction? If so, it was a trap that Beth and I wanted desperately to avoid. So rather than pursue the familiar theme of geological and fossil evidences we sought ancient cultural proofs that would speak in a new language with a new set of authorities and a correspondingly new vocabulary. It was our good fortune to find what we were looking for and it is our hope that the freshness of these discoveries will help loosen the binds of that intellectual trap. The initial thought that a new set of authorities could be found, was acquired from reading Faulkner's *The Ancient Egyptian Pyramid Texts*.[2] Therein Faulkner reveals the existence of some very ancient records that puts the catastrophic episodes of our past in historic perspective. The textural record will not stand on its own merits, however, so we must cross an ocean to put the story together in its proper form, but we must start with the text first.

These ancient texts, as Faulkner's wrote in the Preface, ...were carved on the walls of the pyramids of King Wenis of the end of the Fifth Dynasty and of the rulers of the Sixth Dynasty, and constitute the oldest *corpus* (collection) of Egyptian religious and funerary literature now extant (in existence)...they are the least corrupt of all such collections of funerary texts, and are of fundamental importance...Despite the comparative rarity of corruptions, however, the Pyramid Texts provide problems and difficulties of their own. They include very ancient texts among those which were nearly contemporary with the pyramids in which they were inscribed, imposing on the modern reader problems of grammar and vocabulary; the orthography (language & spelling) is apt to be unusual; and there are many mythological and other illusions of which the purport is obscure to the translator of today.

Robert Bauval and Adrian Gilbert, co-authors of an interesting book on the Egyptian pyramids of Giza called *The Orion Mystery,* give a detailed accounting of the discovery and the meaning of the Texts...

Apparently, [in or around 1881 AD] a jackal or desert fox had been spotted at dawn immobile near a crumbled pyramid in the necropolis of Saqqara. It was as if the animal were taunting his lone human observer, a *reis* or head workman, and was almost inviting the puzzled man to chase him. Slowly the jackal sauntered towards the north face of the pyramid stopping for a moment before disappearing into a hole. The bemused Arab decided to follow his lead. After slipping through the narrow hole, he found himself crawling into the dark bowels of the pyramid. Soon he emerged into a chamber and, lifting his light, saw that the walls were covered from top to bottom with hieroglyphic inscriptions. These were carved with exquisite craftsmanship into the solid limestone and painted over with turquoise and gold. The *reis* had stumbled across one of the greatest archaeological discoveries of the late nineteenth century.[3]

...The inscribed pyramids of Sakkara have given us almost 4000 lines of hymns and formulae... [and] Of the five pyramids involved, the one which was to yield the greatest number of texts was that of Unas..."[4] (It should be noted, however, that no inscriptions have ever been found in the Great Pyramid.)

I want to relate to you three fables which will help me evolve the point that I wish to make. Aesop was a Sixth century B.C. Greek fabulist who wrote, in what we call Aesop's Fables, such stories as, *The Tortoise and the Hare, The Fox and the Grapes*, and *The Crow and the Pitcher.* The first fable, *The Fox and the Grapes,* goes something like this...

> A fox, walking along a trail one day, sees a bunch of grapes hanging high from a vine, and being hungry, attempts to pick some. However, they were much too high for him to reach, but being resourceful, as all fox are, he searches out and finds some rocks that he piles below the vine. Where upon he climbs up and secures the grapes for himself.

The *Crow and the Pitcher* story relates a similar incident:

> A crow, flying about one day, sees a pitcher of water on the trail below, and being thirsty attempts to get a drink. However, the water was much to low in the pitcher for the crow to reach, but being resourceful, as all crows are, he searches out and finds some stones that he drops into the pitcher to raise the water level that he might drink. And drink he does!

These fables are seemingly different, but that difference is only on the surface. Actually they are very similar in that they both relate a story which suggests that you can overcome the odds if you are resourceful. They are also similar in the fact that you can conceptualize both stories with a *single image* in your mind. One of a fox on some rocks picking grapes, and the other of a crow drinking water from a pitcher partially full of stones. They are different only in that the characters and the details are different! The *Tortoise and the Hare* story, on the other hand, has the familiar...you can overcome the odds if you are resourceful theme, but it adds a second, that being that over confidence will cause your downfall unless you are watchful! But even than it is identical to the other two in that you can still put a single image in your mind that will capture the essence of the entire story. The story goes something like this...

> A tortoise and a hare decide to race to decide who was the better runner. Well it seems that the hare being swift of foot easily left the tortoise far behind. But the hare was also over confident, and being that it was a warm day and that he was miles ahead of the tortoise, he decided to lay down and bask in the sun while taking a little nap. The tortoise, meanwhile, having the patience of Job, (In the Old Testament, an upright person whose faith in God survived the test of repeated calamities *(Job* 1-42)), trudged on and passed the hare, who, though half asleep, saw the tortoise pass. He awoke in a bound and sprinted down the road. Well this sprint-sleep-sprint-sleep theme repeats itself throughout the story until the resourceful tortoise prevails in the end when the hare decides to sleep "a little

too close to the finish line" and the tortoise crosses it to win.

So what do these fables have to do with the *Ancient Egyptian Pyramid Texts*? Just this...like the book of Aesop's Fables, the *Pyramid Texts* contain many-many stories with themes and messages, *and images*, but unlike the fables, the stories in the *Texts* are interwoven and stretched out, and interspersed with one another, so that now the theme of a single story is almost indiscernible. As Faulkner put it,

> The rules of grammar are well defined...but within these rules a doubt must often remain as to whether a given sentence is to be understood as a statement or as a wish...a translator can render a passage only as he himself feels it.[5]

The *Texts* do pose a difficult task to the reader if they were to just pick up the book and start reading. But if we likened them to the Fables, i.e., with themes and messages, *and images*, but now interwoven, stretched out, and interspersed with one another, like a rope whose woven strands are multi-colored, with each color representing a theme or message, and whose colors are of many hues, each hue representing a variation in the telling, we can constructed a path to follow for ourselves.

This weaving of a theme with details of many stories interspersed throughout a larger text with apparent randomness, is not without other examples. In *The Mayan Prophecies,* a book co-authored by Adrian Gilbert and Maurice Cotterell, Gilbert narrates Cotterell's discovery of the secrets of the ancient pictorial glyphs found on the "great Lid of Palenque," (The cover for Pacal's tomb in Palenque, Mexico.) It is an interesting narrative that takes the reader into that singular world where ancient mysteries are deciphered by following a weaving theme, a theme that "...challenges the onlooker to probe into its mysteries..." The Mayan Prophecy narrative begins in Palenque where the Pyramid-Temple of Inscriptions holds the 'great Lid of Palenque.'

The great Lid, with its complex interlocking design, seemed to belong to another world, a place where logic and reason are turned upside down. A work of art, yes, but something more than this: a riddle...(that)...challenged the onlooker to probe into its mysteries while denying a straightforward answer.[6]

> Might not the goddess Chalchiuhtlicue, or her Mayan equivalent, be the figure represented at the centre of the Lid? No one had ever looked at this figure as representing a female before, but it seemed to fit. (Now began a search) of the Lid for evidence of other gods in the design...

first there was Chaac, the rain god...(and) there was Tonatiuh...with his tongue poking out, symbolizing that he gave life...

Between the figures representing Chalchiuhtlicue and Ehecatl ("...god of wind and the first born of the gods") there was a shape on the Lid which at one level seemed to represent the Tree of Life...

By discerning meaning in the images of the gods inscribed on the Lid he had broken the first code. The Lid of Palenque...was universal in its imagery. *It was a book of symbols that was intended to be, and indeed perhaps was, read.* Not only that, it was a cultural icon that recorded the passing of the ages...It recorded major events in world history that related to the mythology of the Maya and in a sense illustrated their holy book of Creation, The Popol Vul.

Whoever it was who designed the Lid, Cotterell theorized, liked riddles and enjoyed playing with design elements...[7, A]

Cotterell, while experiencing the magical draw of an antiquity that challenges "...the onlooker to probe into its mysteries," as Gilbert wrote, had discovered in the pattern of the Palenque glyphs the same association that we observed when we discovered that the Nascan figures illustrated the Pyramid *Texts*."[B] Now, this brings us full circle and invites a better characterization of the analogy of the multi-colored rope. As a way to respond to that invitation lets look again at what Cotterell said of The Lid of Palenque,

> "... it was universal in its imagery... it was a book of symbols...it was a cultural icon that recorded the passing of the ages...it recorded major events in world history...it related to the mythology of the Maya and in a sense illustrated their holy book of Creation[a], *The Popol Vul*."[8] It was many things!

[A] This is our point when in the next Chapter we suggest that the site of the Nascan figures is like "...looking at some ancient play ground of the Gods, because they are all so large and they look whimsical and cartoonish." [9]

[B]The recognition of the figures on the Lid betokening the illustrations for the text of the Popol Vul is interesting because the central theme of Part III of this book, *The Pampa Jumana-Colorada*, is that the figures on the plateau above Nasca, Peru are the illustrating agents for the " religious and funerary texts" found in the ancient pyramid's of Egypt.

So it is with the Pyramid Texts. Once it is embodied in our thinking that the pattern of the *Texts*, like the Lid of Palenque, is like that of Aesop's Fables with images, themes and messages, interwoven, stretched out, and interspersed with one another...like a rope whose strands are multi-colored, and whose colors are of many hues, each strand telling its own story, and each hue telling it over again in a varying way, then we can begin to understand the psyche of the Ancients.

The Pampa Jumana-Colorada

a. The Popol Vuh is the Mayan Bible it speaks of the dawn of life and the glories of Gods and Kings.

Chapter 11

Alone On The Equator!

Many of the cultural artifacts found around the world are extremely ancient. So ancient, in fact, that the role that they played in the culture of their time has been lost to history and remain only in legend. But perhaps the greatest of them all is Ōn! Nowhere is there its equal, for Ōn contains the story of Creation as told by the Ancient Gods. Ōn is the ecliptic, and located on Ōn are the twelve Constellations of the Zodiac.

> (§ 1288) O King, you preside over the houses of the Great Ones who are on Ōn; the spirits fear you, and also the Imperishable Stars.[1]

Ōn and the Imperishable Stars! You're not going to believe this, but picture for a moment the view of the Heavens with a billion stars and a hundred constellations, and picture the twelve special Constellations of the Zodiac which encircle the ecliptic plane of the nine planets of the solar system, and picture if you will these nine planets traversing the ecliptic, on and Ōn throughout all of eternity! Now awaken from this and find yourself a survivor of a crustal shift, and you look up into the sky to thank your lucky stars only to find that they have all moved! All that is except the twelve Constellations of the Zodiac, the Imperishable Stars. They still encircle the ecliptic. What has happened is that your spacial-reference to the stars depended upon your latitude, and that changed with the crustal shift. But your spatial-reference to the Constellations of the Zodiac was the ecliptic, and the ecliptic did not change. The Ancients who survived a crustal shift immortalized it on Ōn and in the Imperishable Stars of the Constellations of the Zodiac.

We are going to take an adventurous journey to Nasca. It will be an unusual journey through time and space, a journey normally requiring the power of a Star Ship, but I have chosen the Boeing 757 as my vehicle, and I have chosen my wife Patty to be my traveling companion. I've not chosen her just because she is convenient, though of course she is, but because she is the type of person that you want at your side when your intuition is your only guide.

As our Boeing 757 left the gate and entered the queuing line near the head of the runway I become aware of how strangely quite the engines were for a plane of this size. From the window I could see the aircraft directly ahead of us make the turn onto the runway and lumber off. We were next! We made the turn and the 757 hesitated for a moment to give the turbines time to come up to speed and develop the thrust necessary for take off, and I listened for the comforting storm from the engines that signaled that they had developed the power to do what they have to do, but in place of the storm there is a new sound, quiet, powerful, and reassuring! I was going to count the seconds from the time we started to move to when we were off the ground, but before I could start the countdown the nose of the plane had rotated skyward and we were leaving Cairo, Egypt and were headed for Nasca, Peru. Wow! What a sensation!

We were headed West, to Peru where we'd be walking the plateau, the Pampa Jumana-Colorada, above Nasca where those mysteriously massive animal and geometrical shapes and figures were formed on the rocky plateau so many eons ago. I wanted to lean back and enjoy the ride but my wife and I, needing to get our bearings and plan an itinerary for the weeks ahead, laid out our notes and maps instead and began the task of preparation. But as we leveled off I was able to get one more glimpse of the Great Pyramid...this Ancient Symbol of the past, "...this Only One, who hast no second"[2]. It lay North of us and I could see the North Star above it's pinnacle. The Pyramid and the North Star were lined up with unimaginable precision. The view that I was just given emerged as though the plane had leveled off at this low altitude to give me a special lasting impression.

Our maps of Peru and the South American continent were the typical tourist variety with advertisements for restaurants and hotels, and condominiums printed on the back. Nasca was in the South Western corner of Peru, at about 15° South latitude, or just over a thousand miles south of the Equator, and it was inland from the Pacific Ocean by just a few miles. From Nasca, the stars in the North would not be visible to us, so we'll have to re-orient ourselves to the South and to the guiding constellation Crux, the Southern Cross. Crux is a small constellation in the shape of a cross which lies 30 degrees above the horizon in the Southern sky. But unlike the guiding constellation in the Northern Hemisphere, Ursa Major, or the Big Dipper, whose two outboard stars point directly to the North Star Polaris, Crux only points its long arm to the open emptiness of the sky in the South. It was a divination that I had waited a long time to see.[3]

The maps we had of the Nasca plateau, unlike our tourist maps, were made from aerial photographs and they had brief descriptive text on the side bars. One such insert read,

The Nazca, or Nasca, were an ancient indigenous culture that flourished in Southern Peru around 1000 A.D. They are known for their polychrome pottery and weaving. Aerial exploration of the arid tableland and the surrounding valley has revealed a network of lines interspersed with giant animal forms - probably related to Nazca astronomy and religion.[4]

As we began to examine the map of the plateau and the "giant animal forms," we were struck by the anomalous hit and miss orientation of the figures. They didn't appear to have been drawn with any particular relationship one to another...or to any thing geographical or astronomical. They weren't aligned to any compass point, and they weren't aligned to any feature on the plateau or to the Pacific coastline to the west. Instead they all pointed, seemingly, nowhere. We felt that this randomness was strange for a graphic relic of the past that had an origin in "religion and astronomy!"

There were dozens of caricatures, all upside down and seemingly skewed, but four caught our immediate attention. At the bottom of the map was a whale which appeared to be a humpback. The two central forms, one a leopard with tail erect, was running toward a monkey, or a baboon, with a curled tail climbing a set of stairs as though going to the stars, A forth figure, and the most remarkable of them all because it was almost human in form, was laying on its back with its right arm raised in ghostly greeting. We wanted a more familiar view so we turned the map around and turned it a little toward the Southwest. Now the whale was at the top of the map and everything was right side up. At first we were curious about the figures and conjectured over their meaning, but the curiosity quickly faded and turned into a strange feeling of euphoria. A euphoria that a collage of ancient religious or astronomical figures should not have invoked. We exchanged glances knowing that great things were about to happen.

I was thinking about it, but my wife said it first. "It's like we're looking at some ancient playground of the Gods, the figures are all so large and they look whimsical and cartoonish." "But even in photograph," she added, "They look weathered and wind worn like they've been there forever!"

That's the way the photographs looked, whimsical and cartoonish...and wind-worn! And I wondered aloud whether this was akin to the Elysium fields. The Elysium, or Elysian, fields in Greek mythology, are a happy other world "in the West" for heros favored by the Gods.[5] It is an earthly paradise, or Garden of Eden. There is a Buddhist and Hindu equivalent in the happiness one might achieve in an earthly paradise, it is associated with Nirvana. In the very simplest of terms, Nirvana is a liberation from suffering from ones bondage, which is brought about by desire. Nirvana is attainable in life through moral discipline. But the term "nirvana" has other associations as well, more abstract, but than so are some of the figures. Nirvana also implies in some of these "more abstract" implications, death, oblivion, or abrogation. In that context the central ghostly figure achieves substance - death, oblivion, or abrogation. These abstract meanings associated with nirvana seem to capture part of this human-like figure's character! It was a ghost! But there was another quality about this figure - a quality that was more forceful - a quality that seemed beyond the frontiers of a windswept plateau in Southern Peru - and a quality that seemed unrelated to its prominent ghostly features. It was ithyphallic.

To portray a male figure, symbolically as ithyphallic, was a sculptural tradition in many ancient cultures. The portrayal was commonly achieved by the use of a single line, a series of parallel lines, or with some rectilinear form in combination as with the two central animal figures on the plateau. The leopard, whose male character is formed by two parallel lines, is running with its ithyphallic form extended rearward. The baboon, shown climbing a flight of stairs as though focused on the stars, has a rectilinear form of straight lines issuing from below its tail. It was a way to display the property of fertility, or, in some instances, the facility to self-fertilize. These two must clearly be male. The ghostly figure on the other hand is characterized as an erect penis. There is nothing symbolic about it. It is clearly ithyphallic, and this, in light of the more common custom of using simple lines as an alias, must have rare significance. This figure, as compared to the others on the plateau, must be of immense importance!

As we "awoke" from this period of deep thought and reflection, we became aware that our plane was passing over these very fields. From our vantage point, which must have been from about 2000 feet, we could see all of the figures line by line. The aircraft was on a southeasterly course which, fortunately put the whale at the top of our view and the two central figures, and the ithyphallic ghost, "upright" as we passed overhead. It seemed that our giant 757 once more hesitated in mid-air to give us a lingering look at the figures as it had the Pyramid. But wait! There is something about these.....!

Something kept plaguing my mind about this inanimate pasture. There was something familiar about them that I couldn't grasp. "Patty" I said, "Don't these figures look familiar somehow? "Why do I keep thinking I've seen the theme before?"

"Jim, don't you see." she said, "They are the graphics for the Egyptian *Texts*." Then she repeated it as nonchalantly as if she was playing Trivia Pursuit. "They are the illustrations for Faulkner's *Ancient Egyptian Pyramid Texts*!"[6]

"The graphics for the *Ancient Egyptian Pyramid Texts*?" I repeated it to her aloud. "Good for you hon! You're right, that's exactly what they are!"

It was much easier to relate to the figures now that we recognized their origin, and from our vantage point we could begin to piece together the picture. The spiral of the "baboon's" tail we could identify with the sun God Rē. We could see what appeared to be a "live" tree at the bottom right, and a "dead one" to our left. There were various sized rectangular figures interspersed everywhere. Some of these were open at one end and others were closed! There was a three fingered hand near the top of the field which had a curiously pregnant look about it. The fingers pointed toward two of the opened ended rectangles as though saying something about them. The forms were "drawn" by forming hedges of stone, or by scraping away the dusty top soil to expose the underlying bedrock.

Other than these figures the plateau was bare. There were no trees, no rivers, no streams! We thought the bareness strange but we were leaving the plateau behind as our plane started into a wide bank which was going to bring us into an approach to the airfield, so we settled into our seats and waited.

Utterance 570[7]

(§1461) Hear it, O Rē, this word which I say to you; your nature is in me, ...the baboons are slain by the leopard, and the leopard is slain by the baboons, O you eunuch, O you male, one of you two runs...."[8]

It was getting light in the West as our plane taxied up to its docking station. We'd been in the air for about 9 hours and we were both tired and ready for a break. We looked around half expecting the aisles to fill ahead of us but it happened that just my wife and I stood up. That seemed strange because the plane was nearly full. Well, just the same, it made it easier for us to leave the plane. We stepped out into the muggy air that bore an unusual freshness that was unexpected. Behind us, as we walked away, I could hear that same new sound that accompanied our take-off in Egypt, quiet, powerful, and reassuring! I turned to watch the plane take off, but there was nothing there. The tarmac was gone there was nothing but rolling fields of lush green grasses.

To the South we saw a strange sight. Instead of the long arm of Crux, the Southern Cross, poised over the open waters of the Pacific, pointing to the South Celestial Pole, Crux *was* the pole constellation. Turning northward we could see Ursa Minor, the Little

Dipper with Polaris at the tip of the handle, only it wasn't at the Pole Position anymore. Instead the Little Dipper, and Polaris were 15 degrees to the east. It seemed impossible that we should be viewing both polar skies because Nasca should be at 15° South latitude. We should not have been able to see the Northern sky at all. But there it was!

We didn't fully understand what had happened but it seemed that we were on the Equator. We looked at the stars again - there was no doubt - we weren't at 15 degrees south latitude as we should have been, we were on the Equator! We surveyed our situation and discovered that we were not in Nasca, we were on the plateau with the ithyphallic ghost looking straight at us, with it's arm raised in ghostly greeting.

It was sculpted on a slanted rocky projection making the figure appear to lean backward at about 60 degrees. There was something else, as we looked out across the field we could see that all of the figures were now aligned with perfect precision to the Southern Cross. They were aligned due South. We turned around and, meeting with our expectations, we could see that the figures were aligned true North as well. We suspected that they might have been when we turned to look, but we had to see it for ourselves!

I was sitting quietly on the ground looking at the ghostly figure and contemplating our next move, when I suddenly jumped up, but again it was my wife who said it first. "The ghost is pointing eastward with its raised hand...I wonder what it is pointing at?" Then she added, "If we are on the Equator, and the figures are aligned with the Cardinal points, where is Egypt? Where is the Pyramid and where is the Sphinx?"

Cairo, where we'd been not 9 hours ago, had been at 30 degrees North latitude, "Did it move too?" I wondered! We were almost afraid to look! But we got out our maps and started to redraw the grid lines based on the celestial relationships that we could observe. The answer was quick to reveal itself. Egypt was on the equator. The desert climate of the Sahara was gone and in its place was the lushness of the tropics. The Sphinx, with the head of a female lion lay facing due east.

Our reconstructed map showed us that Giza and Nasca both lay on the equator and the North Geographical Pole lay, not in the Arctic Ocean where it should have been, but on the Alaskan Peninsula east of the Gulf of Alaska. The figures that lay carved in the rock on the plateau about us should not have aligned, at least according to the literature, with anything. But things had changed. Now as we looked about there was meaningful alignment expressed everywhere! It seemed as though we'd entered a time warp that put us in some ancient epoch, and we were on the equator. We were in that strange "happy other world in the West," and we were alone! But 8000 miles to the east, shining in the equatorial sun, lay another lone figure, the Sphinx. Strange indeed. But we shall see!

In advance of this adventure, my wife and I had prepared ourselves for what we would find by reading from Gerald Hawkins's *Beyond Stonehenge*. wherein he tells us that the lines were five miles or more long... and the large rectangle was eight hundred yards by seventy... The surface was ... hard-packed clayey sand... shallow washways...leafless!

This was it, the Pampa Jumana-Colorada. A bare pampa, a simmering pampa without a blade of grass. ...Because of the flatness of the area, because of the sameness, a feature, (the rectangle), 800 yards long could not be seen. Yet it was there, drawn out on the desert blackboard by unknown hands of a lost civilization centuries before.[9]

"... low, long banks of piled stones...covered the undisturbed surface which stretched out to meet the skyline many miles away."[10]

"Nothing changes. No rain — a few drops now and again, but they dry up on contact. The wind's blown away everything that's going to blow away. Footprints stay here for years."[11]

The rest of the story is going to unfold as we read the pages of the *Ancient Egyptian Pyramid Texts* and we walk the Pampas examining the figures one by one. Some will say that our account is wild unsupported speculation. But I think that most of you will see quite differently when we are done!

Atum Rē(
The Ithyphallic Ghost of the Nasca Plateau

Chapter 12

It is No Other

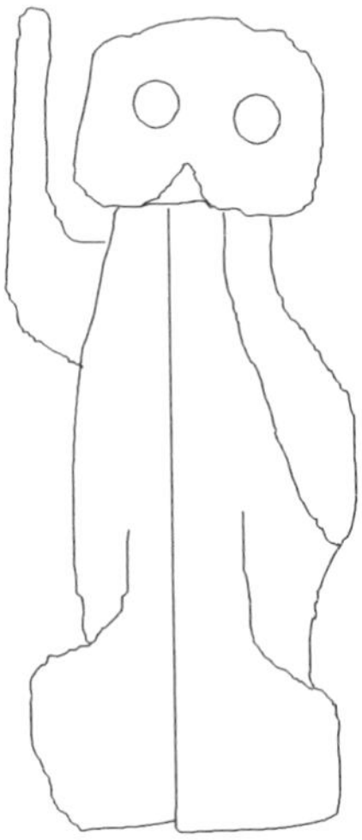

The ghostly figure was portrayed as ithyphallic by its creators. It was an erect penis, and this, in light of the more common usage of a line as an alias, must have rare significance. This figure was pregnant, and compared to the others on the plateau, it must be of immense importance! And so it is. It is no less than the most important of the pre-dynastic Egyptian Gods. It is no other than **Atum Rēʕ** himself.

Figure 1 Atum Rēʕ
The Ithyphallic
Ghost of the
Nascan Plateau

> (§ 1248) Atum is he who (once) came into being, (The primeval god who evolved from the Chaos.) who masturbated in Ōn.[A] He took his phallus in his grasp that he might create orgasm by means of it, and so...[1] (§ 1249)...were born the twins Shu and Tefēnet! May they put the King between them and set the King among the gods in front of the Field of Offerings. Recite four times:[2] May the King ascend to the sky, may the King ascend to the earth.

There is something else, the ghostly figure was sculpted on a rocky projection with its back at about 60 degrees relative to the ground. **It was erect!** And its feet...not shoe-like but more like testicles. The lines that make up the contours of its body...are like veins. The right arm is raised as if to acknowledge a higher Being, and to demonstrate the physical capacity to accomplish the act of masturbation! It is no other than **Atum Rēʕ** himself.

[A] The term "on Ōn," as in "on-and-on," is made in reference to the everlasting plane of the Ecliptic where the Constellations of the Zodiac encircle the sun and the earth. They are visible at the distant borders of the ecliptic and they live Ōn and Ōn as the Imperishable Stars!

The ithyphallic ghost has two eyes as one might expect of a figure that is hermaphroditic. It is capable of self fertilization. It is the Father of all that is. It is **Atum Rĕ(**. In a variation of this rendering, the *Pyramid Texts* speak to the King, **Atum Rĕ(**,...

(§ 1238) O King, raise your self, push yourself off on your left side, sit up on your right side, sit on the pure thrones of Rĕ(, separate your back from the wall, your hand being on your alter: (*phallus*[B])

The importance of the above passage is that it gives us specific expressions that demonstrate the link between this hermaphroditic God, **Atum Rĕ(**, who is carved on the rock of the Peruvian plateau and the Egyptian Pyramid Texts.

"*...separate your back from the wall,*" *...raise yourself*, ie., give yourself an erection that you may "*...create orgasm by means of it*, with "*...your hand being on your alter*," and so... (§ 1249)...*were born the twins Shu and Tefĕnet*! Is there any doubt that this is **Atum Rĕ(** from the Pyramid Texts?

E. A. Wallis Budge[C] adds to this story!

The oldest legend about the origin of the gods is contained in the text of Pepi I., wherein it is said (line 465) that once upon a time Tem went to the city of Ånnu and that he there produced from his own body by the irregular means of masturbation his two children Shu and Tefnut. ... In this crude form the myth is probably of Libyan origin, and it suggests that its inventors were in a semi-savage, or perhaps wholly savage, state when it was promulgated.[3]

[B]Faulkner has not given us an interpretation of "alter" as meaning "phallus."

[C]It must be noted that as the ancient civilizations aged, the records became corrupted such that by modern times one epoch becomes indistinguishable from another. That is to say almost indistinguishable. There is one thing that distinguishes the most early civilizations from the later ones. It is not in evidence here but it is worthy of mention. The earlier civilizations believed, without question, in immortal life. There was no such thing as wholeness or completeness in this life, or the after life, and circles represented both. So they never used circles. It was contradictory to their basic principles. Historians mistook this avoidance as meaning that they hadn't invented the wheel! Hard to imagine a civilization that could carve a figure like the Sphinx out of solid rock— while not knowing of the wheel!

In hymns quoted from Brugsch, [4]

> O Åmen-Rā, the gods have gone forth from thee. What flowed forth from thee became Shu, and that which was emitted by thee became Tefnut; thou didst create the nine gods at the beginning of all things...[5]

And from the *Pyramid Texts*:

> (§ 260) O King, raise yourself on to your side and do my command. O you who hate sleep but who were made limp, arise...take your power in Ōn

> (§ 721) The Great One falls upon his side, He who is in Nedit quivers, his head is lifted by Rē; he detests sleep, he hates inertness.

> (§ 841) O King stand up, that you may be pure and that your double may be pure.[D]

Just as we created an image from the text from Aesop's Fables, we are gathering the text from the pyramids of ancient Egypt so that we can create an image as we read. We are going to need the "art of imaging" when we get to the next chapter, *Thoth*. The image that we should be creating here is that of **Atum-Rē**, the ithyphallic Ghost of the Nasca Plateau, *"...thou didst create the nine gods at the beginning of all things...What flowed forth from thee became Shu, and that which was emitted by thee became Tefnut."*

(§ 1909) May you smite your arm against your foes, whom Anubis who presides over the God's booth gave over to you when he placed you, O King, at the head of the Westerners. The tomb is open to you...

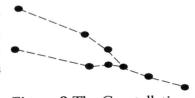

Figure 2 The Constellation of Taurus, ie., **Atum Rē**

(§ 1912) ....give orders to the Westerners, because you are a great and mighty spirit, and those who have suffered death are united for you.

[D] **Atum Rē**'s "Heavenly double" is the Constellation Taurus. See Figure 2, and count the stars. There are nine, one for each of the gods of Ōn. *What flowed forth from thee became Shu, and that which was emitted by thee became Tefnut; thou didst create the nine gods at the beginning of all things...*

Note that there is an inference in the two passages, § 1909 and § 1912 above, that the figure of **Atum Rẽ(** is not corporeal, ie., **Atum Rẽ(** is a spirit, a ghost!

...The tomb is open to you.

...you are a great and mighty spirit, and those who have suffered death are united for you...

The ithyphallic ghost is simultaneously the Gods **Atum Rẽ(**, and it symbolizes, by virtue of the testicles, the god Seth who is the embodiment of the transition to duality in the act of procreation in man. It also symbolizes, by virtue of the two "eyes," Horus who is the embodiment of fertility. It has two eyes because it is simultaneously hermaphroditic and symbolically human. In an allegorical vignette from the *Pyramid Texts* Horus and Seth stage a fight during which Horus will lose his right eye, and Seth will lose his testicles. A vignette is simply a short story with a purposeful intent, and in this case it marks the point it history where the decision was made that man should join with a partner during the act of procreation, and the Gods are no longer hermaphroditic. The figure of the God **Atum Rẽ(** was formed to represent the story of creation before, while, and after, man appeared.

A whimsical rendering by Bauval & Gilbert[6] of the "fight" between Seth and Horus goes like this!

> Osiris was the eldest son of Nut[7], the sky goddess, her other children being Isis, and Seth, ...and others not important to the story...Osiris, a man as well as a god, became the first king of Egypt and his sister, Isis, became his consort...Egypt became prosperous...(but)...not everyone was happy - especially his brother Seth. He plotted against Osiris, murdered him and cut up the body into small pieces, which he scattered all over Egypt.[8]...Isis was childless
>
> So Isis, the sister-wife goddess of Osiris, the embodiment of Wisdom, of whom it was inscribed: I am that which is, has been, and shall be, and no man has lifted my veil[9] ...secretly gathered up the pieces of her husbands body and, by means of her magical powers,[10] reconstituted them into the body of Osiris...she now was able to (conceive a child). Isis (now fearful of Seth's discontent) hid...in the marshes of the Delta near Heliopolis and in due course gave birth to a son, Horus. He grew up to become a powerful prince, and eventually challenged Seth to a duel to see who had the right to rule Egypt in Osiris's stead. During the fight, Horus

lost (his right) eye and Seth lost his testicles. Though the battle was inconclusive, the sun god was eventually persuaded to judge in favor of the young Horus and he was proclaimed king, the first in line of the pharaohs!

The outcome of this "battle" was in actuality a significant point in man's evolutionary history for now he would procreate, not hermaphroditically as a God, but in duality with his own kind. This important turning point is portrayed as a fight between Seth and Horus in the Constellation of Aquarius where Seth, with his testicles laying between his outstretched legs, can be seen putting an instrument, or his hand, into Horus's right eye. See Figure 3.

In Chapter 18, *The Gods, Gemini, and the Great Pyramid*, I state a suspicion of mine that Horus is not a God at all but rather a symbol of both male and female fertility. This suspicion is supported by the following passages from the *Pyramid Texts*. The first passage that is sited below suggests that without union the heart would be broken and it relates to a time before the role of human duality in the act of procreation was decided.

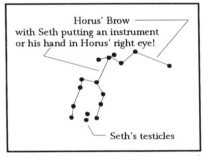

Figure 3 The Constellation of Aquarius depicting the "fight" between Seth and Horus!

(§ 40+10) O Osiris the King, I bring to you the two eyes of Horus which dilate the heart.

The suggestion of a broken heart comes from the meaning of "dilate"; "di" which means "two, or to double" and the word dilate itself which means to expand. The heart would expand "without union" until it was broken, in "two." The next three passages relate to appeals to Osiris by the Gods to save the eye and thereby maintain the hermaphroditic character of the Gods.

(§ 40+11) O Osiris the King, take the eye of Horus, prevent it from being consumed.

(§ 40+13) O Osiris the King, take the eye of Horus and prevent him from destroying it.

(§ 40+15) O Osiris the King, take the eye of Horus which he rescued from Seth when he snatched it.

107

The next two passages relate to appeals to destroy the eye and preserve the necessity for union.

> (§ 43) O Osiris the King, take the water[11] which is in the Eye of Horus, do not let go of it.

> (§ 44) O Osiris the King, I conduct you to your son Horus; put him within yourself. I am Isis; go behind me, O Osiris the King.

These passages take us to a point in history when the decision was being made as to whether man would be hermaphroditic or dependent upon union. The choice that was made is clear. Another thing becomes clear to us at this point as well. *The Ancient Texts*, are more than the reputed religious and funerary texts, they are a history of the spiritual being of man.

IS HORUS REALLY A GOD?

It is Horus who is shown, symbolically, as the second point of ejection of the "egg" on the phallus of the hermaphroditic, ithyphallic ghost. And it is Horus who is the symbol of maternal relationship between Tefēnet and her daughter Nūt, and as the symbol of the maternal relationship between Nūt and her daughters Isis & Nephthys, as we will see in the next chapter where the maternal relationship will be symbolized by a line that crosses the Ambassador God Thoth's arms.

Is it possible that Horus is not a god with presence at all as I have suggested, but just the symbol of eloquence of the male-female roles in procreation? The epitome of fruitfulness.

Chapter 13

Thoth!

Figure 1 The leopard is slain by the baboons, O you male, One of you two runs.

Utterance 570[A]

{§. 1461} Hear it, O Rē´ {§. 1462} The baboons are slain by the leopard, and the leopard is slain by the baboons. O you eunuch, O you male, One of you two runs.

"O you eunuch," (*The baboon*) "O you male, One of you two runs." (*The ithyphallic leopard*) The eunuch is the baboon in Figure 2. He is here climbing the ladder, the stairway to Ōn. He is **Atum Rē(**'s Ambassador God Thoth! But rather than being an actual God himself, **Thoth** is the embodiment of the Ennead, the nine named Gods on Ōn, Atum, Shu, Tefēnet, Gēb, Nūt, Osiris, Isis, Seth, and Nephthys...five male, and four female...and since Thoth is the incarnate of both male and female he is

Figure 2. The baboon is slain by the leopard.

a sexless entity, ie., "O you eunuch." **Thoth,** who is both male and female, who is **Atum Rē(**'s Ambassador, the incarnate bearer of the knowledge and mysticisms of the Gods...is both **Atum Rē(** and the **Ennead.** Thoth is the tenth god...he is ten gods!

[A] Note: The bold high-lighting throughout this chapter is for emphasis.

Hear it, O Rē´ O you eunuch, O you male, One of you two runs.

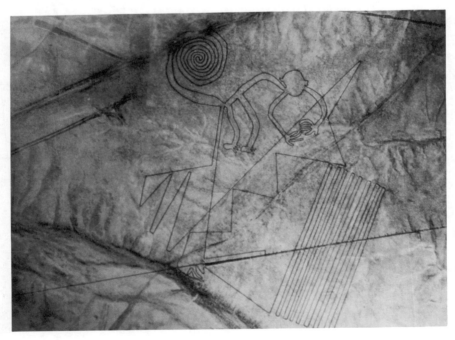

Hear it, O Rē´ The baboons are slain by the leopard.

The leopard...**Oh you male**... and the baboon...**O you eunuch**...are indeed the graphic images that support the text from the Egyptian pyramids.

> {§. 1089} I have gone up in Pe to the souls of Pe, I am grit with **the girdle** of Horus, I am clad with the garment of **Thoth**...the souls of Ōn set up a stairway for me in order to reach the Above...!

THE EGYPTIAN *GOD*— **Thoth**... is represented here as a cynocephalus monkey, with the curl of the tail symbolizing the Spirit and the energy of the Sun God Rē´. He is both male and female...his extremities are the counterparts. The hindquarters are male... characterized by the powerful phallic epitome ascribed by the lines below the tail, and the front quarters are female...the feminine disposition being demonstrated by the maternal "cradling" posture of the arms. You can see this confirmed by the hands of this cynocephalus monkey in the photo on page 110, and in Figure 3. There are five fingers on the left hand and four on the right. Five male and four female, the nine souls of Ōn.

> {§. 1655} O you Great Ennead which is on Ōn, (namely) **Atum**, Shu, Tefēnet, Gēb, Nūt, Osiris, Isis, Seth, and Nephthys; O you children of Atum...![a]

Figure 3 The hands of Thoth show an unusual feature, there are five fingers on one hand and four on the other!

Five male gods, **Atum**, Shu, Gēb, Seth, and Osiris, and four female...Tefēnet, Nūt, Isis, and Nephthys; "O you children of **Atum**...!" **But notice that Atum is named twice!** There is no question of the presence of a tenth God. It is explicit, while at the same time it is only implied...because you don't know how it is that Atum can be named as a member of the Ennead, while at the same time the Ennead is addressed as **"O you children of Atum."** But this is cleared up with the introduction of Thoth, the ithyphallic, cynocephalus monkey...the Ambassador God, the God of Wisdom and Letters, the Allegorical God. Thoth is not only the Tenth God...He is ten Gods. **Metaphorically**, He is both.

I AM THAT I AM.[1]

Actually there is only one God on Ōn! **Atum Rē(**, "Atum is he who (once) came into being...the primeval god who evolved from the Chaos."[2] All the others are His children.

While Thoth is here, **metaphorically**, in representation of **Atum Rē(**, and the Ennead, and as such embraces their combined wisdom. Thoth, therefore, is the embodiment of all, {§. 1235} "Be joyful, you gods, over me when I ascend; my face is that of a jackal, my arms are those of a falcon, my wing feathers are those of Thoth. {§. 1237} ...and there is no god who can lay hold of me, there is no adversary who can oppose himself to my road, for I am Thoth, the mightiest of the gods."

A metaphoric God is absolute because "...there is no god who can lay hold of (him), there is no adversary who can oppose himself to (His) road. Thoth, has no presence, so he cannot be opposed. But he has the quality of being both **Atum Rē(**, and the Ennead combined...he is "...the mightiest of the gods."

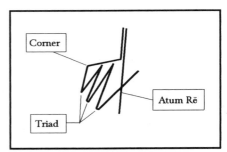

Figure 4. Male Attributes.

The five male gods

When we examine the phallic symbol reproduced in Figure 4, we see two separate aspects to it. First there is the "triad" which is formed by the lines which emanate from the hindquarters, and just above this triad there is a point of sorts which looks more like the corner of a square than a point...add this "corner" to the three points in the triad to form four points. This four cornered image now represent four of the five male Egyptian Gods, **Shu**, **Gēb**, **Osiris**, and **Seth**. The fifth God, **Atum Rē(**, is represented by the single long line that drops vertically from below the tail.

The four female gods

The four female gods, **Tefēnet**, **Nūt**, **Isis**, and **Nephthys** are very cleverly cloaked in the language of symbolism and they are not easily seen so we must uncloak their guise one step at a time. The key is with Horus, and the feminine cradling posture of the arms, hands, and shoulders of Thoth. Lets look at Thoth as he ascends the ladder in Figure 2.

> {§. 976} The Eye of Horus gleams **upon the wing of Thoth** on the left-hand side of the ladder of the god...![B]

[B]Note that the Text is specific in placing the Eye of Horus "...on the left-hand side of the ladder! It demonstrates the consistency between the Nascan Figures and the Egyptian Text!

{§. 971} Hail to you, Ladder of the God!...

Let's start with the phrase "...upon the wing of Thoth..." from {§ 976} above. This phrase has at least two meanings. The partial phrase "...upon the wing" makes reference to the cynocephalus monkey, the flying Lemur.[3] The Lemur "flies" by spreading its arms and legs to unfold the membrane. ie., "the wing" that adjoins the fore-arms and body, hence, "...upon the wing of Thoth..." The second meaning is brought into focus by the partial phrase "...The Eye of Horus gleams...upon the wing of Thoth. This phrase begins the identification of the feminine aspect of the figure. We have previously suspected that Horus is not a God with presence, but simply the personification of fertility. So we should expect that Horus will be playing that role here. And so he is! Recall from the previous chapter that we suggested that the second point of ejection on the

Figure 5 Horus's eye is portrayed by the vertex formed by the two lines, within the circle.

ithyphallic ghost, the second eye if you will, represented one of the two essential elements in the reproductive process of the gods. And **now** Horus will bring fertility onto Thoth! "...The Eye of Horus gleams...upon the wing of Thoth!"

Figure 6. The four female Gods on Ōn. **Tefēnet,** the mother of all, is represented by the shoulders, arms, and hands of the figure on the left. **Nūt,** her daughter, is represented by the upper arms and shoulders of the figure in the middle, and **Isis, and Nephthys,** with Isis on the left, are represented by the hands below the line, in the figure on the right.

The full, all-embracing, cradling aspect of the forearms represents the four female Gods, **Tefēnet, Nūt, Isis** and **Nephthys,** and from this we can develop the individual identities of the female gods! First, however, we must recall that there is an immense precedence for the feminine aspect to be represented by the right hand, or by the assumption of a position on the right. At the Last Judgement, for instance, the female, The Virgin Mary, is on the right, and the male, St John, is on the left[4] ...In China, in times of war yin, feminine, is on the right, and – yang, masculine, is on the left.[5] In times of peace, however, it is reversed. Yin, feminine, is on the left, and yang, masculine, is on the right. Not that they were contradictory concepts, rather...the yin-yang symbol...depicted the perfect balance of the two great forces in the universe...each has within it the embryo of the other power, implying that there is no exclusively masculine or feminine nature.[6]

Let's look at the cradling property of the symbol now to see how it is used to represent the four female Gods. There are four symbolic parts in this characterization. (Recall that a line represents the whole!) The full cradling aspect of the combined shoulders, arms, and hands of the figure on the left in Figure 6, represents **Tefēnet...the mother of all!** She, if you recall, and her twin male God Shu, were the first born of **Atum Rē͛**.

> (§ 1248) Atum is he who (once) came into being, (i.e., the primeval god who evolved from the Chaos.) who masturbated in Ōn. He took his phallus in his grasp that he might create orgasm by means of it, and so... (§ 1249)...were born the twins Shu and **Tefēnet**, (The mother of the female gods!)

Nūt, the daughter of Tefēnet, and the mother of Isis and Nephthys, is represented by the upper-arm-portion of Thoth. The upper-arm-portion includes just the shoulders and the upper arms above the line, as illustrated by the middle figure in Figure 6. The daughters **Isis** and **Nephthys** are represented by the wrists and the hands that appear below the line. Isis is on the left. She is a more important god than Nephthys, and she is therefore represented by the larger image. The *Image* and the *Text* come together in this next passage!

> (§ 1254) **Oh you two kites[C] who are on the wings of Thoth**, you two who are on the crown of the wanderer, bring me this[D] and set me on yonder side...

LET'S GO BACK FOR A MOMENT.

The "corner" as part of the phallic symbol on Thoth has a secondary and very purposeful meaning, see Figures 2 & 4. It is symbolic of the Great Pyramid. The interpretation of

---

[C] A designation applied to Isis and Nephthys, according to Faulkner.

[D] The ferry-boat.

this "corner" as a portion of the phallic symbol having a secondary reference to the Great Pyramid while it also symbolizes the earth as we will see below, may seem a bit obscure at the moment but the rational will become more apparent as we proceed. It is believed, for instance, that another message of the Pyramid, as suggested by Peter Tompkins,[7] is that its pyramidal shape represents the Northern Hemisphere of the earth in symbolic form. It is our interpretation that the comparison might be better represented with the Great Pyramid set upon the ecliptic. In this position it would not be representing the Northern Hemisphere, but rather the hemispheric half of the earth above the ecliptic. (This representation, as you will recall, is in the same pictorial form that we used in calculating the Rotational-Bending effect in Chapter 6, *A Continent Without a Home*.)

As you read this next passage, recall that Ōn is the ecliptic...and recall from the previous chapter that we identified **Atum Rē(**. with the Constellation Taurus, which is also on Ōn!

O you Great Ennead which is on Ōn, {§. 1652-54} O Atum-Khoprer, you became high on the height...in Ōn, you spat out Shu, you expectorated Tefēnet...set your protection over this King, over **this pyramid** of his, and over this construction of the King, prevent anything from happening evilly against it...!

Let's see why this is important!

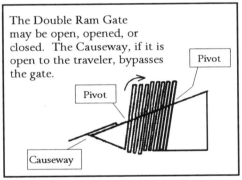

The Double Ram Gate may be open, opened, or closed. The Causeway, if it is open to the traveler, bypasses the gate.

Pivot

Pivot

Causeway

Figure 7 The Double Ram Gate.

The full framework of the rectangular shaped construction below the stairway in Figure 2 and 7, symbolizes the firmament, a term which embraces both heaven and earth. Earth, ie., war, is on left, and heaven, ie., peace is on the right. The seven bars, or eight, depending on how you count them, are set in place to form a gate that separates the earth from the sky, and as we would expect, the presence of this gate bears with it the implication that it is hinged and can be moved, or opened, with the consequential suggestion that there are options! These options are clearly that it could be opened, or it could be closed. Note too that the gate is purposely biased toward the left of the figure to encourage an impression of the relative size of the earth with respect to heaven. The line through the gate symbolizes the presence of a direct causeway. The presence of a causeway has implications of it own...in that it suggests that there is a way around the gate. Which would mean that it may not be necessary in some cases to pass through the gate to get to heaven! A heaven bound traveler could take the causeway. But watch! Now we get a chance to see how resourceful the Ancients really were!

(§. 1726) **The bolt is open for you...in the double Ram-gate...!**

The Ancients show in this illustration that the double Ram-gate "...is open to you" in an unbelievably imaginative way. Notice in Figure 7, that the eight vertical bars are cut by a horizontal line, or axial-pivot bar of sorts, this axial-pivot enables the gate to swing "...open to you" in a vertical swinging motion. It's also interesting to note that when the gate swings open, because of the bias of the door on the hinge, the largest opening is disposed to the right, or in the direction of heaven! This larger opening toward the right is consistent with the ideologies of the Ancients who believed in eternal life while acknowledging the role and consequences of judgement. It's also interestingly to note that one gains entrance to the Great Pyramid through a door that opens by swiveling about horizontal pivots placed at either side of the door in a similar manner.[8]

There are actually four messages, or options, in the structure of the gate and the earth-heaven symbol, and they all have to do with the choices that the ancients say one has in passing "...the double Ram gate!" The Divine Triad on the Plateau, shown in Figure 8, suggests that there are three choices for an extended life *if* the opportunity, by virtue of having chosen a compatible life on earth, is open! Notice in Figure 8, however, that there is the further suggestion, encoded in the respective size of the fingers, that there is a diminishing value among the options! A forth option is also suggested, as we'll see!

Figure 8 The Divine Triad on the Plateau suggests that there are four choices, each with diminishing value with respect to the other!

The first option for an extended life, as indicated by the index finger, is to take the causeway, the horizontal pathway to the right. This option bypasses judgement. But note in the sketch of figure 7, that there appears to be a gate a short way down the causeway that would effectively close this option to a traveler if they are unworthy.

The second opportunity for an extended life is to pass through the gate, pass judgement, and then to turn to the **right** and go into heaven and enjoy eternal life. The middle finger which characterizes this option, however, is reduced in size in comparison to the first option of going directly into heaven via the causeway. The reduced size of the finger is suggestive of the possibility that one might fail judgement, in which case this option is not open and another role would have to be assigned. Hence it is less desirable. The third choice is to pass through the gate and turn **left** – and **re-enter** a life on earth. This is the least desirable passage, based on the smallness of the ring finger, since again it risks the possibility that one might fail judgement, and upon passage back to earth, requires some re-enactment in earthly form. The Divine Triad on the Plateau, in using a gesture that extends the index finger and the middle and ring fingers of the right hand, again in adversity because of the uncertainty in passing judgement, is an impassioned demonstration that there are only three choices for an extended life! Not all being equal – the physical size of the fingers are different. But note too that a small portion of the little finger shows below the hand, this feature is intended to demonstrate that there **is** a portion of the little finger that is actually there and its presence must now be evaluated,

The forth eventuality now, made evident by the near absence of the little finger, demonstrates the unfortunate eventuality wherein the solicitor who has failed judgement will find the gate, and all other options, closed. The solicitor in that eventuality will have exhausted all of their opportunities as a result of the life they chose to live on earth. It is somewhat ironical...can you hear the ancient messengers hailing us? Beckoning for our attention...telling us that the prerogatives are chosen while on earth!

TIME OUT!

We should take time out here to remind ourselves that our intent in examining the figures on the plateau is to bring significance to them by identifying them with their parent passages from *The Ancient Egyptian Pyramid Texts*. We are doing this in order to establish a convincing link between Giza and the Plains of Nasca...thus proving an ancient association between these distant cultures. Once proven, we can demonstrate a spatial orientation of the figures that puts them on the equator with the North Pole in Alaska. With this concluded, we can demonstrate that there have been frequent shifts of the earth's crust. Or, how else could the Pole have shifted away from its ancient home?

LET'S CONTINUE WITH THIS RECAP

In the figures above, the sun God **Rē** is being escorted to the sky by Thoth, as symbolized by the spiraled tail of the Ambassador God on the ladder. While Horus is symbolized by the line that passes through Thoth's fore-arms, and as the second point of ejection for the egg on the ithyphallic ghost. Now lets look closely at Horus!

117

HORUS

The story starts with a fight between Seth and Horus during which Horus losses his right eye and Seth losses his testicles as recited in the previous Chapter, and now we are going to identity Thoth in the following passages as the God of the Pyramid, or if not the God of the Pyramid, than at least the Godly personification of the Pyramid. This God is symbolized by the middle figure in Figure 6. Thoth is represented in combination with Horus in this figure and we use this association to develop the analogy in this manner!

a.   The forearms of Thoth, being the feminine aspect of the personification, identifies the femininity of the Queen's Chamber in the Great Pyramid, while the arms, themselves, make a general reference to the two passages that angle outward from the chamber.

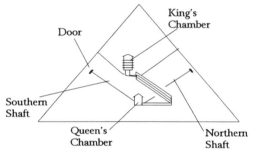

Figure 9 The Great Pyramid of Giza!
and the **Eyes of Horus!**

b.   The hind legs, being the male aspect of the figure, symbolizes the two passages that radiate, one North and one South, from the King's chamber. Hence Thoth's broad stance.

c.   And the ladder of the Gods on the Nascan plateau, is the Double of the steep passageway that is the Grand Gallery in the Great Pyramid of Giza.

Now Horus enters the picture again. Recalling that the Eye of Horus is represented by the apex created by the convergence of the two lines at the upper right of the figure of Thoth...now that same convergence is represented by the sloping lines that form the sides and apex of the Great Pyramid, see Figure 9. That this is the intent of the Ancients can be demonstrated by your inspection of the back of a dollar bill. And if you have a copy of Richard Noone's book, *5/5/2000, Ice: The Ultimate Disaster*, look on page 130 where you will see the Great Seal of the United States reproduced with a mystical Masonic symbol of the Eye of Horus atop the Great Pyramid. The caption reads...*Annuit Coepis*. "He has blessed our beginning."

Horus, the **four** faced God, Horus, who is associated with the **four** cardinal points,[9] had bi-optic vision in each eye, and now his eyes, in another characterization, represent the four passages within the Pyramid. There are two passages associated with each eye. His right eye, the one that he was to lose in battle, represented the two passages that radiate **outward** from the Queen's chamber, one North, one South. His left eye symbolize the passages that lead **outside** from the King's chamber, one North, one South. When Horus lost his **right eye** in the battle with Seth, an allegorical loss of vision in reality, it marked the event when it was decided *not* to open either passage from the Queen's Chamber to the outside. Horus, never a God with presence himself...never had two eyes...neither passage from the Queens chamber were ever open...

THOTH

Before leaving the subject of Thoth, I want to recapture the complete image of this extraordinary figure...Thoth the Ambassador of the Gods!

> {§. 1472-1477} How lovely to see, how pleasing to behold! Says Isis, when you ascend to the sky, your power upon you, your terror about you, your magic at your feet; you are helped by Atum just as he used to do, the gods who are in the sky are brought to you, the gods who are on the earth assemble for you, they place their hands under you, they make a ladder for you that you may ascend on it to the sky, the doors of the sky are opened for you, the doors of the starry firmament are thrown open for you...!

This single passage embraces the essence of virtually every symbolic fiber embodied in the Allegorical God Thoth. You are the eunuch, You are the Ennead...You are Atum. You are the ithyphallic, cynocephalus monkey....You are the Baboon on the ladder to Ōn. Your ladder is the passageway to the stars through the Grand Gallery of the Great Pyramid of Giza!

> {§. 1463} Hear it, O Rē, this word which I say to you; your nature is in me, O Rē, and your nature is nourished in me, O Rē. The baboons are slain by the leopard, and the leopard is slain by the baboons. O you eunuch, O you male, one of you two runs...this one, (Osiris), which was born before anger came into being;

which was born before noise came into being; which was born before strife came into being; which was born before tumult came into being; which was born before the Eye of Horus was gouged out, before the testicles of Seth were torn off...!

Before ending this adventure with Thoth we must be very clear on several points. There can be no doubt that a significant portion of the *Pyramid Texts* are religious and funerary literatures! But I see a second story. This one, and who may know how many others may be intertwined like the strands of a multi-colored rope in this fascinating legacy left to us by the Ancients, tells us about life and creation, about judgement, catastrophe and revitalization, and of love of life. This aspect of these literatures, this second thread, more than the religious and funerary aspects models the true heart of this ancient culture. In support of my belief in this matter, I offer you the testimony given by the traditions and the myths, the legends and the artifacts, that remain of every culture around the world. These, as we all know, are not fables written for children to keep them occupied. They are the remnants of the cultural, scientific, and the religious foundations of very advanced ancient civilizations. It is hard for us to think that the Ancients may have been more advanced than we are in some respects, but how many of us know how to build a Pyramid? How many of us can communicate across 8000 miles of land and ocean without radios or telephones, or how many of us can chart the course of the stars. Many of us don't even know what an eclipse is let alone predict one. But all of this was a vital part of many ancient cultures. I was talking about this to my wife not long ago, and with a deep chuckle of amusement in the style of C. H. Hapgood, she reminded me that they hadn't even invented the wheel yet. Surprised by her remark, I suggested, **"Maybe they didn't need one!"**

a. We know that there is a tenth god on Ōn, so whether an ennead, today meaning nine, should really mean ten, is a matter that has never been addressed. But there is a point that should be made, and that is that the Great Pyramid images ten triangular forms. Eight triangles are obvious from the Pyramids construction, in that each of the four sides of the Pyramid are divided by an indentation that runs from the apex of the Pyramid to the base.[10] The ninth and the tenth are only visible from above. The pyramidal shaped top of the Pyramid is not in place, and this exposes a square form that can be divided into two triangles. Count Goblet d'Alviella...(ref. Pg. 125)

A four-fold heaven and earth...signified by a square divided cross-ways; *Which then becomes two triangles*...Thoth and **Atum RēꟅ.**

Chapter 14

In The Land Of Spreading Darkness

In this Chapter we'll be discussing a most unusual concept. We are going to be looking at the Great Pyramid of Giza portrayed, not as a pyramid, but as a *triangle*. It will be from this perspective that many of the Pyramid's secrets will be revealed, and it will be from this perspective that we'll get corroboration of the ancient association between Giza, Nasca and the ancient Pole in Alaska. In Chapter 18 we'll be examining many more of the Pyramid's secrets, but for now let's just carry this image of a triangle in our mind as we explore the first of the wondrous secrets of the Great Pyramid of Giza. We're going to see why the "Pi" relationship was incorporated in the Pyramid's construction, and what substantiating proof exists, but first turn to page 168 and read the center paragraph and examine the accompanying *Symbol* of Cancer, there's a surprise in store for you there!

The Pyramidal Triangle, as Beth and I are fond of calling it, has some very interesting characteristics. For instance, the area of the triangle is *exactly* the same as the area of the circle from which the triangle is generated.[1] Let's see why this is so! (See Figures 1 & 2.)

1. The area of any circle is: πr^2

2. The equation for the area of any triangle is: $\frac{1}{2}(\text{base} \times \text{height})$

We can calculate the area of the triangle now by substituting the known values for the lengths of the legs, and because the Pyramidal Triangle's side lengths are, respectively, r and $2\pi r$, the area becomes...

3. $\frac{1}{2}(2\pi r) \times (r)$ or, πr^2

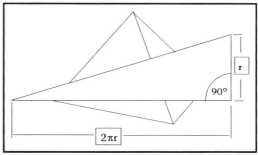

Figure 1 The Pyramidal Triangle illustrates the "Pi" relationship.

So the area of the Pyramidal Triangle (πr^2) is shown to be exactly the same as the area of the generating circle!

SECRETS OF THE GREAT PYRAMID REVEALED

Many investigators of ancient cultures have steadfastly maintained that the Pi relationship in the Great Pyramid is real, but they have been continuously countered by objections based primarily on the argued inability to measure the Pyramid accurately enough to prove that it isn't just a close coincidence. In the world of symbolism, however, it is not true that each symbolic embodiment must be accurate in every detail. In fact the opposite is true. The only requirement is that you are able to perceive the intent however obscure the embodiment. Recall the words of Count Goblet d'Alviella,

> In all systems of writing, in conformity with the popular rule...the part is equal to the whole in the matter of symbols.[2]

Once the existence of a symbol is perceived, the next move for the observer is to determine how to apply the message. That's what we are doing here. We are applying the *message of the symbol* by combining the two concepts that were employed in its portrayal, the pyramid, which is actually a figure constructed of triangles, and the circle, which is required because of the Pi relationship. When we put these two concepts together the Pyramid relinquishes some of its secrets!

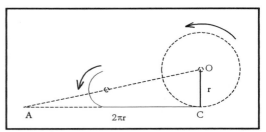

Figure 2 Triangle AOC is generated by "rolling" circle, 'O' with radius, r, and circumferential length, $2\pi r$, out to form side A-C. Side A-O is formed by the locus of the center point of the circle.

The first discovery, from which others will be revealed, is an equation for the average length of term of the precessional cycle. In regard to this, I have to say that the feelings that I had at the discovery of this equation were like those that one might have at the discovery of the Arc of the Covenant. I was completely overwhelmed! Perhaps the most overwhelming aspect of it was that it was found despite the obscurity of the clues. It required that we associate two seemingly unrelated artifactual codes from two very distant continents. We had to put the Pi relationship from the Great Pyramid together with the Cosmic Tree on the Nascan Plateau. This in itself is important! *This secret* of the Pyramid could not have been solved until various pieces of distantly stored information were put together. Can you imagine

122

the opportunities this opens up for investigators? Now instead of wearying a path around some ancient edifice looking for its secrets in vain behind some hidden door, we can start to amalgamate elements found separately from artifactual searches that might take us anywhere in the world.

The Cosmic Tree, a term that I have chosen to use for this figure, is illustrated in Figure 3. There are a number of features about it that I'll discuss in detail in Chapter 18, but for now I wish only to draw your attention to the undulating character of the trunk of the Tree. Please accept for now that these undulations, and I'll give you reason later, represent a series of four precessional cycles of the earth's axis. I have marked them out on the tree as, 1, 2, 3, & 4. The equation that we are going to derive is actually going to give us a value of 103,712 years which is a period of time that covers all four precessional cycles which the tree

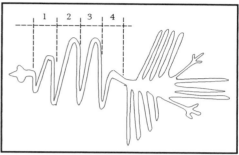

Figure 3 The Cosmic Tree from the Nascan Plateau illustrating a period of time spanning four precessional cycles!

characterizes. When we divide 103,712 years by 4, (or multiply by ¼) to get an *average* value for one precessional cycle we get 25928 years. Interestingly modern science holds fast to the belief that the period of the precessional cycle, 25920 years[3] by some accounts, has been constant over time. NOT SO! Says this Cosmic Tree from the plateau.

DERIVING THE EQUATION!

We are going to be working from the triangle, "AOC" in Figures 2 and 4. Our first step will be to express both Angle 'G', and the Hypotenuse "AO" in terms of the opposite and adjacent sides relative to angle 'G'. Then we will evaluate their equivalence.

First, we will express angle "G" in terms of the opposite and adjacent sides...

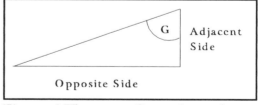

Figure 4 The terms **Opposite** and **Adjacent** are in relation to angle "G."

4.   Tan G = Opposite Side / Adjacent Side = $2\pi r / r$

The (r's) cancel and we are left with...

5.   Tan G = 2π

The value of angle 'G' (in degrees) is obtained by using the ArcTan, thus...

6.   Angle 'G' (in degrees) = ArcTan 2π

Now we will express the length of the hypotenuse AO in terms of the opposite and adjacent sides using the Pythagorean thorium.

7. $AO^2 = (\textbf{Opposite Side})^2 + (\textbf{Adjacent Side})^2$

      $AO^2 = (2\pi r)^2 + r^2$

The equation may now be derived in final form by evaluating the equivalence of the respective values of Angle "G", and the Hypotenuse AO! First, however, I must introduce you to a mathematical term called 'absolute value.' For instance, I would use two vertical lines with a mathematical expression set between the lines, like this, $|xxx|$, to let you know that I want you to determine the numerical value, or the absolute value, of the expression between the lines, in this case "xxx", but to ignore the units in your response.

For example, if you were asked to count the pieces of furniture in a room you could come back and say, "There are 12 chairs, 3 tables, and 2 lamps." Or I could say, "Give me the **absolute value** of the number of pieces of furniture in the room." In which case you would ignore the fact that some pieces are chairs, and others are tables and lamps, and you would come back and simply say, "There are 17 pieces of furniture in the room." So as we evaluate the up-coming equation we should recognize that the vertical lines that bracket the terms, $|\text{ArcTan } 2\pi|$ and $|[2\pi]^2 + 1|$, mean for us to obtain the *numerical value* of the expressions but to ignore the fact that the "ArcTan" actually yields an answer set in degrees of arc, and the expression "$([2\pi]^2 + 1)$" yields an answer set in linear dimensional units, such as inches or feet.

The equation, solved for r = 1, can now be expressed as the equivalence, or *difference*, between angle "G" and the length of the hypotenuse "AO." The equation for the four precessional cycles depicted on the Cosmic Tree becomes...

8) $[|\text{ArcTan } 2\pi| - 2(|[2\pi]^2 + 1|)] \times 10^9 = 103711.8^4$

The equation for the *average* length of a precessional cycle is...

9. $\frac{1}{4}[\,|\text{ArcTan}\,2\pi\,| - 2(\,|\,[2\pi]^2 + 1\,|\,)]$ x 10^9 = 25927.95, or simply... 25928

The individual elements of the equation are explained in this manner...

10.   The $\frac{1}{4}$ in equation (9) above is an averaging figure, required because the initial equation which was, $[\,|\text{ArcTan}\,2\pi\,| - 2(\,|\,[2\pi]^2 + 1)\,|\,]$ x 10^9 yields a value of 103,712 years which is a number that spans all four precessional cycles. So as our goal was to get a value for one cycle, we multiplied by $\frac{1}{4}$.

There is an interesting point to be noted here. There is a commonality between all ancient cultures in that "four," is held with almost sacred reverence in both legend and myth.[5] One such tradition as told to us by Count Goblet d'Alviella speaks of ....

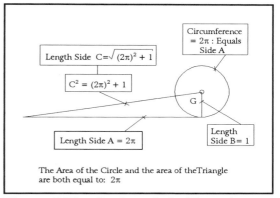

Figure 5 The Circle and the Triangle leads us to the Precessional equation

> A four-fold heaven and earth...signified by a circle, or a square divided cross-ways; (*Which then becomes two triangles!*) from which...a "heavenly garden," watered by four rivers, and of a four-square "heavenly city" with its four went ways gradually (modeling)...four-square well watered "paradises"...[6]

BACK TO THE ANALYSIS!

11. $|\text{ArcTan}\,2\pi\,|$, expresses the absolute value of angle G.

12.   From the $|\text{ArcTan}\,2\pi\,|$ we subtract *twice* the value of the length of the hypotenuse, and the term looks like this: $2([2\pi]^2 + 1)$.

We *subtract* because we started out as our objective to obtain the equivalence of, hence the difference between, the largest angle in the triangle, excluding the right angle, and the longest single boundary of the triangle, that being the hypotenuse. We double the part of the expression that gives us the length of the hypotenuse, ie., ($\left|\,[2\pi]^2 + 1\,\right|$), because in this comparison, where we only used the hypotenuse, we forfeited two boundary surfaces, so we have to make-up their values. So now the expression becomes $2(\left|\,[2\pi]^2 + 1\,\right|)$.

13.　The numerical value of $\left|\,\text{ArcTan}\,2\pi\,\right| - \left|\,2([2\pi]^2 + 1)\,\right|$ is 0.0001037118. We have to convert this decimal fraction to a whole number by multiplying by 10^9. From this we obtain 103711.8 (Why not 10^{10}? Because we didn't have two tens!)

Here again, in following the popular rule of the part representing the whole in the matter of symbols, we can factor the 90° right angle in the triangle into its component parts, 9 and 10. We needed these two numbers to compose the term, 10^9, for the equation above, and we needed the 10^9 term to convert the decimal fraction into a whole number.

But we must be careful at this point and not be arbitrary by saying that the unitless number, 103711.8, all of a sudden now has units, in this case a quantity expressed in terms of years. We cannot do that because we were very specific in the beginning to say that we were to ignore the units, and obtain only the absolute values. So at this point 103711.8 is simply a unitless number. But lets go back and recall that we interpreted each undulation on the trunk of the Cosmic Tree to mean "one precessional cycle." We didn't know what amount of time was represented be each cycle, though we measure precession in terms of solar years, but we did apply a unit of measure when we said that each undulation represented *one* precessional cycle, and from this we can derive the proper units, ie., "four precessional cycles per time span represented by the Tree, in years"

14.　So now when we divide 103711.8 by 4 we have a number with the proper units. The answer becomes: 25927.95 (years per precessional cycle.)

Precession, which we'll look at in greater detail in a later chapter, is a slow gyrating motion of the earth's axis of rotation. It is an astronomical phenomenon of great importance to science but whose rate of motion can only be calculated by empirical methods. To the average person, however, neither the motion nor the method of calculation is of any real consequence because precession is not a phenomenon that bears us much interest in our daily lives except in astrology. But just for the sake of interest lets get a comparative value for the precessional cycle from a couple of sources. We can get one from The Concise Columbia Encyclopedia[7] which suggests a value of 26,000 years. The Encyclopedic Dictionary of Physics[8] gives us a rate of motion of 50 seconds of arc per annum, which will yield us a cyclic duration of 25920 years, which agrees in essence with the 25928 year figure from the Great Pyramid and the Nascan figures! That's pretty good for an ancient culture that hadn't even discovered the wheel yet!

BUT WHY SUCH INTEREST IN PRECESSION?

If the subject of precession lacks popular interest, as I suggested above, why should we spend so much time examining it in such minute detail? There is a six fold answer to that question. **First**, it was the only tool that an ancient mathematician/astronomer had that could be used to establish a date, or a series of dates, that had any chance at all of being understood by a later generation. **Secondly**, precession conveys to the later generation a message of the level of technological development achieved by the ancient society. **Thirdly**, and this is perhaps the most important reason of all...it is difficult in the first place to catch the attention of a later generation to tell them that you have an important message to pass on to them. In order to solve this problem the Ancients built anomalous characteristics into their monuments, in this case precessional codes, in the hope that we would take notice and pursue the intent. In modern telegraphy a radio operator, in order to get attention, will transmit the code "CQ"..."CQ"..."CQ" meaning "All receivers! Attention, I have a message for you."

This communication, "All receivers! Attention, I have a message for you." is precisely the intent of the ancient's anomalous architectural works. They are transmitting the code, "CQ"..."CQ"..."CQ" in their monuments to get our attention. In morse code "CQ" is transmitted by a series of dots and dashes, (— · — · , — — · —). Phonetically the "CQ" message is pronounced, dā-dit-dā-dit, dā-dā-dit-dā. Interestingly, the Columbia Encyclopedia states that the origin of this "CQ" code sequence is unknown! Well perhaps the origin of the specific letter code "CQ" is unknown, but certainly the origin of the meaning, *"All receivers! Attention, I have a message for you,"* is not. That part of the code, *I have a message for you,* can be found all around the world in the form of ancient stone monuments. It is up to us now, if we have any thoughts of surviving the next cataclysmic event, to listen to the rest of the ancient transmission!

It is worthy of note, regarding the inseparability of the Egyptian Hieroglyphics and the Nascan Art in deciphering the code of the Pyramidal Triangle...that we could not have derived this equation had we not recognized the ancient "CQ"..."CQ" transmission and stopped to listen to the message. We had to accept as valid both the Pi relationship from the Great Pyramid and the precessional cycle interpretation of the undulations on the Nascan Tree figure. For some reason the Ancients are leading us on a merry chase with all these codes and secret messages. I wonder why they are being so devious? Could it be as Maurice Cotterell expressed it! "Whoever it was who designed the Lid (with "...images of the gods...")...liked riddles and enjoyed playing with design elements..."

So far I've given you only three of the promised six reasons why there is such an intense interest in precession. Here is the **fourth**. When we examine the precessional equation, $[|ArcTan\ 2\pi| - 2(|[2\pi]^2 + 1|)]\ x\ 10^9$, we can see that it is based on *geometric* factors only. This makes the precessional phenomenon, at least in the minds of the ancient astronomers, *independent* of all physical attributes, such as size, or mass, or orbital and rotational velocities, etc. Is this surprising? I don't know, but it sure is consistent with the physics of free falling bodies on earth. So would it be proper to say that the earth is in a pseudo-state of free fall as it orbits the sun? If so than this is a pretty valid equation.

The **fifth** reason that this subject is pursued so ardently is as we said in an earlier chapter, we saw that the thickness of the crust, hence its size and mass, which is established by gravitational influences through the RB-Effect, had no governing control over a catastrophic shift. We know that the precessional phenomenon is independent of size and mass as well. The significance of this, providing we continue to believe the ancient astronomers, is that the apparent character of the precession cycle and the character of the earth's crust as it prepares to shift, is nearly identical in character.

LETS LOOK AT THIS THOUGHT IN DETAIL

a.   There are two forces that affect the antarctic ice mass, one is the gravitational force that holds it in place on the surface, and the other is the centrifugal force that wants to move it in catastrophic fashion toward the equator.

Similarly, there are two forces in affect on the earth as it orbits the sun, one is the gravitational force that holds the earth in orbital place, and the second is the centrifugal force that wants to hurl it catastrophically out into deep space.

b.   The size and mass of the crust has no influence on the character of a crustal shift, despite the fact that it is being worked upon by gravitational forces.

Similarly, the precessional wobble is also independent of size or mass, though it is being brought about by gravitational forces, as shown by the ancient equation.

c.   And both processes, precession and earth's shifting crust, are cyclic in character.

This last consideration has a quizzical character to it! It is no secret among authors and researchers of ancient lore, that the concepts of astrology, if only in the identification of the twelve constellations that circumscribe the ecliptic, are ancient-ancient-ancient. As, in fact, are the antediluvian names and symbols that identify them. So as we enter the age of Aquarius, *The Water Bearer*, and as we recall the characterization of the shift of the crust that I made in an earlier chapter where we saw the waters of the earth cascading across the continents and laying waste to every thing in their path, should we now be mindful of the possibility that the Ancient's obsession with precession might be a clue awakening us to the forces of cyclic cataclysm that are brought about by the shift of the crust? Is it possible that the similarities between precession and the shift of the earth's crust is the ultimate message of the Ancient transmission?

In a later chapter we will be looking at the strange recurrence of the number "66" during a more detailed analysis of the Pyramidal Triangle. That number is present in the current analysis as well. Look at the absolute value of the number, 103711.8, and note that if we divide the number, |1037118|, in the following fashion, 10 + 37 + 11 + 8, and then add the elements we get 66.

Somewhere in the ancient messages there are clues that will help us derive the proper interpretation to this ubiquitous number 66, unless, of course, we already have it in hand and don't know about it, which might be the case. But for now we'll just have to give the interpretation our best guess.

SO HERE'S MY BEST GUESS

The number, 1037118, which has an association with precession and adds up to '66', along with the Ancient's obsession with the subject of precession, opens up the possibility that these are clues that might tell us of the dreaded character of the shifting-crust phenomenon. They all certainly seem to go together. If this is anywhere near true, than it may be possible that the number "66" is in reference to a latitude! This possibility immediately brings to mind the thought that both the Arctic and Antarctic Circles are at 66° of latitude. One North latitude and the other South.

The Arctic and Antarctic Circles are imaginary lines of latitude which mark the northern and southernmost points at which the sun can be seen at the respective winter Solstices in the Northern and Southern Hemispheres.[9] More importantly, the Arctic and Antarctic Circles run tangent to the northern and southern precessional planes that their revolving motion establishes in the heavens, as shown in Figure 6. So they make excellent tools to transmit associated messages by. The fortunate part of this is that the latitudes of these circles are readily determined by methods of geodesy, ie., the science of the size and shape of the earth. Now if we adopt this idea that the number '66' actually means 66° of latitude, and conclude that the overall message is one of warning, then we might tentatively conclude that a crustal shift is eminent. Here is the rational behind this. First if we were to choose between the message referring to a measure of latitude or a measure of longitude, we would have to pick latitude. The reason for this is that the starting point for a measure of **latitude** is known by everyone to be the equator. However, the starting point for a measure of longitude is as arbitrary as the imagination of the helmsman. So logic points us away from the thought of longitude and directs us to conclude that the value, 66, is a measure of latitude.

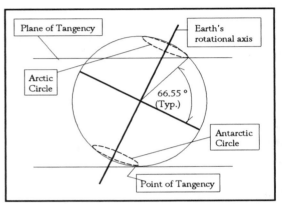

Before we take off on what might be a fallacious tangent, however, we should consider an alternative possibility. It may be that we should look at both 66° of latitude and its compliment, or the *difference* between 90°, ie., the pole position, and 66° of latitude because this difference, more to the scientific point, is **Figure 6** The Arctic and Antarctic Circles run tangent to the northern and southern precessional planes that their revolving motion establishes in the heavens

a measure of the earth's obliquity relative to the ecliptic. This relationship is expressed mathematically as, 90° − 66°= 24°.

Another way to look at this is to look at the spacing of the two precessional planes, or Planes of Tangency, shown in Figure 6. Currently these planes are 133.10° of arc apart, (2 x 66.55° = 133.10°). If a crucial value of the angular distance separating these planes marks an initiating condition for crustal shift, marked as we said by a change in the angle of obliquity, then we should look for a number that repeats itself in the ancient clues. There is validity in this because the centrifugal forces on the Antarctic ice increase with increasing angles of obliquity. One such repeating number, as we'll see in a later chapter, is 66, or an angle of obliquity of 24°.

It is interesting to note that as the angle of equatorial obliquity increases, say from our current angle of 23° 27' to 24°, [10] the winter darkness of the polar regions moves slowly to lower latitudes along with it. There are traditions among the Northern tribes that speak of past occurrences of the stealing away of the sun's light.

LAND OF THE LONG NIGHT

With creation by a Great Spirit, there came dangers from evil spirits. Such spirits carried away the sun and moon, and hung them to the rafters of the dome-shaped Alaskan huts. The World became cold and cheerless, and in the land of Darkness white skins became blackened by contact with the darkness. So it became necessary to search for the sun and hang it again in the dome-shaped sky above them. Darkness in the Land of the Long Night was the cause, through magic, of the bitter winds of winter — winds which came down from the North, bringing with them ice and cold and snow. This was the work of some Great Spirit which had loosened the side of the grey cloud-tent under which they lived, letting in the bitter winds of another world. Spirits blow the mists over the North sea so that canoes lose sight of their home-land.[11]

NINE LETTER WORDS

To many modern day geologists and geo-physicists, cataclysm is a nine letter word! So any argument that affords them an antonym is incarnated immediately. And so in explaining some ancient evidences of climatic change it is common for the cause to be attributed to the precessional phenomenon.[12] This brings us to the **sixth**, and last reason that we have pursued the examination of the precessional cycle. We want to examine the equation above one last time and satisfy ourselves that there are no physical attributes associated with it. From this we can conclude that precession has neither the power nor the will to put a single cloud in the sky. A process that takes 25928 years to complete after all cannot have any interest in rain, or snow, or clouds, or weather systems...at least to much of the world this is true. But there are the few who live in the land of spreading darkness where the "Great Spirit (will loosen) the side of the grey cloud-tent under which they (live), letting in the bitter winds of another world..." and to them it is another story.

The Whale of the Modern Epoch
Giving Birth to a New Generation

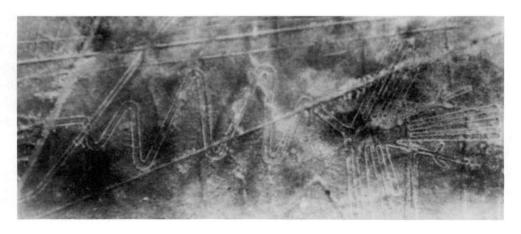

The Tree of Knowledge
On its Bier Awaiting Resurrection

Chapter 15, **The Whole of Manifestation**

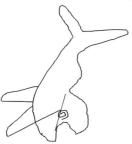

Figure 1. The
Humpback Whale,
the embodiment of
the South Celestial
Pole and all aquatic
life!

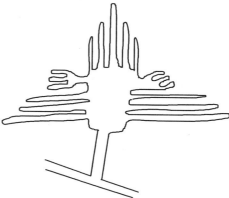

Figure 2. The Tree of Knowledge,
The Tree of Life, The Cosmic Tree,
The Whole of Manifestation;
The Key!

THE MESSAGE OF THE HUMPBACK WHALE:

The North Pole, because of the ancient epoch that we find ourselves in, is centered in the Alaskan Peninsula a short distance inland of the Bay of Alaska, and again, because we're in this ancient epoch there is no land mass, and no opportunity for a geodetic marker at the South Pole. The nearest land is Antarctica, or what was to be called Antarctica in a far distant century. In this ancient time, however, Antarctica is simply a very large island surrounded by the waters of the great oceans.

We know too, from the maps that have survived from these ancient times, that there was a flourishing maritime trade that engaged Antarctica, and in all probability, Peru as well because Peru lay on the equator where its warm water ports would attract the maritime travelers. We know too that the artisans of the Peruvian plateau, for what ever reason, had a deep interest in the polar region south of Antarctica. Wanting a representative form of characterization for the region, they chose the Humpback whale.

Up to fifty feet long, with a rounded back, a horizontally flattened tail and knobby flippers — Humpbacks communicate in orchestral vocalizations that we call song!

The humpback whale, was chosen to personify the deep ocean life forms for a very specific reason. We can see why as we note the similarities between the whale and the lotus plant in Figure 3. One of the more obvious similarities is the wide spread nature of the upper and lower appendages of both the whale and the lotus. Another obvious likeness is in the line that projects toward the right from the whale's eye in comparison to the extended root of the lotus plant. We spoke of the lotus plant in the introduction to Part Three, saying that, "...the outward projection of the right stem of the (lotus) root...depicts a state of change directed toward propagation." The whale is depicted in a like manner, except for one difference, it is not only the personification of its own species, it is the

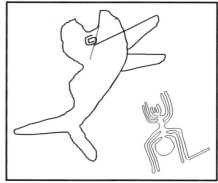

Figure 3 "...in a state of growth directed toward...propagation."

personification of all ocean life...it is a geodetic marker...it is the physical-biological personification of the entire South Polar region.

Another point can be made without objection, and that is in the prominence of the open mouth and the strongly opposing jaws. Is this a clue to another message? But what? The whale, we concluded, represented both the physical and the biological worlds...so there may be a suggestion of some significance here! If the clue is in the jaws, than which side of the mouth is the physical world and which side is the biological world? We'd not be inconsistent if we placed the biological world on the right and the physical world on the left. No certainty here, but the right *is* generally associated with the feminine principle, ie., biological. So let's go that way. Right *biological*, Left *physical*.

A PATTERN FOR US TO FOLLOW

In the forth Star Trek movie, *The Voyage Home*, the Enterprise took two humpback whales, George and Gracie, from 20th Century San Francisco, to the 23rd Century in order to repopulate the species. If you'll recall in that movie, Gracie was not only pregnant, she was *very* pregnant...I think that our Peruvian humpback whale, GeoGracie, is also pregnant! This would certainly be consistent with our earlier statement...ie., the outward projecting line from the eye of the whale depicts a state of growth directed toward propagation. If we accept the idea of the whale being pregnant and the feminine principle being on the right, then we could also accept the fact that it signifies a time of unrest. Recall that the Chinese Yin-Yang doctrine puts the feminine principle on the right in times of war, and if you'll recall the Virgin Mary was on the right at the Last Judgement. Both were on the right during adverse times. I believe the humpback whale, with the feminine principle on the right, stands as a warning to mankind of impending change!

Our conclusion, because this symbolization is in a state of growth, is that the message of the whale is a communique suggesting that the physical and biological forms in the Polar regions are due for a change, a cataclysmic change! Why cataclysmic? Because this whale, this geodetic marker, this personification of all ocean life, is in a state of growth directed toward *propagation*, ie., renewal. This implies a renewal of life and land, ie., a new South Polar region, ie., new families of aquatic life, ie., a crustal shift!

THE COSMIC TREE, THE WHOLE OF MANIFESTATION. THE KEY!

The Tree of Knowledge, The Tree of Life, The Cosmic Tree, The Whole of Manifestation, by what ever name...a tree whose summit is the sky, and whose trunk is the earth,[1] was constructed majestically on the Nascan Plateau as the Key to the question of time, and place. To understand the tree we must apply to the symbol what is written in the myth.

> (§ 1760) ...may you lift me and raise me up to the Winding Waterway, may you set me among those gods the Imperishable Stars that I may fall among them; I will never perish nor be destroyed, but I will sit between the two great gods who give judgement among the gods.

> (§ 1454) Do not break up the ground, O you arms of mine which hold up the sky as Shu; my bones are made of iron and my limbs are the Imperishable stars...

> (§ 1456)... I live beside you, you gods of the Lower Sky, the Imperishable stars.

In order to proceed we must picture The ancient Tree...The Key, as it was meant to be understood! We must think in a new way and follow the astronomical phenomenon of precession. We must walk the Milky Way and visit the Constellations of the Zodiac, and we must visit the Imperishable Stars! We have the capacity, it is said, to catch a glimpse of this higher truth through the opening of a new window through which we can view the past and, if for just a moment, become an Ancient who is composing a message for an unknown people in some unknown epoch far in the future! If we will allow ourselves the pleasure for a moment we would be one with them. Only that way will we understand the ancient Tree. To catch such a glimpse, Count Goblet d'Alviella tells us, is the most manifest sign of the greatness of the human soul and the proof of its faculty for infinite growth and development.[2]

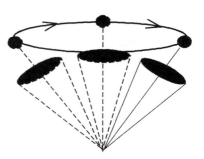

THE KEY

The astronomical phenomenon of precession is our key to discovering the message of the Cosmic Tree. So we'll start there. The precessional motion of the earth's axis has all of the appearance of the decay of

Figure 4 The gyrating motion prescribed by a toy-top, as the spinning motion decays, is like that of precession.

the uniform spinning motion of a toy-top. A top begins with a uniform spinning motion about a stable axis, but as the spinning motion begins to decay a gyrating motion sets in and the rotational axis begins to wobble. It is a phenomenon easily observed by watching the decay of motion of a quarter that has been set to spin. When the uniform spinning motion is lost to wobble, you're observing precessional motion. Discovered in recent times by the Greek astronomer Hipparchus, the wobble of the earth's rotational axis causes an outlining of a circle with a radius of 23.5 degrees around the earth's north ecliptic pole, a circle which progresses at a rate of 50.27 seconds of arc a year, and comes full circle, ie., one complete precessional circuit, in 25,800 years,[3] or 25892 years by ancient interpretation.

Another common reference is thought of in terms of the Precession of the Equinox. The Precession of the Equinox is the slow apparent westward movement of the equinox along the plane of the ecliptic brought about by the precessional wobble. The equinox is a function of time and place. The place is on the earth's equator, and the time is the precise instant that the sun is directly overhead on the first day of Spring, to observe the Vernal Equinox, and the first day of Fall to observe the Autumnal Equinox. Now as we establish a relationship between precession and the Tree, put in mind that the Tree's apparent meaning will change character from one concept to another as the investigation progresses. The Tree, of Figure 5, for instance, demonstrates a relationship between the

136

earth's equator, its axis of rotation, and the ecliptic. It confirms the interpretation of this relationship through the illustration of a gimbal. A gimbal is a ball and socket of sorts used mechanically to provide gyrating capabilities to a joint. The wrist joint, which gives the hand 360 degrees of freedom to move, is a good example. The Gimbal is the Ancient's message that The Celestial Tree is gyrating. It is precessing! It is a time clock!

THE MILKY WAY

The Milky Way is a large spiral galaxy of 100 billion stars, including our sun, and it appears as a wide band of closely packed stars that span the night sky from horizon to horizon. In its path lie the constellations of Sagittarius, Aquila, Cygnus, Perseus, Auriga, Orion, and Crux, the Southern Cross.[4] The Path of The Milky Way is illustrated on the Celestial Tree by the doted line through the Constellations of the Zodiac in Figure 6.

THE CONSTELLATIONS OF THE ZODIAC[5]

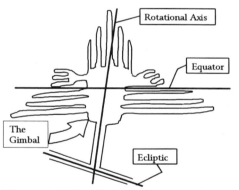

The Zodiac occupies that zone of the sky that includes 8 degrees of arc on either side of the ecliptic. It is divided into 12 equal parts of 30 degrees each, with each part being named for the constellation that dominates it. The Celestial Tree and the twelve constellations of the Zodiac is shown in Figure 6. There are six constellations above the equator, and six below, in this illustration, and there are six constellations on one side of the Milky Way and six on the other. Sagittarius and Scorpio are shown as the Gate-Keepers of the Path of the Milky Way in the South, and Taurus and Gemini hold the Gate in the North.

Figure 5 The Celestial Tree is the Earth. It is the Constellations. It is the Zodiac!

(§ 1220) You shall set me to be a magistrate among the spirits, The Imperishable Stars in the North of the sky, who rule over offerings and protect the reaped corn, who cause this to go down to the chiefest of the food-spirits who are in the sky.

(§ 1376) My ropes are tied,[6] my ferry-boats are made ready for the son of Atum, who is hungry and thirsty, thirsty and hungry on this the southern side of the Winding Waterway, (ie., the Milky Way).

The finger like projections that extend laterally from the trunk of the Tree, form a double ram gate which can be swung open...pivoting about the path of the Milky Way.

> (§ 1726) The bolt is open for you in the double ram-gate which keeps out the plebs; may you number the slaughterers, (the celestial door-keepers[7]), may you take the hands of the Imperishable Stars.

THE IMPERISHABLE STARS

Imagine, as we did once before, it being midnight and directly overhead is the Constellation of Orion, *The Hunter*. Now picture the earth's crust shifting and your position of latitude relative to the equator changing with it. Now as you observe Orion it is no longer directly overhead as it was previously, now it is 30° north of you. Orion hasn't changed position, but you have. Your change in latitude has changed your frame of reference for all celestial bodies *except* for that singular star group...the twelve Constellations of

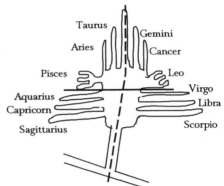

Figure 6. The Celestial Tree and the Constellations of the Zodiac.

the Zodiac which lay Imperishably on the plane of the ecliptic. They do not change reference with a shift of the earth's crust! The Imperishable Stars of the Constellations of the Zodiac, the celestial door-keepers which lay Imperishably on the ecliptic, are your proof that the Celestial Tree is a historical record of cataclysmic change!

> (§ 818) May you go on that road whereon the gods go. Turn yourself about (ie., look across the stretches of the Milky Way) that you may see this offering which the King has made for you, which the Foremost of the westerners has made for you; may you go to those northern gods the Imperishable Stars.

IN REVIEW

We know that the Tree, and specifically the line across it that represents the equator, symbolizes the earth in its precessional path about the sun, and we also know that the ecliptic symbolizes the heavenly expanses of our solar system. We also know that the ecliptic incarnates the souls of the ancient dead as they enter into Heaven through the Double Ram-Gate to traverse the sky along the *Wandering Waterway* of the Milky Way! And we know that the history of the Plateau begins when the North Pole was in Alaska and Nasca and Giza were on the equator. So for the Ancients to have drawn the Tree in all correctness following the last shift of the earth's crust, which according to Hapgood was approximately 17,000 years ago, the people(s) of the plateau would have need to know of the previous positions of the Pole. If they knew it 17,000 years ago then wouldn't there have been a written record of it somewhere? Can we surmise that the Tree(s) are a library of historical facts? To learn the answer to this question we have to look at the other whale, and the other Tree on the plateau.

Figure 7. The whale of the modern epoch giving birth to a new generation

THE OTHER WHALE ON THE PLATEAU.

With the feminine principle again on the right during a time of unrest, the "other whale" on the plateau is caught in the process of giving birth to a new generation. It is the manifestation of the prediction made earlier that its expectant condition was directed toward propagation. It symbolizes an episode of renewal of aquatic life, of the birth of new species of fish and marine mammal. It is the advance messenger of revitalization. Could Figure 7 also be giving us an advanced look at what the new species of Humpback whale will look like! See photos on pages 88 and 132.

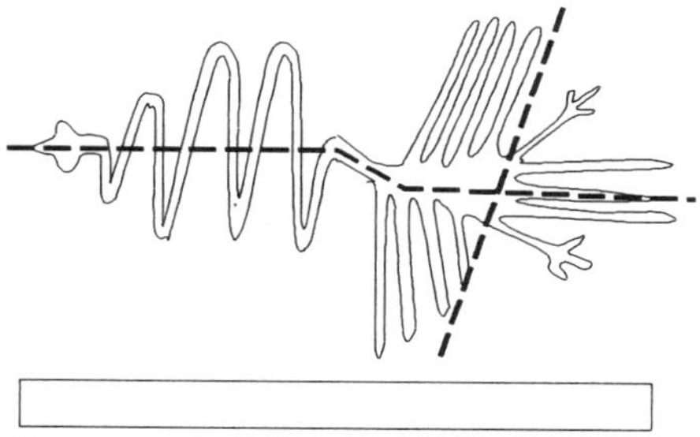

THE TREE OF KNOWLEDGE:

We must now look at the Tree of Knowledge in a completely new light. The Gimbal, as shown in

Figure 8 The Tree of Knowledge, on its bier awaiting resurrection.

Figure 8, has moved from below the lower branches, where it was in the Celestial Tree, to below the trunk. It is now part of the root. The number of branches are the same, but note that the three fingered branches, the Triads, have moved, and the oblique attitude of the axis which gave us six constellations above the equator and six below is different. In Figure 8 there are eight constellations below the equator and four above, and the trunk, by virtue of the variation of frequency and amplitude of the undulations is suggesting that the precessional cycle, as previously suggested, has not been stable over time. If this is the case, than any date that is set on the basis of precessional consistency

139

is incorrect! There is some modern thought that supports this contention. In the February 18, 1993 issue of the journal *Nature*, there appeared an article by J. Laskar & P. Robutel, titled "The Chaotic Obliquity of the Planets."

> The numerical study of the global stability of the spin-axis orientation of the planets against secular orbital perturbations shows that all of the terrestrial planets could have experienced large chaotic variations in obliquity at some time in the past. The obliquity of Mars is still in a large chaotic region, ranging from 0 degrees to 60 degrees. Mercury and Venus have been stabilized by tidal dissipation, and the earth may have been stabilized by the capture of the Moon. None of the obliquities of the terrestrial planets can therefore be considered primordial.[8]

In Part 4, *Earth's Hidden Unrest*, we'll see that the earth is far more dynamic than we'd ever imagined. The earth and the moon exchange elements of angular momentum, and during that exchange the moon's orbit broadens and goes chaotic, and the earth strains and the core gives up angular velocity as if it was a governing device. The Chinese called the period between world-destructions a "great year." Each great year ends "in a general convulsion of nature, the sea is carried out of its bed, mountains spring out of the ground, rivers change their course, human beings and everything are ruined, and the ancient traces effaced.[9] Chaos has always been accompanied by the death of some and the birth of others.

But never has a period of maelstrom taken all that was!

Chapter 16

The Lineage is Broken!

The chance discovery of a triangle that was laid out on the earth in cartographical form, by an ancient association of advanced civilizations that joined Nasca, Giza, and a site in Alaska near the modern site of Juneau, had a profound affect upon our research. The **Ancient Terrestrial Triangle**, as we lovingly call it, has Nasca at the Western base angle, Giza at the Eastern base angle, and Juneau at the Northern apex. It would have been laid out at a time when Alaska was at the North geographical Pole and Nasca and Giza were on the equator. The lines that form the triangle, form angles at the base and at the Northern vertex that are identical to those of the elevation view of the Great Pyramid of Giza. To have made such a construction, the sites of the vertices must have been surveyed in advance of the building of the Great Pyramid, and in advance of the layout of the figures on the Nascan plateau in Peru. There can be no doubt that this construction was intended to be the Double, or one of the Doubles, of the Great Pyramid of Giza.

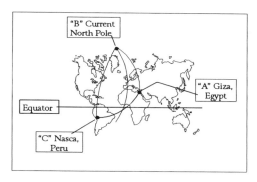

Figure 1. This is the current triangular relationship between Nasca, Giza, and the North Pole.

The procedures and a demonstration of the analytical proof in Spherical Trigonometry is performed in Appendix II and III. The proof makes for some laborious reading so I'll not reproduce it here, but for those who are interested, the analysis is straight forward and anyone familiar with plane trigonometry should have no trouble following the course of the proof. It may be of some interest even for those who are not familiar with spherical trigonometry because, as I have found in my own readings, there is some pleasure in confirming for ourselves what others have claimed to be true!

In reality, where I believe the discovery of this ancient artifact to be an incredible find, I don't consider it unusual that it should exist given the nature of these ancient people. It is altogether consistent with their native beliefs to have laid a Double of the Great Pyramid out on the surface of the earth for themselves, and for a later generation to discover, for what ever reason they had to do it. It is consistent with everything that they ever believed in.

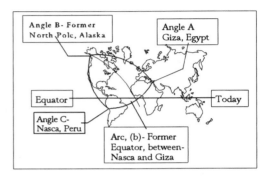

(§ 1277) A boon which Gēb and Atum grant: that this pyramid and temple be installed for me and for my double, and that this pyramid and temple be (§ 1278) enclosed for me and my double...As for anyone who shall lay a finger on this pyramid and this temple which belong to me and to my double...will have offended the Lady of the Mansion.

Figure 2. The Terrestrial Triangle. The base angle, C, at Nasca, and, A, at Giza, are identical to the base angles of the Great Pyramid. They are both 51°52'

LET'S TAKE A LOOK AT THE TRIANGLES

The calculations in Figure 3, show that the base angle of the Great Pyramid is 51°52'. Now lets look at the base angles of the Terrestrial Triangle. The meridional distance along the line of the ancient equator from Nasca to Giza was 111.099°, as it is today. There's been no change! This is a point of interest in itself. We have been led to believe that the continents move about the earth's surface, colliding at some points and subducting at others through a process called plate tectonics. However, Nasca, in South America, and Giza, in Northern Africa, have managed to maintain their relative positions over many thousands of years and through two shifts of the earth's crust. This is mind-

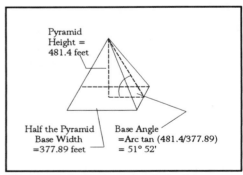

Figure 3 Calculation of the base angle of the Great Pyramid

boggling! So despite the fractures, despite the apparent motions, despite the shifts of the crust, the crust must act pretty much, except for changes in elevation, as a solid unit. It apparently changes very little with time. This is so important that we'll revisit it before we leave this chapter. But back to the matter at hand!

The problems associated with calculating the base angles of the Terrestrial Triangle were not in themselves difficult, but because the meridional lines, ie., the lines that form the vertical land grid, intersect at right angles at the equator, they are meaningless in the world of spherical trigonometry. So we had to convert the triangle to a plane figure with the likeness of the vertical elevation of the Great Pyramid in order to solve for the base angles in any meaningful terms. Such a construction is shown in Figure 4. There it can be seen that the base angle of the Terrestrial Triangle, at 51° 53', is virtually identical to the 51° 52'

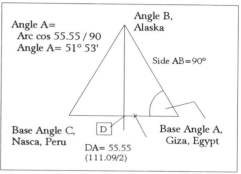

Figure 4 Calculation of the Base angles of the Terrestrial Triangle

base angle of the Great Pyramid of Figure 3. One is the Double of the other!

The Ancients have left us a meaningful message in this Double of the Pyramid and it is not the least bit subtle. The message of the Terrestrial Triangle, as with the Triangle of the Gods that we will study in Chapter 18, *The Gods, Gemini, and The Great Pyramid*, is that the Pyramid, as all faithful investigators have alleged, carries a Communiqué. We don't know the full extent of the message yet, but it is there. For one thing the Communiqué tells us that the Ancients had a command of the world of science, mathematics, and navigation! They wrote their story in the *Texts* of Giza and the *Graphics* of Nasca! Some were Gods some were *Man-Gods*. Some were Male and some were Female. They were in a state of transition!

Osiris and Isis made the transition. They were the first of the *Man-Gods*. But for some reason their son Horus, and Osiris's brother Seth, didn't make the transition. Horus, who would have retained the power of the Gods to procreate but for the loss of his "eye", and Seth who would have had the gift of procreation with a female partner, but for the loss of his testicles, were left as lone actors on an emptying stage. Their lineage was broken! But Horus remained in symbol the human gift of union in the act of procreation even though he himself would never experience its meaning. Seth on the other hand was

143

the embodiment of the transition from the single act of a God in the roll of procreator to the duality of the act in the human species. It has been suggested that the ultimate message of the Ancients is the story of the ancestral history of man, and by implication, his destiny. We say implication because it was the chance discovery of the Terrestrial Triangle, and the implicit reference to a crustal shift that it bore, that led us to that part of their message. Without this we'd never have realized that a part of the message of the Triangle is that the earth's crust shifts...in tact. This conclusion is obvious from the fact that the Terrestrial Triangle has not changed, its meridional lines are as they were laid out eons ago. They originate from a polar position and terminate on the equator and replicate the angular dimensions of the Great Pyramid.

Figure 5. The Ancient World!

A globe of the Ancient World would have looked like that of Figure 5. Antarctica would have been in the South Pacific Ocean and Alaska would have been at the Pole! Nasca and Giza would both have been on the equator and their weather would have been like that of the rain forests of the Amazon river valley. The European, and African climates would have been modernly familiar to us, but the climates of Canada and the United States, as they are called today, would have been vastly different. Ice would have covered all of Canada and vast stretches of the United States. Europe and Greenland would have been enjoying the mild weather of the mid-latitudes and Antarctica, with a climate like that of England today, would have had another name. The name Antarctica is of modern origin and indicative of the current polar climate, and hardly suitable for a mid-latitude island continent with warm water ports as it once was!

A TRUE ICE AGE!

The ice, as it accumulated around the Pole, would have thrown the northern countries into the throes of an Ice Age. It would have pushed its way, scrapping, gouging, and destroying its passage southward until the climate of the lower latitudes stopped its advance...there it would have sat, two miles thick, with its leading moraines fluctuating slowly to mild changes in the climate. This was the true Ice Age!

The Ice was to build in thickness while the lower extremities of the crust were ground into submission by the relentless action of vibration, fretting and fatigue, occasioned by the gravitational forces of Rotational-Bending. Thousands of years were to pass while the surface ice grew and the sub-surface conditions deteriorated...when, not of a sudden, but

144

following the frequent warnings occasioned by increased earthquake activity and more frequent and more violent rising and subsiding of continental surfaces, the crust shifted. It moved 30 degrees, no more, no less. It moved from the Alaskan Peninsula to Hudson Bay, either directly, or in a bobbing motion, that took the polar land from Alaska to the Arctic Ocean, and then to Hudson Bay. (This bobbing motion, as we mentioned earlier, is becoming our scenario of choice.)

The climates around the world would change gradually, as the ice receded from Siberia and Alaska, and it strengthen its grip on the higher latitudes of Canada and the United States and Eastern Greenland. Nasca and Giza both moved to 15° North latitude and into the lower tropical climates of modern day Central America. Again the ice sat and the moraines moderated with the climate while conditions built-up for another movement of the crust. When it came Hudson Bay moved southward and the Arctic Ocean moved into its current spot at the North Geographic Pole. This formed the world as we know it today...two generations after the time of the Ancient Peoples of Nasca and Giza.

The mechanics of the movements have been the same since the continents formed eons ago, and fortunate we are for them, because these movements bring re-vitalization to the wearying surface. Without them the world would have died years ago.

Chapter 17

In Perfect Alignment

We're leaving Peru now and are headed back to a modern time, but it will be a much different world from the one we just left. The crust will have shifted twice since we journeyed from Giza into Nasca's past. The Arctic Ocean is centered at the North Geographic Pole and Polaris is the guiding Star in the North. Antarctica, having been jostled from ocean to ocean, has found a temporary home at the South Pole and is burdened with miles of glacial ice. Everything is as it was, except one thing has changed. The Sphinx, having once been purposefully aligned eastward with unerring precision, still faces east, but now the sacred alignments have been exchanged for an alignment brought on by coincidence and the intervention of man.

The Sphinx was carved from the rock of the Giza plateau eons ago with the noble head of a female lion facing the equatorial sun. But the unerring precision is not in evidence in the 20th century structure. Now the equatorial sun rises far to the south, and the once proud face of the Sphinx has taken on human qualities. The evidence for this most coincidental event is a matter of history whose detail is in the records left by the ancient Peruvian and Egyptian civilizations...we have examined them all!

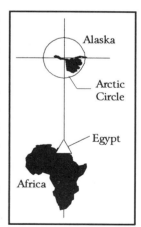

Figure 1 The world before everything went "topsy turvy."

The first piece of evidence was the precise alignment of the Sphinx's body toward the east and the rising sun when Alaska was centered at the North Geographic Pole.

The second was found in the alignment of the Nascan figures with the Northern Pole in Alaska.

The third piece of evidence was the discovery that the hieroglyphic narratives of

147

Egypt told the same story, with the same cast of characters as the graphics on the Nascan plateau.

The forth was the discovery of the Terrestrial Triangle whose sides join Nasca, Giza, and the ancient Pole in Alaska.

FORBEARANCE IS LOST IN TIMES OF CHAOS

Nasca, was racked by uncommon tectonic disturbances during the shifts of the earth's crust. The farm lands, once lush and productive, changed to mountainous terrain as the Andes, known as the Western and Eastern Cordilleras in Central Peru, grew to new heights and drove the inhabitants to the warmer temperatures of the lower elevations. The people suffered greatly during these turbulent times, and their religious beliefs must have been strained to the point of change. Today we know that there was no intervention in the processes...though many may have thought so at the time! No! the processes were the devastating consequence of the RB-Effect and the centrifugal pull on the polar ice caps. These deadly processes work silently deep within the earth with only the unvalued vibrations detectible. They are both natural enough, but unless recognized as the signs of warning, their consequence comes unexpectedly, and so for those who were caught unaware, there may have been a search for a defense or an understanding. But where does one begin such a search, and upon what do you concentrate, and if found, how do you recognize the discovery? Certainly there is no single fissure in a dike that one might place a finger to curb the threatening waters. So would they have turned to a religious solution, and perhaps deified everything in their frantic efforts to regain the sanity of the pre-cataclysmic world? We think of polytheism, the belief in many gods, as the religion of heathens...but than we have never faced the trauma of a world put into chaos.

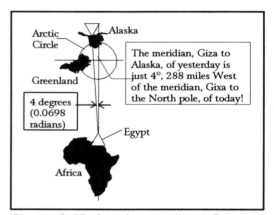

Figure 2. Today the meridian, Giza to the past position of the North Pole in Alaska, misses alignment with the North Pole in the Arctic Ocean by a scant 4.0°, 288 miles.

But while the world was going topsy turvy,[1] the Sphinx, though turned and jostled by the processes, somehow managed to retain, except for a very slight margin of error, its eastward bearing. How? We'll never know for sure, but it did, that much is clear. We can retrace the events easily enough by examining the orientation of the figures on the Nascan plateau, and the orientation of the Sphinx, past and present. The map shown in Figure 1, shows an ancient world in perfect alignment with the former Alaskan Pole. A world that would have remained in perfect alignment, had the crust remained stable. But that wasn't to be the case, change through the intervention of chaos is natural, so crustal stability is not in the cards. You can see it with a quick look at a modern world globe. Stretch a string from Juneau, Alaska, which is very close to the center of the ancient ice sheets, across the top of the globe to Giza and the Pyramids. Stretch the string taught and cause it to form a straight line. This is the alignment that existed 30,000 years ago, when Alaska was at the Pole and Giza was on the equator. Now, with your string still

taught and forming the same straight line between Giza and Alaska, note that the string misses the current polar position by a scant 4 degrees, a mere 288 miles. It will look like Figure 2! The 20th Century alignment of the Sphinx is an illusion. It isn't anywhere near as perfect as some think, or others would have us believe.

I have assembled some geographical facts in Table 1, to illustrate how the Peruvian figures at their inception, and how the Sphinx at its inception, exhibit today their ancient alignment with Alaska, and not the North pole as we know it today. Here is how to

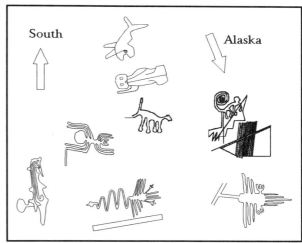

Figure 3 The Nascan figures align with the ancient Alaskan Pole, not the modern one!

make the Table work for you. To recreate the Nasca alignments use the data in Column 3. Position a modern world globe in front of you, for convenience and imagine that you are standing on the plateau above Nasca. Now position your body to align with the **current** pole in the Arctic Ocean. Remain facing the North Pole and with your left hand, point to Alaska.

Now compare the angle that your left arm makes with your body to the orientation of the Nascan Figures in Figure 3. Wō-La!

For the Giza alignments, use the data in Column 5. With the modern world globe and Egypt in front of you, position your body to align with the **current** pole in the Arctic Ocean and with your left hand, point to Alaska. Now compare the angle that your left arm makes with your body with the angle data in Table 1, and with the picture of the Sphinx in Figure 4 on page 157, and the alignment map in Figure 2. Wō-La!

Geography		Column 3		Column 5
	Latitude of Nasca	**From Nasca, the direction to Alaska.**	**Latitude of Giza**	**From Giza, the direction to Alaska.**
The North Pole is in the Arctic Ocean	15° South	15° NW	30° North	4° (Due North, if we were to judge by eye!)

TABLE 17-1. The History of the Shift of the Pole!

After two shifts of the earth's crust, the Sphinx was brought back to within 4 degrees of the ancient religious associations. If we look carefully now at the perpendicular alignment of the Sphinx's spine in Figure 4, we will see that it does not pass over the North Arctic Pole, but instead it follows your string a little to the west. It is aligned unerringly toward the ancient Alaskan Pole. The eastward orientation of the Sphinx today is no more than an illusion created when man intervened by resculpting the lions head to face the new East. But there had to have been purpose here, though obviously lost to us now!

Could it be, do you suppose, that the post-equatorial Egyptians re-carved the head to align it with the rising sun to correct what they may have perceived to have been an ancient error in orientation! Or could it have been that the lions head had become so eroded by time and water that it had lost its distinguishing features and so a new likeness was created to fit the culture of the day. Which ever the case the illusion was complete.

NATURE WORKS IN CATASTROPHIC OUTBURSTS OF ENERGY

But let's not close the book on the Sphinx quite yet. Lets go back for a moment to the precise time that the face of the Sphinx was reoriented and humanly reconfigured. Could the anomalous reconstruction, with the anomalous placement of a human face on a lions body have been intentional? If so, where would it direct us in this modern day? Ancient Cardinal references were purposefully created, and the head of the Sphinx would most certainly have been constructed to match the orientation of the body. With this thought in mind, lets remind ourselves that there were numerous clues in the West that spoke of frequent displacements of the crust, not the least of which is the modern mis-orientation of the Nascan figures. But there is no equivalent clue in the East, unless by intent the role of the re-configured Sphinx is our guide. Could this be the clue that we are looking for? Was the re-configured Sphinx intended to attract our attention? Perhaps the disparity in the orientation of the modern day Sphinx, like the angle between your arm and your body moments ago, is facing one way and pointing another in a plea for understanding!

The purpose in my having you go through those finger pointing exercises was to have you observe for yourself the coincidence that fate dealt. The alignments of the ancient structures are not true to 20th century compass directions. Perhaps we have learned something new from this...the Nasca figures and the Sphinx are both pointing to the ancient pole, and somewhere within their respective structures we may find a coded communiqué, saying, "These mis-alignments are a signal, CQ, CQ, CQ! Let me have your attention!" If so, we might better heed their message!

MOTHER NATURE IS TWO FACED

Let's assure ourselves that these mis-alignments are not just the result of the tectonic motion of the plates. We can examine this thought by looking at the two faces of Mother Nature. She wears one face as she works methodically behind the scenes to prepare the world for turmoil, and she wears quite another as she goes about the extended task of evolutionary change. The preparations for turmoil eventually come to the surface in cataclysmic form, they always come unexpectedly, and sometimes in mild doses, but just as often devastatingly. There are two activities of chaotic proportion that are going on at this very moment that are easily recognizable. The accumulation of ice at the poles is well known and of awesome proportion, and so are the rumblings within the earth which are the sounds made by the Rotational-Bending processes as it breaks the ties that bind.

ACTIVE GEOLOGIC CENTERS

One of the most, geologically, active centers in the world is the zone along the northern and eastern edges of the African plate where it is in contact with the southeastern edge of the Eurasian plate and the western edge of the Arabian plate.[2] This rift between the plates follows a path through Gibralter, along the northern shores of the Mediterranean Sea, hence through a passage from Jerusalem to the Red Sea...then moves on to the Gulf of Aden in the South, and out into the Arabian Sea. Reports have this rift opening at Djibouti, in Ethiopia, in modern times. Active tectonics along this fault would cause the African plate to rotate clockwise, with the pivot point in the area of the Aegean Sea, where flanked by Greece and Turkey the seismic activity is most pronounced. So rather than opening the meridional gap and wresting Giza from its Alaskan alignment, any tectonics along this fault would be closing it. We must conclude, therefore, that tectonic movements of the African plate to be of no consequence!

The Great African Rift

Velikovsky tells us that in recent geological time Africa was in tension and torn by north and south fractures (which) along with the sinking of a strip of the crust formed the longest meridional land valley on earth. From Lebanon almost to the cape there runs a deep and comparatively narrow valley, margined by almost vertical sides, and occupied by the sea, by salt steppes, old lake basins, and by a series of over twenty lakes, of which only one has an outlet to the sea. This is a condition of things absolutely unlike anything else on the surface of the earth.[3] J. W. Gregory, in an article titled "Contributions to the Physical Geography of British East Africa," published in the *Geographical Journal*, and quoted by Velikovsky adopted the view that a general common cause created the entire Rift from its north end to its south.

> The Rift begins in the valley of the Orontes River in Syria; at Baalbek it goes over to the Litani River valley, then to Lake Huleh in Palestine; along the Jordan River to the Sea of Galilee, called also Gennesaret or the Sea of Tiberias, which lies in a depression below the level of the Mediterranean; from there to the Dead Sea, the deepest depression on earth, between the Judean and Moabite mountainous plateaus that were torn apart; then along the Araba Valley to the Gulf of Aqaba in the Red Sea and across the channel of this sea into Africa; thence for an enormous distance to the Sabie River in the Transvaal, branching, on the way, eastward to the Gulf of Aden and westward to Tanganyika and the Upper Nile, and the rift valleys of Lakes Moeris and Upemba in the central Congo— all the way from about 36° north latitude in Syria to about 28° south latitude in East Africa, in a sinuous line along a meridian for more than a third of the way from one pole to the other.[4]

The movements along the Rift and their geological consequence are not events of ages past, but rather according to Gregory, are actually quite modern. This wide-spread valley system, he adds, is obviously not the result of some local fracture. Its length is about one-sixth of the circumference of the earth. Gregory describes it thus...

> It must have some world-wide cause, the first promising clue to which is the date of its formation...Some of the fault-scarps are so bare and sharp that they must be of very recent date. This continuation of earth-movements into the human period is one of the most striking features of the district...All along the line the natives have traditions of great changes in the structure of the country.[5]

PERU! An emphases on change:

Other parts of the world report similar change. One of the best records is in the history of Lake Titicaca. The Lake, about 140 miles long by 70 wide, is situated 360 miles east, as the crow flies, of Nasca. It lies on the border between Peru and Bolivia at an elevation of about 12,500 feet.

Graham Hancock tells us that Lake Titicaca had a puzzling geological history...

> Though now more that two miles above sea level, the area around Lake Titicaca is littered with millions upon millions of fossilized sea shells. This suggests that at some stage the whole of the Altiplano was forced upwards from the sea bed.

> Lake Titicaca has retained, until the present day, a marine icthyofauna, ie., ocean marine rather than fresh water fish and crustacea...and...Since its formation this great "interior sea" and the Altiplano[A] itself, has undergone several other drastic and dramatic changes. Of these by far the most notable is that the lake's extent appears to have fluctuated enormously, indicated by the existence of an ancient strand line visible on much of the surrounding terrain...

> Much harder to explain is (the) irrefutable evidence that the city of Tiahuanaco,

---

[A] The Altiplano is the elevated plain that is situated between two branches of a range of mountains known locally as the Cordilleras. More accurately the Cordilleras comprise the entire complex of mountain ranges in the western parts of North, Central and South America extending from Alaska to Cape Horn.

(pronounced Tē´a-wa-nö´kō) was once a port, complete with extensive docks, positioned right on the shore of Lake Titicaca...Tiahuanaco's ruins, (the builders being unknown) are now marooned about twelve miles south of the lake and more than 100 feet higher than the present shore line.[6]

Velikovsky, adds to the mystery of Tiahuanaco.

With the present climate (of the Altiplano) it would not have been suitable at any period as the asylum for the great human masses of the most important prehistoric center of the world. (Although) endless agricultural terraces of the people who lived in this region in pre-Inca days can still be recognized. Today this region is at a very great height above sea level. In remote periods it was lower...the terraces rise to a height of 15,000 feet, twenty five hundred feet above Tiahuanaco.[7]

Another singularly impressive piece of evidence for recent (movements) of the crust, may be found in the journal of Charles Darwin. Sir Archibald, as related to us by Charles Hapgood[8], summarized Darwin's findings...

On the West coast of South America, lines of raised terraces containing recent shells have been traced by Darwin as proofs of a great upheaval of that part of the globe in modern geological time. The terraces are not quite horizontal but rise to the south. On the frontier of Bolivia they occur from 60 to 80 feet above the existing sea-level, but nearer the higher mass of the Chilean Andes they are found at one thousand, and near Valparaiso at 1300 feet. That some of these ancient sea margins belong to the human period was shown by Mr. Darwin's discovery of shells with bones of birds, ears of maize, plaited reeds and cotton thread, on some of the terraces opposite Callao at a height of 85 feet. Raised beaches occur in New Zealand and indicate a greater change of level in the southern than in the northern end of the country...[9]

The Great Extinctions of recent times

The closing millennia of the ice age saw an enormous mortality of animals in many parts of the world.[10] Hibben estimated that as many as 40,000,000 animals died in North America alone.[11]

Many species of animals became extinct, including mammoths, mastodons, giant beaver, sabertooth cats, giant sloths, wooly rhinoceroses, camels and horses. No one has been able to explain these widespread extinctions.

Velikovsky adds...

> In bogs covering glacial deposits in Michigan, skeletons of two whales were discovered...How did they come to Michigan in the post-glacial epoch? ... Was there a sea in Michigan *after* the glacial epoch, only a few thousand years ago?

It seems hardly possible because the surface of Lake Michigan is 582 feet above sea level.[12] In further regard to Michigan, let me add this note. North of Clare, at about 45° north latitude, at an estimated elevation of 850 feet, there is an ancient beach that runs east and west across the face of the state. I pass by it every year on trips north. The beach marks the previous shore line of a single lake which now, because of geologically recent changes of elevation of Central Michigan, has been divided to form Lake Michigan on the west, and Lake Huron on the east.

Velikovsky continues...

> Bones of whale have been found 440 feet above sea level, north of Lake Ontario; a skeleton of another whale was discovered in Vermont, more than 500 feet above sea level, and still another in the Montreal-Quebec area, about 600 feet above sea level.

> A species of Tertiary whale, Zeuglodon, left its bones in...such abundance in (Alabama and other Gulf States), and were such a nuisance that the farmers piled them up to make fences.

> A most striking phenomenon (among those observed by Joseph Prestwich, Professor of geology at Oxford 1874-88) was in the fissures in the rocks. In the neighborhood of Plymouth, (England) on the Channel, clefts of various widths in limestones formations are filled with rock fragments, angular and sharp, and with bones of animals— mammoth, hippopotamus, rhinoceros, horse, polar bear, bison. hyaena, wolf, bear and lion. ...No skeleton is found entire. If the crevices were pitfalls into which the animals fell alive, then some of the skeletons would have been preserved entire. But this is "never the case."...These conditions are similar to those found in England and Wales, in the valleys around Paris, and in the hills in central France, and all over western Europe...every where the fissures are found

choked with the bones of animals, some extinct, others still surviving.[13]

And the Rock of Gibraltar is intersected by numerous crevices filled with bones. The bones are broken and splintered. The remains of panther, lynx, caffir-cat, hyaena, wolf, bear, rhinoceros, horse, wild boar, red deer, fallow deer, ibex, ox, hare, (and) rabbit have been found in these ossiferous fissures.[14]

Ancient Beaches:

Comparatively radical vertical changes in positions of land masses are evidenced by a considerable number of ancient beaches (some of them, however, are not very old) which are now found at great elevations above sea level, and sometimes far inland from the present coasts. Thus the geologist P. Negris claimed to have found evidences of beaches on three mountains of Greece: Mt Hymettus, Mt. Parnassus, and Mt. Geraneia, at, respectively, 1400 feet, 1500 feet, and 1700 feet above sea level. (And) He found a beach on Mt Delos at 500 feet. William H. Hobbs cited a particularly interesting case of a beach of recent date now 1500 feet above sea level, in California.

Upon the coast of Southern California may be found all the features of wave-cut shores now in perfect preservation, and in some cases as much as 1500 feet above the level of the sea. These features are monuments to the grandest of earthquake disturbances which in recent times have visited the region.[15]

We've read about ancient beaches in an earlier chapter, but I would like to end this section with a comment made to me by Fred N. Earll in a letter dated October 26, 1993. Fred, now retired, was a Professor of Geology at Montana College of Mineral Science and Technology, and wrote the forward to Charles Hapgood's second book on the shifting of the earth's crust titled, *The Path of the Pole*. Fred wrote...

Last July I had the good fortune to visit Freeport's Grasberg Mine in Irian Jaya. There, where the Pacific and Australian Plates have collided, I saw cretaceous sea floor sediments (65 to 130 million years old) atop the highest peaks of the Sudirman Range at elevations in excess of 15,000 feet! Sheared, folded and intruded by magma, but there never–the–less.[16]

This group of islands formed since Cretaceous time almost within sight of Australia where the oldest rocks yet found on the planet occur.[17] I guess what I am saying is that we should quit arguing about the existence of these things, (i.e., sea floor sediments thrust upon the continent, and sea floor sediments atop the highest peaks.) and concentrate on explaining them.

We've been examining the circumstances and the evidences of recent geological change in order to establish a scientific foundation in support of the ancient cultural messages. It would be possible to multiply endlessly the evidence of the raised beaches, and ancient lakes, the displaced sea floor, and the bones and the pebbles, the hundred foot deep lava beds with human artifacts at their base, and the glacial swept terraces that are found in every part of the world. The evidences have not been fallacious computer modeling efforts...they have been drawn from the field by researchers and independent authors. In each instance, they are verifiable by anyone who cares to reach out and examine them.

We've also presented multiple pieces of evidences that demonstrate that the Sphinx was carved when Giza was on the equator many eons ago. We also suggested that the alignment of the Sphinx eastward is no more than an illusion. The illusion being created by the intervention of man when the Sphinx's head, which was formerly that of a female lion, (See Figures 5 & 6 on Page 158) was carved in human likeness. We saw that the body and the spine of the Sphinx are not pointing eastward but rather are oriented 4 degrees north of east. A line drawn northward from the primordial spine can be seen to align, not with the North Pole of today, but with ancient pole in Alaska. Looking back at the reconstructed head, we can see that only the face of the Sphinx is facing due east. And we showed you where the alignments of the figures on the Nascan plateau were consistent, not with any modern day marker, but with the North Geographical Pole in Alaska.

So in closing this chapter on the ancient alignments I would like to comment on their discovery. The discovery of the Terrestrial Triangle, and the discovery that a relationship between the Egyptian hieroglyphic text and the Nascan graphics existed, since there was no material evidence to be found linking them, came about through the intervention of pure chance. I cannot see where the clues were that lead me to them. But isn't that the way of all discovery? Don't we kind of stumble onto things? Because, after all, we don't really know what there is to be found, so we can hardly be looking for something specific to discover. So again I am reminded of Edward Bacon's "*...love of an ideal beauty...*"

The instinct to find out the past has many sources: idle curiosity...the material of magic...a desire for romance...or a love of an ideal beauty![18]

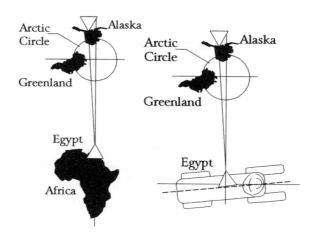

Figure 4 Today only the face of the Sphinx faces east.
The rest of its body, forgotten as to purpose, aligns
with its ancient origins.

We have said that the Sphinx is female. Now judge for yourself, the answer is in the
Constellations of the Zodiac. The Celestial Double of the Sphinx, the Constellation Leo,
is undoubtedly female. But there is a particular item of interest here...note the lines that
join the heart to the ovaries and the breast. What do you think they mean?

Figure 5. The
Celestial Double of
the Sphinx, The
Constellation Leo.

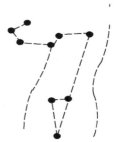

Figure 6 Well?
Female, or not?

Chapter 18

The Gods, Gemini, and the Great Pyramid!

In the opening chapter of Part III, *The Story Begins*, we examined a body of clues that demonstrated an anomalous height to perimeter ratio in the structure of the Great Pyramid involving the value Pi, which, as we noted then, is a relationship known only to circles and related shapes. We also suggested, without providing you proof, that the Ancients took the value of Pi out to 9 decimal places in their mathematical expressions. The proof, which combines somehow with an anomalous number 66, is linked with a new geometrical representation for the Pyramid which we demonstrate below, and we'll find verification from, of all places, the constellations and the astronomical calender we call precession. The answers that will evolve from these proofs will also suggest to us what the Great Pyramid may be, at least in part, and where the Gods[1] may be now, or at least where they may have been at one time.

BY DEFINITION

By definition a tangent is a short excursion off the beaten path...and that's what we're going to be doing now in order to establish some background. The height of the Pyramid is about 481 feet and the perimeter, the distance around, is close enough to 3022 feet to have established for investigators, like Peter Tompkins[2] and others, the clue that the relationship between the height and perimeter of the Great Pyramid is the same as found between the circumference of a circle, C, and its diameter, d. The relationship is expressed vocally using the word Pi, and mathematically with the Greek letter, "π."

The mathematical expression for the Pi relationship is, $C=\pi d$, but when we substitute the radius for the diameter, the expression becomes, $C= 2\pi r$. But we'd want to use the height of the Pyramid, h, in our expression rather than the radius, and we'd want to use the perimeter of the Pyramid, P, for the circumference so when we do this the expression becomes, $P = 2\pi h$. This is the expression that the Egyptians used in the construction of the Great Pyramid. Now, let's substitute known values into the equation...

159

Perimeter of Pyramid = 2 πh   Where "h" is the height of the Pyramid, or 481 feet.
           = 2 x 3.14159 x 481
           = 3022.2   (This demonstrates the Pi relationship mathematically.)

In reality the height and perimeter of the Pyramid will have no bearing on the outcome of our analysis what so ever, as we are about to see. The only item of importance, the only message that was ever encrypted, was that there *was* a Pi relationship to be discovered. Getting this connection accepted by many investigators, however, has been an up-hill battle for all who sought the answers, because every suggestion of a mathematical or celestial relationship regarding any feature of the Great Pyramid, or the Giza site as a whole, was summarily rejected. How? By simply ignoring the evidence. So its been that the discovery of the true meaning of the Great Pyramid has evolved only very slowly.

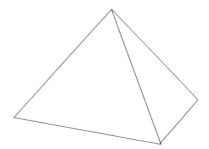

Figure 1. The Pyramid!

The Great Pyramid sits upon the Mokattam plateau of Giza six miles west of the Nile with the sides oriented to the Cardinal points with nothing but the imagination to suggest that it is anything else but a simple pyramid. None the less, it has been measured every which way but up in the hopes of discovering its suspected secrets. If we were to continue this line of exploration in hopes of discovering why the Pi relationship was encrypted into the Pyramid's construction, we'd see two obvious ways to look at it. This would be to examine the base angles and the corner angles separately. To analyze the base angle we'd examine the elevation view, and to analyze the corner angle we'd examine the Pyramid diagonally. But neither of these would prove to be of any value to us! What we'd want to do instead is to look at the Pyramid in the precise metaphoric relationship that the builder had originally expressed, and that is to view the perimeter directly in relation to the height. This is going to give us a totally different perspective and it will provide us with some very unexpected answers.

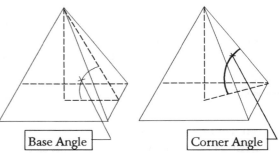

Figure 2 There are two angles of possible interest in the Great Pyramid: The base angle and the corner angle.

160

The builders had never intended for us to view the Great Pyramid in geometric form for analysis, rather, it was their intent that we'd view it as a plane **triangle**. After some examination it becomes apparent why they did this...it was because they had encrypted their message in the mathematical logic embedded in the precepts of algebra, geometry, and trigonometry, and a triangle, because of it's simplicity, is a unique vehicle for doing this. But the Ancients had to get our attention first. So they chose to use the anomalous Pi relationship. That's the wonder of an anomaly...it gets our attention! And that it did, the Pi relationship was discovered a long time ago. (See Figure 3.)

A tangent, besides being a short excursion off the beaten path, is also a mathematical formulation used in trigonometry to express the relationship between two sides of a triangle in relation to a designated angle.

THE RIGHT TRIANGLE

The Tangent of the Angle β (pronounced Beta) in Figure 3, is the ratio of the length of the side opposite Angle β, in relation to the length of the side adjacent to Angle β. Mathematically it is expressed this way.

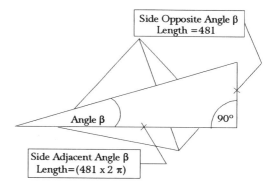

1.   The Tangent of Angle β =
        481 ÷ (2π) x 481

The 481 values in the numerator and denominator of this expression will cancel and the term will become...

Figure 3. The Pyramid as seen by the Builders. The answers, we're are embodied in the characteristics of a triangle, not those of a Pyramid.

2.   The Tangent of Angle β = 1 ÷ (2π)

Solving the expression, 1 ÷ (2π), for its numerical value we have...

3.   The Tangent of Angle β = 0.15915494307 (This is both a transcendental number and an irrational number as are all of the values we will be examining below.)

The 481 foot height of the Pyramid canceled when we solved the equation, as you can see, and it left us with the simple expression, 1 divided by 2π, or, 1÷(2π).

So it made no difference what the measured height or length of the perimeter of the Pyramid was, or in what units it was measured in. It could have been measured using a broken stick dipped in mud as long as the Pi relationship was observed. It made no difference! The answer was going to be the same in any case, because it was not based on the dimensions themselves, since these canceled, but simply on a ratio of numbers involving the mathematical constant, Pi. This encrypting logic is precisely what is required when the intent is to speak across great spans of time. Their message is being revealed in a language that is itself transcendental, their clues are everlasting and they are independent of measuring systems and accuracies.

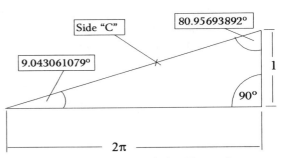

Figure 4. The angles of the Triangle.

So as we continue, keep in mind that the builders of the Pyramid are speaking to us in the only language that will transcend time. It is the transcendental language of science and mathematics. So don't expect a message that will say, "Hey, let me tell you a story." Expect, instead, a message written in mathematical expressions. Expressions that will require that we explore the possibility that each and every number that evolves from the investigation could be a clue. So we must try to examine everything that we encounter within the framework of the Ancient's culture and within their ability to convey a coherent message across the ages to a people that they would never know.

WHERE DO WE GO FROM HERE?

We need a path to follow, so let's recap our position. We know that there are 9 Gods on the Plateau...Atum, Shu, Tefēnet, Gēb, Nūt, Osiris, Isis, Seth, and Nephthys, so the number 9, must have some lingering significance. Another point stands out, everything worked mathematically when we applied *modern* algebraic techniques to solve the Pyramid Triangle so the Ancients must have developed a form of trigonometry if in fact they didn't invent ours! And I'll wager you this, a dollar says they used a numerical system written to the base ten, and if I am right they would have written our tangent of Angle $\beta = 0.15915494307$ from equation 3 above, as $15.915494307 \times 10^{-2}$. So we'll follow the numbers 9 and 10 as we pursue this analysis further. A number like 10 as a clue, however, is all too familiar to us, it's not anomalous it'd never be recognized. But what if, in searching for a way to express the number 10, we used 9 plus a tenth element, like (9 + 1 = 10), that would be sufficiently arbitrary to catch our attention! It was a wild guess, but it was going to pay off. So based on this logic, I started to look for the number 9 along with "an anomalous reference" to a tenth-figure, perhaps a reference to a tenth god. But if it was a god, which one? And within what context would we find the answer? It was going to be somewhat of a puzzle. As a preliminary guess Thoth stands out as the hands down favorite because Thoth was the tenth god on the plateau. Thoth, who is **Atum Rē('s** Ambassador, the incarnate bearer of knowledge and mysticisms.

We'll start our analysis with the number that we just calculated from the tangent, (Tan $\beta = 0.15915494307$), and search for a clue in numerology. The number 9 is important some how, so we'll use it in re-expressing the number 0.15915494307. If this bothers some of the readers, let me remind them that the art of deciphering ancient codes doesn't come packaged with instructions. We don't know what exists in the way of clues, we just have to experiment. So let's continue.

We'll re-express the Tan β by dividing the absolute value into 9 segments...[A]

4. $|15915494307| = 15+9+15+4+9+4+3+0+7$ (There are 9 numbers in the set.)

Now we'll add them using each of the 9 numbers in this set as a unique number.

5.   The sum of $15+9+15+4+9+4+3+0+7 = \mathbf{66}$

For the time being, we will interpret this as meaning that there are 10 Gods, 9 plus 1, with the "1" identified as number "66," this being our anomalous entity. So now we have Atum, Shu, Tefēnet, Gēb, Nūt, Osiris, Isis, Seth, Nephthys, and perhaps Thoth, who is represented by the number **66**! Some may say that it is possible to play around with numbers and make them say anything that you want them to say. Well that's true, and under most circumstances I'd not pursue such an analysis, but the Ancients have given us a most unlikely puzzle to solve, and we have to use everything at our command to solve it. What makes it worth while to go on in this fashion, as you'll see, however, is that the ancient people never...as in never ever did anything just once. They expressed themselves over, and over again in an assortment of different ways, but always with the same intent and meaning! What we should do at this point is to keep going, and we'll see that the number 66 keeps coming up as it did in Chapter 14, *In the Land of Spreading Darkness*, when we divided the absolute value of the number, 1037118, ie., $|1037118|$

[A]The reader will recall our definition of absolute value from Page 124.

which related to the length of the precessional cycle, into elements and added them to get 66 in this fashion, $10 + 37 + 11 + 8 = 66$.

Having calculated the tangent of the angle β from the triangle we can now determine the value of the angle in degrees. Using a calculator and the following expression...

6. The arc tan of $0.15915494307 =$ Angle β $= 9.043061079°$

The angle, $9.043061079°$, is the base angle of the **triangle** that characterizes the Great Pyramid in this new geometrical format, and we see the number 9 again.

We'll separate the 9, and then partition the remaining 9 digits as we did before.

7. $|043061079| = 0+4+30+6+10+7+9$

8. The sum of $0+4+30+6+10+7+9 = $**66**

Here again we have **9 + 66**.

Now lets take the absolute value of the transcendental number Pi, 3.141592653, out to "9" decimal places, and we'll partition it and see what we get. (Here is part of our proof!)

9. $|3141592653| = 31+4+1+5+9+2+6+5+3$

Now we'll add them, using each of the 9 numbers in this set as a unique number.

10. The sum of $31+4+1+5+9+2+6+5+3 = $**66**

And here again we have **9 + 66**

Now let's take an in-depth look at the 90° angle in the "right" triangle of the Pyramid.

11. 90 is the product of 9 and 10 (No surprise here!)

We have here the very elements of our investigation, 9 and 10. In themselves, they have an interesting history. The symbols and legends that have come down to us through the ages, those at least that demonstrate a certain permanence, can usually be traced to some ancient truism, and as we might expect it is true of the numbers nine and ten. Nine is the number of the circumference, hence its division into 90 degrees and into 360 degrees for the entire circumference. Ten is the perfect number[4]...it is the foundation of all counting. It is also the sum of the number nine of the circumference with the unity of the center.[5] Yup, you guessed it, (9 +1=10). So as you can see there are some interesting associations here! But there again...not surprising...and it encourages us to continue this line of investigation! So lets continue with the square root of 90.

12.   The square root of 90 is 9.48683298. (And here is our number 9 again.)

We'll separate the 9 as a unique number and divide the decimal in the following manner!

13. $|48683298| = 4+8+6+8+3+29+8$

14. $4+8+6+8+3+29+8=\textbf{66}$

LET'S SUMMARIZE ALL THE ABOVE

In demonstrating this extraordinary association between the Great Pyramid and the right triangle,[6] I've attempted to show you that there was a repeated reference to a tenth entity which was implied in four instances when the transcendental numbers we analyzed added up to 66! Reviewing, these four instances we have...

1.   The tangent of the base angle of the triangle. (Tangent= 0.15915494307)

   $|15915494307| = 15+9+15+4+9+4+3+0+7=\textbf{66}$

2.   The base angle of the triangle. (Angle β= 9.043061079°)

   $|043061079| = 0+4+30+6+10+7+9=\textbf{66}$

3.   The transcendental number Pi. (3.141592653=31+4+1+5+9+2+6+5+3)

   $|3141592653| =31+4+1+5+9+2+6+5+3=\textbf{66}$

4.   The square root of 90 from the "right" angle of the triangle. (Sq-root=9.48683298.)

   $|48683298| = 4+8+6+8+3+29+8=\textbf{66}$

In each instance we obtained a set of numbers equaling, (9 plus 66)! Is this coincidence? We can't analyze the figure ten in this numerical decryption because the number doesn't actually exist. The number "ten" was always expressed as 9 plus 1, besides, it isn't transcendental, and all the other numbers that we analyzed were transcendental. But on the other hand we can't overlook the number "one" from the expression $(9+1=10)$, because *it is* a valid number, and as it turns out it is important to our story. The number "1" represents primordial unity, the beginning, the sum of all possibilities. It is the principle which gives rise to duality and thence to multiplicity,[7] and it is this matter of *multiplicity* that we are primarily interested in here. There is an algebraic axiom that states that a numerical equivalent may be substituted for any number in a mathematical expression. For example, if we had a number "4" in a mathematical expression, we could substitute an equivalent expression in its place like, 2x2, which equals 4. To arrive at this we factored the "4" into the 2x2 expression.

So following this mathematical rational we can substitute "66" for the *one*, because we learned above that each mathematical attempt to evaluate the *one* in the expression $(9+1)$ yielded "66." So apparently *one* and "66" are equivalent in some manner. We're on some shaky ground here, but let's proceed by substituting the value "66" for the *one*, except that we'll express it as the *product* of the two sixes, ie., 6x6, in accordance with the principle of substitution...just as the product of 2x2 was substituted for the number "4" above. This done our number "1" becomes 36, ie., 6x6=36. We don't know the significance of this yet, but certainly as important as the numbers themselves is the realization that the relationships that are expressed by them illustrate some thought-provoking facts about the Ancients. For instance, these *Gods,* and I don't know what else to call them, most certainly had a commanding knowledge of the mechanics of geometry, algebra, trigonometry, exponential functions,[B] and irrational numbers, as well as the deductive system of logic and proofs that is associated with each of these separate disciplines. Irrational numbers, by the way, are numbers that cannot be expressed as an integer, or by a ratio of integers, Pi, is an example.

THE MATH OF THE GODS, The Gods of the plateau clearly understood...

1. The significance of Pi, ie., π, as a transcendental, irrational number,
2. The trigonometric functions of an angle, ie., the tangent, sine and cosine, etc.,
3. The arc functions of angles,

[B] An example being $10^{1/2}$, where the "½" means to take the square root.

4.   Exponents, whole and fractional,
5.   Set functions,
6.   Factoring,
7.   Number Theory...

And on and on, or should I say Ōn and Ōn? In addition, since we were able to use an Arabic numbering system to the base 10, it follows that the Ancients used an Arabic style numbering system as well. Or could it be that we 20th century *moderns* are using *their* system? That wouldn't surprise me! Another point to consider is that we were able to use angles measured in degrees, thus demonstrating that the Ancients used degrees as a construct for their circles as well, and since the mathematics of our analysis worked out, we can be pretty sure that they divided their circles into three hundred and sixty degrees (360°) just as we do. There are alternative numerical systems that would have worked for them, they could have used a system of radians, or grads, or a system with degrees but not totaling 360°, but apparently that was not the case.

BACK TO OUR STORY!

The biggest question of them all is what is the significance of all the numbers (1, 9, 10, 36, & 66)? Could it be more than just the singular reference to a tenth entity? I am ready to accept the probability that it has several meanings at this point. It all depends upon which path we are following. But it would be uncommon to suspect that the Ancients would have used the same shaped figure for a six (6) or a nine (9) that we do. They could have used figures of any shape or description. But interestingly enough, or maybe I should say "not surprisingly," their number "6" seems to have been very similar to our own. But how about the additional fact that we have two identical symbols side by side, ie., "66", twins as it were? Could this be a subtle suggestion to look at the Constellations for an answer? We'll see in a minute, but lets set some ground work first.

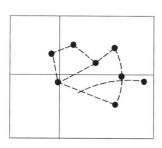

Figure 5 Sagittarius

Constellations are identified in a variety of ways...we'll be interested in just four. The first means of identification is by the appearance, and the second is by its name. The third way is by a descriptive pseudonym, or nickname, Sagittarius, for instance, is known in this manner as *The Archer*. The forth means is by the constellation's Sign. The *Sign* of Sagittarius, *The Archer*, is an arrow!

Figure 6
The Sign is an arrow!

Now back to the Constellations in search for an answer. If we look to Gemini, because it's pseudonym is *The Twins,* we're going to be disappointed. Because when we look...we discover that the *Symbol* of Gemini, which should have been complimentary, and perhaps even the twin "6's" that we were looking for, is anything but complimentary. But our disappointment is not long lasting because the next Constellation in the precessional cycle is Cancer, and you guessed it! The Symbol of Cancer **is** a pair of sixes.

BUT THIS IS ALL WRONG!

The trail left by some clues is obvious like the Pyramid-Triangle relationship. Others are subtle! We make guesses and if they lead us somewhere we keep following. But when we come up against a brick wall we have to turn around and start over, and that's where we are now...we are in front of a brick wall. What has apparently happened is that some of the Signs, Symbols, and even some of the names of the Constellations of the Zodiac have been switched around. It's

Figure 7 *The Twin Embryo of Gemini.*

beyond the scope of this book to find out when it happened, but happen it did. We believe that switches were made between Cancer and Gemini, for instance. The Sign of the *Twin Sixes,* now associated with Cancer, actually belongs to Gemini. The *Twin Sixes* depict Siamese Twins, and the Sign portrays unborn *Twin Embryos.* Tables 18-1 and 18-2 illustrate this story. Now look at the Sign of Cancer in Figure 8. It is the ancient mathematical symbol for Pi, and not by coincidence, it is also the over head view of the Great Pyramid of Giza, so you'll not be surprised to learn that the small pyramidal shape at the top of the Great Pyramid, and whose absence would give the square shape in the *Sign* of Cancer lasting significance, isn't there. The Sign of Cancer actually authenticates the relationship between Pi and the Great Pyramid. But now that we have reunited Gemini with the twin embryos, who are Gemini's *Siamese Twins?*

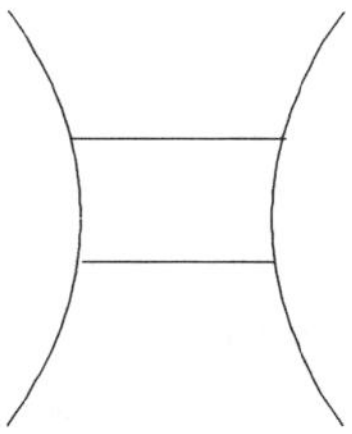

Figure 8. Cancer, the ancient Pi Symbol.

I believe that they are the Celestial Double of the subject of the opening passages of Genesis in the Old Testament. *In the beginning God created the heaven and the earth.* (Genesis, 1:1) If so, then the *Twin Embryos,* the ever encircling twin sixes of Gemini, are the Twins Shu and Tefēnet, and in the ancient world they would have personified Heaven and the Earth.

I believe that Shu and Tefēnet are the *Celestial Twins,* the Ecliptic, which spreads across the Heavens, and the Equator, which encircles the Earth, ie., *Heaven and Earth.*

It would seem, from all evidences that I have uncovered, that the Constellations of the Zodiac were instruments of illustration for numerous ancient texts. One text example, as we've demonstrated throughout this book, is Faulkner's, *Ancient Egyptian Pyramid Texts*.

Table 18-1

The Constellations of Gemini and Cancer as we know them today. They are mixed up!			
Name/Comments	Pseudonym	Sign	Appearance
Gemini. The Pseudonym, the Sign, and the Appearance of modern day Gemini are not consistent with one another! **They don't match!**	*The Twins*		
Cancer. The Pseudonym, the Sign, and the Appearance of modern day Cancer are not consistent with one another! **They don't match!**	*The Crab*		

Table 18-2

Gemini and Cancer as they should be!			
Name/Comments	Pseudonym	Sign	Appearance
Gemini. The left leg of the Constellation of Gemini shows to be pregnant, *The Twins* are Siamese, and the Sign is the unborn embryo.	*The Twins*		
Cancer. The *Sign* of Cancer is the ancient symbol for Pi, and it's the plan view of the Great Pyramid. It is a Terrestrial Crab, a tropical variety characterized by a large square body.	*The Crab*		

169

And I'm convinced that, for the Ancients, the conjunction of the Sun, ie., the Sun God **Atum Rĕ(**, ie., the Father, ie., the ithyphallic ghost, with the Equator at the vernal equinox, chronicled not only the first day of Spring, but the birth of man.

> (§ 1248) Atum is he who (once) came into being, (The primeval god who evolved from the Chaos.) who masturbated in Ōn. He took his phallus in his grasp that he might create orgasm by means of it, and so...(§ 1249)...were born the twins Shu and Tefĕnet.

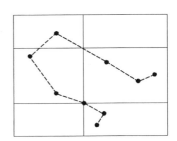

The ever encircling *Twin Embryos* of Gemini! *Heaven* and *Earth*! Do you see the same implied association between the Father, **Atum Rĕ(**, (§ 207) *May you come into being with your father Atum*, and the Ithyphallic Ghost from the Nascan plateau that we do? If you do than you are entitled to feel the same kind of chills down the spine that we feel!

Figure 9. Gemini, *The Twins* a constellation in the Northern Hemisphere with nine primary stars.

> (§ 1249)...and so were born the twins Shu and Tefĕnet! May they put the King between them and set the King among the gods in front of the Field of Offerings. Recite four times: May the King ascend to the sky, may the King ascend to the earth.

In Chapter 15 *The Whole of Manifestation*, we associated the branches of the Tree with the Heavens and with the Constellations, and now if you'll look at the root, you realize the association of the root with the nutrients from the soil on earth. (§ 1249) **Recite four times** May the King ascend to the sky, may the King ascend to the earth! *The Twins*, the Equator and the Ecliptic, *Shu* and *Tefĕnet!* The ever encircling *Twin Embryos* of Gemini! See Figure 10

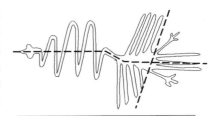

Figure 10 (§ 1249) Recite four times! May the King ascend to the sky, may the King ascend to the earth. *The Twins*, the Equator and the Ecliptic, *Shu* and *Tefĕnet!*

The number 66 has taken us to the Constellations, to The Father, **Atum Rĕ(**., and to the *Twins* of Gemini, Shu and Tefĕnet, and it has taken us to the Ecliptic ...Heaven, and the Equator...Earth, and it has taken us to the ithyphallic ghost on the plateau.

Could the ubiquitous number "66" also be in reference to a date told by the astronomical phenomenon of precession? If so, should we include the number "9"? My guess would be to include it because, as a first clue, there are nine primary stars in the Constellation of Gemini, and as a point of interest there are ten primary stars in the Constellation of Cancer. But what date could be associated with "9 & 66?" The construction of the Sphinx perhaps? The drawing of the figures on the Nascan Plateau? Or perhaps both? Lets do this, lets find out when "9-66" on the precessional calender was. It would be reasonable that it would mark either the beginning or the end of the Age of Gemini, or the Age of Cancer, or somewhere in between! We are currently in the Age of Pisces, *The Fish* and fast approaching the Age of Aquarius, *The Water Bearer*. The Age of Gemini, *The Twins* lasted from about 6860 B.C. until around 4700 B.C. The Age of Cancer started where Gemini left off at 6860 B.C., and ended in 9020 B.C. Or 11018 years ago. So what time slot do we slip into? Interestingly enough, we're going to be getting a hint from a totally unexpected source. The head-to-tail position, symbolic of the embryonic twin six *Sign* of Gemini, is one that is assumed by a pair of horses as they doze on warm summer days. This may sound like an unrelated circumstance, but as we've said, deciphering codes does not come with a set of instructions, so all we can do is to keep following our instincts until something starts to conflict. So until we hit that brick wall again we'll just continue along this line of investigation.

The set of clues that we have been following have led us to the tentative conclusion that the numerology of the Pyramid-Triangle, through the repeated reference to the number 66, was a precessional date that takes us back to sometime between 4700 and 9020 B.C. But this is uncertain ground, because even if were right, we still wouldn't know the event! What I think we should be looking for is something that has some elements of commonality between then and now. The Pyramid, for instance, is said by some to house all of the knowledge of the Universe! Could it also house the history of mankind? Does it stand as a record of our past? Richard Noone, who interviewed G. Patrick Flanagan, a child prodigy, inventor, and a person recognized by Life magazine[8] as one of the top ten scientists in America, writes...

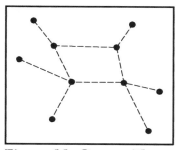

Figure 11. Cancer, *The Crab*. A Constellation in the Northern Hemisphere with ten primary stars and one step further back into antiquity.

As you may well know, in any legend there is usually some basis of fact somewhere in the background, and there are enough stories from different sources that the Great Pyramid has a secret chamber and that within that chamber is a library of knowledge which will indicate to modern man his true history, why the Great Pyramid was really built, and where we really came from, and why we're really here on this planet. This legend has been going around for literally thousands of years. When I was in Egypt[9] I had the opportunity of interviewing various Bedouin chieftains and Arab guides. They all told this story, the story that the Great Pyramid is considered to contain within it the knowledge of man's past, present, and future, and that some day a person will come from the West,[10] and that person will ultimately reveal to the world the secrets of the Pyramid.[11]

Is there a Chamber of Knowledge of the Universe, or a Burial Chamber of the Dead in the Pyramid? And where are the Gods today? The clues that we've been examining seem to associate the Gods with the Great Pyramid. Are they there now? Are they entombed in the Great Pyramid? But who would be there? The original nine, Atum, Shu, Tefēnet, Gēb, Nūt, Osiris, Isis, Seth, and Nephthys? Or is the tenth one there too? Or, since the Tenth Entity represents them all, is that One Entity entombed alone? I'd say this, if they are, or ever were in the Great Pyramid, I'd score one for the Egyptologists! They have said that the Pyramid was a mausoleum all along. But here's another thought, is the trove of Knowledge of the Universe embodied in the Gods themselves or, perhaps, in just the Tenth Entity? If the store of knowledge is in one Entity, than we'd know that the Tenth Entity is the God Thoth, the God of Letters and Wisdom! We're going to see.

Again Richard Noone writes...

Citing some evidence and ignoring vast sums of other evidence, Egyptologists espouse their belief that the ambiguous Egyptian Pharaoh Khufu (sometimes known by his Greek name "Cheeps") built the Great Pyramid as a tomb.[12]

If Khufu built the Pyramid, for himself, it would seem that it would leave little room for the Gods. But it would be my thought that if the gods are entombed in the Great Pyramid, the Egyptian Pharaoh-Horus-King Khufu would have had little to do with its construction!

THE ANSWER AND THE MEANING OF THE PYRAMID:

I think the answer to the Pyramid is expressed in the precessional clock, the Zodiac, and the Triangle-to-Pyramid characterization. All of the mathematical extrapolations were singular in their expression of 9+66! The Nine Gods of Ōn and Gemini. But where does

Thoth fit into this? Are Thoth and Gemini affiliated in some manner? Or is it possible that *The Twins* are, symbolically, the *Twin Gods*...Thoth[a] & Gemini, Osiris & Isis, Shu & Tefēnet, The Ecliptic & The Equator, Heaven & Earth? Before we go on I would like you to look at the Constellation of Virgo in Figure 12. What I see is a woman's breast at the upper right, feeding the King's Chamber in the Great Pyramid as though it was her child. If the angular structure that I have identified as the King's Chamber on the left, looks a little like a baby carriage to you, than all the better, because it looks that way to me!

Now look at Virgo, *The Virgin*, in Figure 13. This time I've turned the Constellation a little clockwise, so that you can see how it was that *The Virgin*, if such she was, was able to breast feed the child in the King's Chamber. Take a close look, her head is at the upper left, her legs are spread wide and she is watching the process. She is being made pregnant while in the redundant style of the Ancients she is simultaneously in child birth. Where and how the Pyramid fits into this role of union that's being played out in the Zodiac, you'll have to wait and see. But in the mean time, what of the tenth god Thoth? Thoth is portrayed on the plateau as a cynocephalus monkey. He is an Ambassador bearing the other nine gods with him. But

Figure 12 Virgo, *The Virgin*?

then in Chapter 13, entitled *Thoth*, we see Horus symbolized in association with Thoth by a line that crosses the *Wings of Thoth* and in this form Horus represents the genetic symbol of relationship between Tefēnet and her daughters Nūt, Isis & Nephthys. But Horus, we said, was not a god at all, but just the *eloquence* of the male-female roles in the newly acquired need for union! Horus, the son of the man gods, Osiris and Isis, Horus we said was the epitome of fruitfulness.

> (§1199) Stand up, Osiris, and commend me to those who are in charge of the Causeway of Happiness north of the Field of offerings just as you commended Horus to Isis on the day on which you made her pregnant.[13]

Figure 13 Is the Constellation of Virgo really a virgin? Here, she is not!

This analogy would solve some earlier problems. For instance, In ceremony each of the Pharaoh-Kings of ancient Egypt identified himself as a *Horus-King*. Could this have been in reality a Ceremony to bestow the new Horus-Pharaoh-King with the gift of fertility? It would be a rear gift indeed! Thoth than is not only **Atum Rē('s** Ambassador, the incarnate bearer of knowledge and mysticisms, who bears with him the nine Gods on Ōn, as the tenth entity he also carries with him the god Horus, who is the genetic symbol of relationship...the *eloquence* of the male-female roles in the newly acquired need for union! Le Plongeon writes...

> The ape god is still held in great veneration in the Asiatic peninsula and the Island of Ceylon. Pompous homage is paid to him. The pagodas in which he is worshiped are adorned with the utmost magnificence and the Portuguese in plundering the temple of the ape god Thoth, made themselves masters of immense riches.[14]

While Budge tells us,

> The cynocephalus ape, which plays such a prominent part in dynastic Egyptian mythology, are supposed to be inhabited by divine spirits and to possess extraordinary powers of intelligence.[15]

SO IN FACT THOTH AND GEMINI ARE TWINS!

Gemini, the mother of the *Twin Embryos*, and Thoth, the bearer of the symbol of relationship...the *eloquence* of the male-female roles of union required of man! {§. 1089} I am grit with **the girdle** of Horus, I am clad with the garment of **Thoth**...the souls of Ōn set up a stairway for me in order to reach the Above...![b]

> (§ 1655) O you great Ennead (you Nine) which is on Ōn, (namely) Atum, Shu, Tefēnet, Gēb, Nūt, Osiris, Isis, Seth, and Nephthys; O you children of Atum, extend his goodwill to his children in your name of Nine Bows.

Let's look at the Constellation of Sagittarius one more time. In Figure 14, you can see the quiver and the Roman Numeral Nine in the formation of the stars. "O you children of Atum, extend his *goodwill* to his children in your name of Nine Bows."

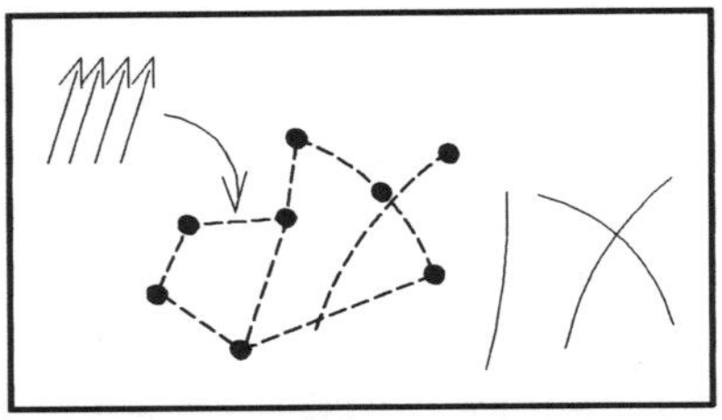

Figure 14 Nine Bows, The Constellation of Sagittarius.

Study now the *arrows* of Sagittarius, the one on the left is male, while the **BOW** on the right is female, a second arrow (male) is inserted into the **BOW**...O you children of Atum, extend his *goodwill* to his children! Atum's *goodwill* is sex...and Sagittarius is the *Celestial Cupid!* This important passage, (§ 1655, O you children of Atum, *extend his goodwill* to his children), is addressing the Ennead, the nine Gods, to procreate with "...His (Atum's) children!"

174

In reality the Zodiac contains the history of the ancient world and the Zodiacal Constellations are a pictorial representation of the tales that are told elsewhere.

IF NOT VIRGO, WHO IS THE VIRGIN?

If not Virgo, who is the virgin? Capricorn is! Look very carefully at the Constellation of Capricorn in Figure 15, and you will see the pubic region of a woman with the legs apparently held tight together as would be those of a virgin. You can also see that Capricorn is in the shape of a veil, and now let's recall the words that were written of Isis, the sister wife of Osiris, "I am that which is, has been, and shall be, and no man has lifted my veil."[16]

Figure 15 This is the Constellation of the *Virgin*

In EXODUS 3:14, God responds in a similar way when Moses on the occasion of asking of God's name, replies, I Am That I Am.

HORSES, YARDS, AND LATITUDES

We need an explanation now for why the symbol of Gemini looks like a pair of horses standing head to tail, and we want to know the significance of the number 36. In the summer, when the days are warm and quiet, and the winds are light, a pair of horses will stand head to tail swishing the flies off of one another's faces with their tails. They will stand this way for long periods of time, heads down, half asleep, slowly creating light breezes with the back and forth swish of their tails.

THE HORSE LATITUDES

The horse latitudes are those zones of latitude ~36 degrees North and South of the equator, where the barometric pressures are high, and the winds are calm, light, and changeable,[17] like the swishing back and forth of a horse's tail. It is said that the origin of the name "horse latitude" is obscure,[18] but the obscurity is only because the story of the Zodiac has been dismissed as folly.

YARDS AND YARDS

A yard is simultaneously, a unit of measurement, 36 inches long, and it is also an area of ground, sometimes around a home, but just as commonly, out by the barn where it would be called a stock yard where horses might be kept. There in the summer, when the days are warm and quiet, and the winds are light, the horses will stand head to tail swishing the flies off of one another's faces with their tails. It is a time when storms can develop suddenly, and without warning! It is...the quiet before the storm! A yard is simultaneously, the lower yard on the main mast of a sailing ship, sometimes called a fouryard, it is the long tapering spar used to support and spread a square sail, and it is common with the term yard goods, referring to fabrics. Now let's take another look at the Symbol of Cancer, and in the redundant style of the Ancients we can see the square sail, ie., the yard goods, the tapering spars that support the sail, and we can see the horizontal yards of the main mast. (See Figure 8, on page 168)

THE COMBINED MESSAGE

The possibility that the numbers 9, 10, 66, and 36 could lead us to a date is remote. It is more reasonable to accept the alternative path that the Ancients laid out which took us to Gemini, and the Great Pyramid, to the pictorial character of the Constellations of the Zodiac, and through the reference to *The Twins*, to Genesis, Thoth, and the Creation of man! But what of the Great Pyramid? I believe that it is a monument, not to a God, but to the Birth of Man. The child within the Kings Chamber is being breast fed as would a new born. And does the Pyramid contain the wisdom of the ages? Is Thoth, or any of the Enneads of Ōn there? We can only speculate, but it has been the fortune of man to achieve any goal that he sought. So it may be that *we*, man, are the embodiment of the God Thoth, the God of Wisdom and Letters!

Now let's see why Cancer is called *The Crab*. The term "crabbing," refers to a waddling side wise form of movement, like the yawing of a ship searching for the wind in a zone of light breezes, as in the horse latitudes. The square *sail* of Cancer...is **Rē('s** reed-float in the sky, it is yawing, it is crabbing, it is looking for the wind!

> (§ 337) The reed-floats of the sky are set in place for **Rē(** that he may cross on them to the horizon.

a. The *Celestial Twins* are many things. Shu and Tefēnet, and Gemini and Taurus. Taurus on the other hand is also the Celestial Double of **Atum Rē(**, and since Thoth *is* **Atum Rē(**, and the Ennead, and on and on, or is it Ōn and Ōn?

b. See Chapter 13, *Thoth*, Page 111.

Chapter 19

And the Sphinx Faced East

In the modern setting the figures on the Nascan Plateau are without meaning or direction. They are from a time past and have no links to the modern age. They were constructed on a stage of pantomime by a people so deeply religious that their lives embraced the very consciousness of Creation. For that is the story of the Plateau. It is the story of the creation of life as they knew it...told in a language that was never spoken and never written. One can tell from the cartoon-ish look of the figures that they were a fun loving people who had a deep appreciation for life and love, who probably had few possessions or needs for them. I suspect that they were communal in their habits with no need to communicate through the vocal cords because they spoke from the heart in a form of telepathy that was highly instinctive. But their story of the creation, their unspeaking Gods wrought in pantomime, plead to those with voice in Egypt!

The figures on the plateau and the hieroglyphics from the pyramids of Egypt are so different in form that they appear to be the individualistic religious expressions of two separate societies. Except that both exhort to an order of awareness of man's origins and to an awareness of the sciences of the world and the course of nature that they bespeak of common ancestry. Were they a people then who had survived the agonies of a cataclysmic change of environment who were working to preserve their heritages in the only way that their respective environments allowed? Being separated, having to fend for themselves, might we expect their respective record forms to evolve differently? If we were compelled to search further, might we find that a difference arose because the inhabitants of the plateau had to yield to a harsher environment? We don't really know, but we do know that a written form of expression, such as the hieroglyphics of Egypt, evolves from a spoken language, while the more primal graphic form, of the type on the Plateau, comes from the heart and mind without language. This speaks of a chronology.

We don't know when the inscriptions were placed on the walls of the pyramids, or in fact when the pyramids themselves were built, and we don't know when the primal graphics of Nasca were formed. The only thing that we can be sure of is that both artifacts give the same accounting. The Ancients were, from all appearances, so intimate with their origins that time and catastrophe could not erase their religious consciousness. Richard Noone, whom we've met as the author of the book 5/5/2000, suggests that the Ancients possessed what he called a *science of the soul*...

> The idea of antiquity was that there was something to be *known* in religion, secrets or mysteries into which it was possible to be initiated; that there was a gradual process of unfolding in things religious; in fine, that there was a science of the soul, a knowledge of things unseen.

> A persistent tradition in connection with all the great Mystery institutions was that their several founders were the introducers of all the arts of civilization. Analyze any of the great religions, and you will find the same factors at work, the same problems of human imperfection to be studied...

> Who were the founders of the great mystery institutions of ancient Egypt? Who they were and where they came from is itself a mystery; we may know the gift but not the giver.[1]

He describes them as being no ordinary men (but) survivors of a civilization destroyed by a sudden shift in the earth's terrestrial axis[2] triggered by a massive accumulation of ice at the South Pole."[3,A] He believes them to be the architects of the ancient Order of Free Masons and the civilization being that from the continent of Mu. A continent once located in the Southern reaches of the Pacific Ocean.[4] Noone writes...

> ...one may learn the name Musons, sons of Mu, the motherland, it is where the ancient name of the Order of Freemasons originated... In Finlayson's Symbols and Legends of Freemasonry it is stated: "AMEN— This untranslatable word, the same in all languages, is a name of the Great God of Egypt." In Revelation 3:14, God is called "the Amen,"

If Noone is correct, and the ancient heritages of Egypt came from the Continent of Mu than it might be, since Nasca, lies on a direct navigational route from ancient Mu, that

---

[A] We agree in detail with Noone, but we would suggest that the geographics of the time would have the accumulation of ice at the North Pole, rather than the South.

the peoples of the Nascan Plateau are of the same origin. So might it be too, that the Nascan civilization, simply progressed along a slower evolutionary path than their descendant brotherhood in Egypt? There is some support for this since we know that there was a commonality in the *science of the soul* that guided both the East and the West, because even though the Gods on the plateau were nameless, we recognized them from the sameness that was woven in the fabric of their story. So wouldn't this alone suggest a common origin but an independent cultural development?

Count Goblet d'Alviella on the evolution of the religious spirit

In all nations that have admitted the existence of a Supreme Being, He has always been regarded as the beginning and the end of all things to which men have aspired, and do aspire, to be united after the dissolution of the physical body. This reunion with God, this Nirvana, this End, has in all ages been esteemed the greatest felicity to which the spirit can attain.[5]

At first there were the obvious ideographs of the phenomena of nature that made the deepest religious impression on archaic man, such as the outstretched heavens above him, and the outstretched earth beneath; both of which he naturally divided into four quarters. The east "fronting" him as he watched anxiously for the returning sun, the south on his right hand, the west backing him, and the north on his left hand...[6] Then came the observation of the daily renewed miracle of the phenomena of vegetable, animal, and human reproduction, expressed at first... by the most direct realistic types, and afterwards by the lotus bud and flower, the date palm, and other conspicuously phallic flowers and trees. And for the entering of the oracle he made doors of olive tree.[7]

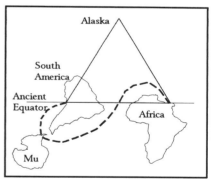

Figure 1. The Ancient cultural trade routes and the Terrestrial Triangle.

And as the Heavens...came slowly into the observation of archaic man, and the whole universe was perceived to be full of moving life, and was now symbolized by a Holy Mountain with its cosmical palm, deep rooted in the earth, (and) the Garden of Eden...[8] Everywhere he saw creative force in operation, and everywhere adopted the most homely and personal implements of the force as the visible and material symbols of the invisible and spiritual Creator, of Creators, in whose express image he postulated that the worlds were made.[9]

The Count expressed it as "This reunion with God, this Nirvana, this End." But was it an End, or was it a beginning, a dawning? With "the gradual process of unfolding in things religious," and with "a science of the soul" in guidance, "the east fronting him and the Heavens coming slowly into observation," man grew as the realization dawned upon him that the returning sun brought with it a new day, and with the returning of the Vernal Equinox...the first day of Spring and the beginning of a new year. And the Sphinx, the most mysterious of all ancient cultural edifices, the embodiment of ancient man honoring his origins, the embodiment of the *science of the soul* and the blossoming *religious spirit*, the Sphinx in representation, lay on the equator and in proxy watched purposefully throughout the night for the returning sun and the beginning of a new day. And in proxy the Sphinx, facing east on the equator, watched purposefully across the endless plane of the ecliptic for the first day of Spring and the beginning of a new year with the returning of the Vernal Equinox.

The Sphinx, facing east on the *Equator*, in adjunct representation of the *spirit of the soul* of man, circled with endless intent, mindful that there was an instant with each new day when it's emplacement on earth would cross the plane of the ecliptic and it could gaze across the *Heavens* in adjunct honor of man's origins.

Graham Hancock described the Sphinx as "Vastly, remotely, fabulously ancient."[10]

> As long as a city block, as high as a six-storey building it was perfectly oriented due east and thus faced the rising sun on the two equinoctial days of the year. Man-headed, lion bodied, crouched as though ready at last to move its slow thighs after millennia of stony sleep, it had been carved in one piece out of a single ridge of limestone on a site that must have been meticulously preselected. ...

> The first and lasting impression of the Sphinx, and of its enclosure, is that it is very, very old – not a mere handful of thousands of years, like the Fourth Dynasty of Egyptian pharaohs, but vastly, remotely, fabulously old.[11]

Today, at 30 degrees north latitude, only the face of the Sphinx looks east. Though still the wondrous edifice, and still the cornerstone of an exultant Triad between Nasca, Giza, and Alaska, the Sphinx is now forgotten as to purpose and forgotten as to origin, and we

180

are singularly ignorant of its wonders. I quoted Graham Hancock in an earlier chapter, "We are people with amnesia, we have become a people who have forgotten our past."

THE FIBER OF TELEPATHY

Our story of the Plateau doesn't end here. I owe you an explanation for why I believe the ancient people on the plateau were telepathic. This impression stems from three sources. First, telepathy is one of the few forms of expression that one must possess in the heart in order to understand it in the mind, and that this was their form of expression is avowed to by the reality that there is not even a hint of a word or a phrase on the Plateau. Everything is expressed symbolically in a metaphoric style that exhibits a complexity of form that is of another age and without language. Secondly, as Gerald Hawkins is going to acquaint us with below, the figures are so large, and the terrain is so flat and strewn with boulders and rocky projections that it is impossible to see from one end of a figure to the other. Some of the lines are five miles long and are straighter than a taught string. It is an unusual feat to accomplish without instruments, but the task is the heart and fiber of telepathy. And lastly, the story on the plateau is not one of hit and miss. It is a single story of creation spread about on thousands of square feet of desert and visible, in this modern age, only from the air. It is a relic of the past lost even to the later inhabitants of the area. It was too large to be seen, and is too old to be appreciated.

THE OLD STRAIGHT TRACK!

This is not the only story of mystery involving lines that project onto the horizon! On 20 June 1921 Alfred Watkins "...saw a web of lines linking the holy places and sites of antiquity...without warning...his mind was flooded with a rush of images forming one coherent plan...all tracks were in straight lines marked out by experts on a sighting system. The whole plan of the Old Straight Track stood suddenly revealed."[12]

> Mounds, old stones, crosses and old crossroads, churches placed on pre-Christian sites, legendary trees, moats and holy wells stood in exact alignments that ran over beacon hills to cairns and mountain peaks. In one moment of transcendental perception Watkins entered a magic world of prehistoric Britain, a world whose very existence had been forgotten.[13]

> In China...every building, every stone and wood, was placed in the landscape in accordance with a magic system by which the laws of mathematics and music were

expressed in the geometry of the earth's surface. The striking beauty and harmony of every part of China, which all travelers have remarked, was not produced by chance. Every feature was contrived.[14]

On a mountainous landscape in Bolivia,[15] as in all places around the world, old and new, there lays a network, "...an astonishing pattern of trackways in straight lines, from horizon to horizon, criss-crossing in sacred manners. In China they are known as Dragon Paths, in other parts of the world they are called Ley Lines.

I don't want to leave the subject of telepathy without giving you this one last accounting. It started at 9:10 PM on June 18, 1988. I was laying crosswise on the bed in a room just off the living room of our home on the lake. My wife was watching television, and I was watching it with casual interest through the open door. Then of a sudden I told her that our horses were out of the pasture. Twenty five miles west of this lake home we had a farm where my son lived and tended our two horses, Ben and Gypsy. The pasture was about a thousand feet deep, and at the western end it had a somewhat broken down wire fence and a hedge row of stones, that though shabby, had looked to us adequate to hold the horses. But this night Gypsy led Ben across the barrier into the adjacent land.

My wife, without questioning me, which in itself was surprising given the gravity of the matter, asked me if we should go into town and rescue them. I told her no, and I assured her that they were safe and that the next day would be soon enough. The next day we drove into the farmhouse and looked for the horses. They were gone just as I had told my wife the night before. We hooked up the horse trailer and drove around the corner to the property that adjoined ours to the west, and there, tucked safely in a separate pasture provided them by the neighbors who had horses of their own and so had all the provisions, were our two horses. I had assured my wife that the next day would be soon enough, and sure it was, Ben and Gyps were quite at home!

The image of Ben and Gyps crossing that stone barrier didn't come to me in words or phrases, it came as a moving scene. I watched Gyps lead the way with Ben following hesitantly after her. There was no history of them crossing this fence so it was not a re-enactment of a previous adventure. It was as new for them as it was for me.

The point of the story is that, though we tend to discredit anecdotes of this type, extrasensory perception is common among peoples of all nationalities. Some accept it more readily than others and the skills get developed to a greater level of meaning in these people. But once someone has experienced it, particularly over great distances as

I had occasion to, they become aware of the form that it takes in the mind. There are no words or phrases, as I said, there are merely moving images with as much detail as you want to take in, and surprisingly, you can sense the spirit of the event. I knew that the horses were feeling mischievous and that they were safe. And for me, the worrier supreme in our household, admitting to their safety was an astonishing acclaim. But their safety was confirmed by what I saw as the horses left the pasture. I have no doubt that the people of the Plateau had these powers developed to a level beyond our comprehension.

Let's go back to the plateau now and have Gerald S. Hawkins answer all your other questions. He is talking to Tony Morrison, who Hawkins describes as "...a film director specializing in the South American tropics..."[16]

> "How long are the lines?" Hawkins asked.
> ..."Five miles or more," Morrison replied.
> "And the rectangle?"
> ..."Eight hundred yards by seventy."
> "What are these black spots?"
> ..."Piles of stones...a mound of boulders 30 yards across and 3 feet high...In some places the mounds are set out in rows, like a network of some type of grid."[17]

Hawkins...

> It was a moonscape of dust and rock. Without landmarks there was a feeling of disorientation...It was an endless desert-sea, with an unreal coastline...I had the sensation of moon-blindness at Nasca, directionless walking. The sun was no help ...it was overhead, intense, white, swollen...[18] The underlying soil is a light-yellow mixture of sand, clay, and calcite...fragments are red-colored underneath, hence the name Colorada. The top is blackened with a thin coat of desert varnish— manganese and iron oxides—caused by long term exposure to the atmosphere.[19]

Hawkins had computerized the data that he and Tony Morrison had gathered with the intent of putting the computer to the task of proving an astronomical purpose in the layout of the figures, but the computer had failed, so in puzzlement, while knowing that they were in no way connected with flying saucers,[20] they asked of themselves, "Then what are the lines for?"[21] They had no answers...just these reflections...

> The markings in the desert are dead, unspeaking, geometric patterns, rectangles, triangles, zigzags, but the figures are of living things. Most of them can be directly

linked to fertility; that third leg of (the) *Ricinulei,*(spider),[B] the genitals of the monkey, and dog,[22] the hairpin pathway leading to the pollen of the flower.[23]

The life signs in the desert seem to show a preoccupation with nature, and the same awareness is in the motifs on the Nascan ceramics, and I could believe that the mesa, suspended below the violet mountains, was an ancient Peruvian holy place, an abode of spirits...[24]

B. The *Ricinulei* spider is indigenous to the Amazon jungle and is the rarest of spiders. It is unique in that "the third leg is used for copulation.

INTRODUCTION, Part 4. Earth's Hidden Unrest

Past catastrophic events took various forms, volcanic eruptions, subterranean upheavals, passing comets, ... the Deluge. But as Chorley explains in, *The History of The Study of Landforms,* only the Deluge, as a catastrophic ordeal, was recorded at length, and this only in the Bible. So its explanation of geological events, since there was no other, was sanctioned and championed by the Church.[1]

> In the six hundredth year of Noah's life, in the second month, the seventeenth day of the month, the same day were all the fountains of the great deep broken up, and the windows of heaven were opened. And the rain was upon the earth forty days and forty nights.... And the Flood was forty days upon the earth... and the waters prevailed exceedingly upon the earth, and all the high hills, that were under the whole heaven, were covered, fifteen cubits upward did the waters prevail and the mountains were covered,... And the waters prevailed upon the earth an hundred and fifty days.
>
> Genesis 7:11-24

Chorley adds,

> Considering that the Church dated creation at 4004 B.C., for the world to assume its present shape in the brief interval allowed, the application of catastrophes was inevitable and yet fossil evidence pointed to slow processes and immense intervals of time....however, there were superficially good scientific grounds for believing in the existence of the Flood....there are innumerable glacial features... erratics or far-traveled boulders foreign to their present resting place...large patches of clay and of ill-sorted gravel and sand...(and) the presence of river terraces and of marine and lake beaches...at high altitudes...[2]

The dichotomy advanced by the evidence, ie., fossil evidence, pointing to slow processes and immense intervals of time on the one hand, and glacial features, erratics, river terraces and of marine and lake beaches...at high altitudes...on the other, served to do nothing more than to partition the antagonists. There seemed to be no middle ground.

But perhaps there is one! For no place can we go but what we are confronted with the wonders of nature, no place can we go but what someone has gone before us. We only have to look, and question before we condemn.

A CASE FOR PROCESSES SET INTO PLACE.

The butterfly, this wondrous creature of Nature, who in the course of its life undergoes four stages of metamorphosis; the egg, the caterpillar, or larva; the pupa, or chrysalis, and the adult butterfly. It epitomizes the case of a process set into place, with a stimulus to set it into motion, and the ability to proceed undisturbed, on its own, to its prescribed end. But caterpillars are not alone in this wonder. We could begin a long list of items, starting with the marvel of life itself, with healing and reproduction, with the unerring repeatability of the elements to combine, and the endless motion of the planets to follow their prescribed orbits about the sun.

We could continue from a list of a hundred individual wonders of nature. Through the principles of hydrology, which to supply the earth with a constant supply of water, starts its cycle with evaporation – and the mists so generated – are transported everywhere, and precipitation brings it in final form to all living things.[3] So it is too with volcanos, though not generally thought of in this manner, that bring renewing products to the surface as fertilizers that are so badly needed by the soils to grow cover and life sustaining crops. We cannot leave the subject without recognition of the system that is so important to sustaining the life of plants themselves. This is the carbon cycle. This system moves carbon dioxide from animals and oxidation processes through the atmosphere to the plants where it is synthesized into food. Water and oxygen are given off as by-products by the plants only to enter the life cycle of the animals, and the cycle continues.

All are processes set into place when the planet was born. Among them there are no apathetic contributors. They are all in conformity with some unknown law that assures us that everything is in place to serve some undivided purpose. Even the earth's magnetic field and the fearsome earthquakes are the progenies of the system that is in place, and working, and enduring.

> In the whole machinery...of springs and rivers...constructed hills and valleys...and the apparatus that is kept in action for their duration...of never-failing fountains...as to supply the earth by constant evaporation...in...these we find such undeniable proofs of a nicely balanced adaption of means to ends...[4]

> *William Buckland (1830)*

Now to Part IV!

Chapter 20

370 Million Year Old Coral

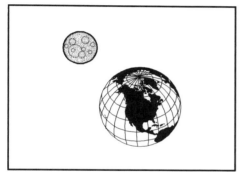

Figure 1 The Apollo astronauts conducted experiments on the moon that showed a measurable relationship between moonquakes, the moon's orbital position, and the earth.

Most earthquakes, it is said, occur within a few kilometers of the earth's surface by the process of "...brittle fracture and frictional sliding."[1] Others occur hundreds of kilometers down in the earth's mantle where the pressure is thought to prevent rock from cracking.[2] While still others occur at the more intermediate depths of 70 and 300 kilometers. The most devastating of these, however, tended to be the shallow events which occur at depths of 50 kilometers or less.[3] And so it followed that a form of classification based on a criterion of depth of occurrence evolved. On this basis three depth ranges were identified, high-focus events which have sources near the surface; intermediate-focus events, which take place at roughly 150 kilometers down and are the most plentiful, and deep-focus events which have focuses at depths of as much as 650 kilometers.[4]

These conventional views are descriptive, but they are vague as to the mechanism that would cause the earth to fracture in the first place. Just as important, they are vague about where the forces originate from that would cause the fracture to slip, or where the sliding fault goes, surrounded as it is with rock. It's not as though there are only a few earthquakes here and there. We could accept the brittle fracture and frictional sliding concept if that were the case. But there were over 270,000 earthquakes in the 25 year period between 1964 and 1989.[5] The mantle would have to look like a sieve or Swiss cheese or something with that many events occurring. Is there really that much room for this rock to go sliding around down there? Cliff Frohlich, author of the *Scientific American* article, "Deep Earthquakes," that we quoted above, wondered too! "How can rock slip abruptly," he asks, "if the enormous pressures of the mantle rule out brittle fracture?"[6]

EARTHQUAKE

We believe that earthquakes are more than movements along fault lines. We've been stressing the fact that forces, and only forces are capable of doing work, that is of producing motion. When earth's "bell gets rung" a force has yanked the lanyard and a clapper has struck something solid. Only forces do this, nothing else works! Myeung Hoi Kwon & Randal D. Peters, in a study of Free Earth Oscillations have written...

Figure 2 When Earth's bell gets rung!

> ...we have almost continuously observed long period oscillations of the earth during January to August in 1990. Periods of those vibrations are correlated with more than ten of known long periods of spheroidal and torsional oscillations of the earth which result from the occurrence of large earthquake. The amplitudes of the fluctuation we have observed are correlated with the lunar synodic period, indication that they are driven by tidal forces.[7]

THE SEARCH FOR THE ORIGIN OF EARTHQUAKES

Man is forever measuring everything. It's a passion that must have been acquired in antiquity. It may even have been that the mastery of measurement was the first technological advancement after making the cave a home and the club a weapon. So it was natural that this passion would have survived the ages and that two scientists, John W. Wells who discovered the daily growth characteristics of ancient coral, and S. K. Runcorn, who continued the study, would have investigated its significance. The research that followed suggested that the earth's 24 hour daily clock does not tick at a constant rate. The point of interest that intrigued Runcorn was...

> ...if a "clock" could be found that had recorded the days of ancient geological periods, it would be possible to arrive at a more precise measurement of the number of days in the year and so to obtain evidence about the earth's rotation and the factors affecting it. ... The intriguing possibility now under investigation is that the ...fine ridges or bands found in some corals represent daily growth. If

this is the case, a coral that could be accurately assigned to a particular geological period (by radioactive dating or the evidence of stratigraphy[a]) would provide a measurement of the number of days in the year at that time.[8]

THE ANCIENT CORAL SERVED THE PURPOSE!

The banding on certain corals, as furthering investigations revealed, represented not only annual growth, but monthly, and daily growth as well.[9] Ancient coral thus provided clues to changes in the earth's rate of rotation, and hence to the length of the year and the length of the day in past eras.

Wells reported in 1963 that his count of the fine bands within the annual bands in several corals dating from the middle of the Devonian period (370 million years ago) ranged between 385 and 410 and averaged 400.[10]

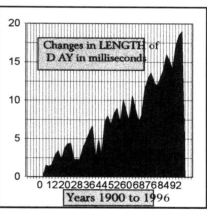

Wells' conclusion was that there must have been just 22 hours in a day in ancient times. The historical events that led Wells to the inquiry of coral as a fossil clock were actually independent of the coral. The events started, surprisingly, in the middle of the 18th century when navigational needs for measuring the meridional longitude led to an intense inventive research program directed toward the development of an accurate chronometer. The chronometer's use by mariners to determine the longitude is a fascinating story onto itself, and the books that elucidate this developmental story make very interesting reading.[11,12] But once the inventive mind created the sought after accuracy and demonstrated its usefulness and dependability on shipboard, time and its measurement began to occupy man's mind in a continuing manner, and the quest for even greater accuracy and broader application began in earnest.[13]

Figure 3. The length of day has been slowly lengthening since antiquity, from an average length of 22 hours per day to the current 24 hours per day.

Following this passion for measurement, and encouraged by ever-improving accuracy, the clock was applied to the task of measuring the length of the day.[14] But there was a surprise in store for those who made the studies because, not only had the length-of-day changed since the Devonian, but it was changing on a daily basis! Something, very powerful, was affecting the earth's rate of rotation. That's the only way time could change! Earth's rotational speed was being altered! The time measurement changes were not large, a millisecond here and there, but the surprise was not that time was changing so much, because that fact was known, what was surprising was that the length-of-the-day would lengthen and then shorten...the first measurement would show that the earth had slowed and the day had lengthened...and the next measurement would show that the earth had speeded up again. On average the slowing process was winning out and earth's day was getting progressively longer. Something was slowing the earth down...and as we know only forces can do that...but where were these forces coming from?

The earth, though small in comparison to some of the other planets, is still a pretty big piece of celestial rock, and it can't slow down, or speed up without some measurable consequence, particularly with respect to the moon! The earth and the moon are actually coupled, hand in hand, in a preservation of angular momentum agreement in accordance with Kepler's laws of planetary motion. Angular momentum **must be** preserved. A slowing of the earth's rate of rotation, i.e., a loss of angular momentum, can only force, or occasion, an exchange with the moon. The moon must accelerate, it simply has no choice...and forces are involved. Runcorn...

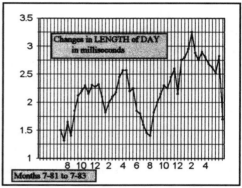

Figure 4   Changes in length-of-day are seen to occur strongest in the summer months in the Northern hemisphere. As a matter of interest, most 6-8 point earthquakes occur during this period also.

Angular momentum of the earth-moon system is conserved, slowing of the earth is accompanied by an acceleration of the moon...and an increasingly wide lunar orbit, so that the moon's angular velocity decreases.[A] (On average) Delta, ie., the change, is a minus 22 seconds per century...over the last 370 million years.[15] And this must be accounted for within the system.

[A]The idea of the moon accelerating on the one hand, while its angular velocity decreases may sound contradictory, it is not— think of it this way: If a runner on a race track wishes to move to the outside lane, he must accelerate, ie., run faster to keep up with the crowd, as he has further to run on that outside track.

190

This was a very exciting discovery. Having coral act as a Paleontological clock was like having a time machine at ones disposal. This would be a machine that could travel to times past and actually permit the investigator to observe things as they happened first hand. The days would have been 22 hours long and the moon would have been much closer to the earth than it is today. It would have appeared like a giant in the midnight sky...with the look throughout the night of the full moon today as it breaks fresh over the Eastern horizon. I was interested in whether Dr. Runcorn had continued his work on the associations of the ancient coral, and I wrote to him in late 1993. Here is his reply.

> The work on biological growth lines has not progressed since the 1960's— you will find a book edited by G. D. Rosenberg & me on this question 'round about 1970' which will be useful to you. The ideas in the Oct—1966 issue of Scientific American are still correct, but it would be very good if more work was done. The problem is finding well preserved coral (or mollusc) on which accurate counts of lines into various bands can be made.[16] (*S. K. Runcorn*)

A SERVO SYSTEM AT WORK!

But there were discoveries made here, though not recognized, that are more engaging than the single fact that the length-of-day was increasing by a second now and again,[17] or that the moon would have been much closer in antiquity than it is now. What is more interesting is that we are actually looking at some sort of joint activity between two forces hard at work to change time. One force causes the day to lengthen, and another force is acting to shorten it again. The day lengthens, and then it shortens, lengthens and shortens. Some servo system is at work, a servo system with two active forces. Something is providing a feedback signal that triggers a response! (See Figure 4.)

Two tremendous forces operating on the earth in opposite directions, each capable of changing the rate of rotation are at work! But fascinatingly enough, and true as it is that two interacting forces must exist, no one actively pursued this consideration. Some saw the possibility that tidal friction, ie., ocean tides acting against the shores and ocean bottoms, and to some extent acting upon the land mass, could act as an agent to slow the rate of earth's rotation. Others saw an opportunity for the earth's moment of inertia, a figure that sums up the earth's shape, size and mass distribution,[18] as exerting the necessary influence. But no one pursued either course of investigation beyond the point of conjecture. There was talk, but no action. It was as if everyone was acting blind to the possibility of real discovery opportunities.

191

There is another view regarding the exchange of angular momentum which involves core-mantle interactions that should be mentioned before going on. John Wahr suggests...

> Information about core-mantle interactions can come from a variety of sources, including (and perhaps surprisingly) from changes in the earth's rotational period, inferred from astronomical observations over the past two centuries. The Earth's rotation period (nominally one 24 hour day) fluctuates irregularly by up to 4-5 milliseconds over periods of a few decades or so, which has long been recognized as being due to angular momentum exchanges between the core and mantle...What is less clear is the mechanism by which angular momentum is exchanged.[19]

My analysis of this same subject would suggest that the exchanges are not just between the core and mantle, but are exchanges between the core, the mantle, *and the moon*. In such exchanges the mechanism is clear...it would be occasioned by earthquake activity.

EARTH'S HIDDEN UNREST

Had the question of the changing of the length-of-day been pursued a little further it might have been realized that a very significant clue to earth's unrest was being demonstrated by earthquake activity! The progressive lengthening of the day through a long series of alternately applied lengthening and shortening "tugs" by forces of sufficient magnitude to change the earth's rate of rotation, and hence change time, relays a rather bold message to anyone listening! The message relays the suggestion that these time-altering tugs do not act autonomously. It suggests, instead, that when one pushes to shorten the day, the other acts in response and pushes back to lengthen it again. One, it seems, does not work without the other...and it is clear that the lengthening of the day effort **is** the perpetrator!

THE INITIATING FORCE SLOWS THE EARTH & LENGTHENS THE DAY!

The notion of two forces acting with strict dependance is central to all understanding of mechanical interactions. We'll see below that there can never be a single acting force. There must always be a reactive force accompanying the initiating one. This is central to our understanding of the earthquake mechanism because the earth's rate of rotation, and hence the lengthening and shortening of the day, cannot occur by itself, there must be an operating system involved. The earth slows and then the gears of adjustment engage and the earth speeds up again, but as we learned, the recovery never succeeds in full or there wouldn't be a lasting trend for a slower spin and a longer day. The two forces are clearly working together, they are part of a servo system, and they act in opposite directions, and they obey, as they must, natural law. These facts should have been an alarm going off that would have alerted us to look deeper than our interest in time to see what laws are involved. There is no instance in all of nature where forces are not involved in producing natural events. We know this, we should have been looking!

The primary forces that slow the earth and lengthen the day are earthquakes. By our analysis, these create a **reaction force**, a force that wouldn't exist otherwise, and this reaction force responds to cause the earth's speed to recover. But the fact that there is a slowing trend proves that the reaction force is losing some of its influence in its administration, a loss probably due to friction. Because of this loss the earth will gradually slow down and the length of the day will continue to increase over time. This action-reaction combination can be better appreciated if we think of a branch that we might push aside in passing...only to have it slip from our grasp and smack us in the face. If, instead of being walloped, we step aside and watch the branch swing freely, we will see its oscillations grow shorter and shorter as internal friction consumes the energy. The **action** is administrated when we push the branch, and the **reaction** is created in response. The consumption of energy that slows the branches's oscillations is due to internal friction. The important point of note here is that the responsive oscillations of the branch would never have occurred had the active force not been administered.

Let's move to the length-of-day-graph shown in Figure 4. A brief study shows that the lengthening of the day is pretty nearly scaled in magnitude with the subsequent shortening. Notice too how the August data, ie., that data corresponding to the 8th month on the graph, always takes a significant dip, and notice too that there is a very significant seasonal characteristic. The shape of the curve, August to August, though different in amplitude, is similar in shape. This long term graph shows us that the forces that are effective in influencing the rate of rotation are not in balance and the days, in consequence, are getting longer. But why should a long term trend develop if there is a reactive force to shorten the day each time the initiating force causes it to lengthen?

The answer is in the measure of the amount of **effective** work being performed. The forces are actually equal in magnitude initially, but motion is involved and motion always creates friction. We are losing out to friction, and any loss to friction means a loss to heat, and in the form of heat it is simply gone, at least to this process! That is not to say that it won't show up somewhere else. There is a lot of heat below the planet's surface that is not accounted for so we'll be revisiting this topic later.

The forces that we are talking about in these processes are performing work. They are making things happen. They are changing things. That is what work is all about. So factors like friction, the magnitude of the force, the distance moved, and the length of time the force is applied, all become important. It's like stopping an automobile, you want something to happen. Friction, being a force, will do the work. So how hard you apply the brakes, ie., frictional magnitude, and how long you keep your foot on the brake pedal determines how fast you are going to stop. (Force, magnitude, & time.)

LETS SUMMARIZE!

Some force is acting to slow the rate-of-rotation of the earth and the days are getting longer! Another force is awakened by this initiating action and it speeds the earth back up again, thus shortening the day. The restorative force, however, falls short in its effort to restore the earth's rotational speed due to frictional loses and an ever increasing trend towards a lengthening day ensues.

THE FORCES INVOLVED

We're now in a position to consider the forces at work here. The restorative forces are the easiest to describe and the easiest to comprehend, so let us start there. In the most simplistic form we can state them using Newton's First and Third Law of Motion.

We'll look at the Third Law first. Newton's Third Law of Motion, which relates to the restorative force, is expressed in this fashion.

1.   For every **action** there is an **equal** and opposite **reaction**.

We can state a corollary to Newton's Third Law that would be expressed as follows...

2.   Since it is known that every **action** creates an **equal** and opposite **reaction**, it follows that there can **never** be a single isolated force, one creates the other.[20]

In order to apply Newton's Third Law we must take a look at the principle of angular momentum, and in *very simplistic terms* angular momentum can be defined in terms of Newton's First Law of Motion.

3.   A body at rest remains at rest, and a body in motion remains in motion, unless acted upon by an outside force.

194

Angular momentum in a sense is a derivative of Newton's First Law of Motion except it is not a law, it only acts like one. Angular momentum is about objects that are rotating, or bodies that are spinning on an axis, like a top, or ice skaters who spin. It is about bodies in rotational orbit, like the moon rotating about the earth. It is about a bucket that is being twirled about on a rope. If the bucket gets ahead of the twirler, because the action slows, it will keep going and the rope will wrap around the twirlers legs. In this instance the bucket is demonstrating its angular momentum...its desire to keep going.

We're talking about the Conservation of Angular Momentum when a skater's rotational speed increases when they close their arms about their bodies, or when the earth slows down and forces the moon to speed up in response. Angular momentum can be expressed as the product of an object's linear momentum, in a sense the bucket's weight and speed, and the perpendicular distance from the axis of rotation to the centroid of the revolving body, essentially the length of the rope. The greater the speed, the heavier the bucket, the longer the rope, the greater the angular momentum.

DEMONSTRATING THE RESTORATIVE FORCE WITH AN EGG!

We don't really have to know all of that, because we can demonstrate the principle of the Conservation of Angular Momentum, and hence the restorative forces that act within the earth, with an old fashion chicken egg. What we want to do is to go to the refrigerator and get a fresh egg. Be sure it's fresh! Now set it on the table and let it assume a stable position. Now put a finger to each end of the egg and set it to spinning. The egg is now the earth. At some point while it is still spinning fast, take the tip of your finger and gently, but very briefly, touch down on the spinning egg and then let up. Three things are going to happen, (Four if you press too hard). The first thing to happen, will be that the egg will slow down. It will take longer to make one revolution...you will have caused the egg's day to lengthen.

The second thing to happen will occur during those brief seconds that your finger is on the outside shell of the egg as you slowed it down. The shell will try to transferred this work that you are performing to slow it down to its viscus interior, and it will try to slow it down too. But the transfer of work will not be fully successful because the albumen, the white of the egg, is viscus and it will continue spinning at a slightly faster rate than the outside shell despite the efforts to slow it. So for a very brief period of time the inside of the egg will rotate faster than the outside shell. (A body in motion tends to remain in motion...Newton's First Law.)

195

The third event, and remember the inside of the egg is spinning faster than the shell at this point, will be initiated the instant you lift your finger from the outside shell. The restorative forces inside, (i.e., the viscus forces which are common every day shear stresses), will start to take over. They will re-couple the faster spinning viscus interior to the outside shell and the shell will begin to pickup speed again. The re-coupling will continue until the shell and the albumen are spinning at the same rate. It will pick up speed as you watch it. The final rotational speed of the egg will depend on a number of factors...the freshness of the egg, the friction of the egg against the table, how long your finger was in contact with the shell, and how hard you applied the force.

But the end result will always be that the egg, once having been slowed and seemingly now on its own, will begin spinning faster again. Not all of the rotational speed will be recovered because some energy will be lost in the turbulence and strain that occurred when the viscus interior broke continuity with the outside shell. It will be lost to friction, and slightly, only slightly, the inside temperature of the egg will increase![22]

The point of this exercise was to demonstrate the action of the restorative forces.

a.   The egg represented the earth...the shell was the crust...the viscus interior represented the earth below the plastic layer...and the yoke was the earth's core.

b.   The egg was put to spinning...it represented earth's ancient 22 hour day!

c.   Work was performed on the outside shell of the egg to slow the spin rate down, and the egg's day got longer. (Earthquakes do the same to the crust of the earth as you'll see in the next chapter.)

d.   The brief contact with your finger reduced the rotational speed of the shell but the viscus interior kept turning at a faster rate and shear stresses built up inside of the egg. When your finger disengaged, internal shear stresses went into action to re-couple the shell...the shell picked up speed...and the egg's day got shorter.

e.   Some energy was lost to internal friction so the final rotational velocity of the egg was slower than before, its day was forever lengthened, and it got warmer inside!

HERE'S THE EYE OPENER!

The yoke of the egg was not much different in its function, and influence on rotation,

196

than the core of the earth! The mass of the yoke of the egg, being large in comparison to its surroundings maintained its speed and energy level better as compared to the shell and the albumen...it acted as a buffer, so to speak. To some extent it stored some of the energy and it rotated a little faster than either the shell or the albumen for a brief moment after the shell and the albumen re-coupled. The yoke, just like the core of the earth, smooths the exchange of momentum between the shell and the egg's interior. While the albumen is a sort of "plastic zone" a viscus interior zone where energy can be transferred smoothly from the shell to the yoke...or in the case of the earth, to the **core**!

Interestingly, it has been discovered that the earth's core rotates at a different speed than the crust. It was reported in many of the Nation's papers and periodicals. The New York Times article headlined the story as "Earth's Core, a Planet Within the Planet, Is Spun by Twin Streams of Molten Iron."[23]

We'd want to step lightly here I should think, because if there were "Twin Streams of Molten Iron," acting about the core of the earth, it would seem that the streams **are the result** of other energies that are being exchanged and **are not** themselves causing the core to spin at a differential rate. They would be a waste-by-product of the exchange. They are not there to do any work! We will revisit this question of a separately rotating core in a later chapter because it is an interesting discovery and matches well with our proposal that earthquakes are the culprit in the change of the length of our day!

Another accounting of the phenomenon of the independent rotation of the earth's core, is reported in the January 1997 issue of *Discover,* magazine under the heading of "The Top 100 Science Stories (of 1996)." The article, entitled "In the Earth but Not of it," suggests, from data generated by computer simulations, that two independent jet streams of molten iron encircle the core...

> ...the churning iron of the outer core...deep counterparts to those (air currents) in the atmosphere...organizes itself into two jet streams that ring the inner core's north and south poles. Racing eastward, the jets carry a magnetic field that in turn drags the inner core like the rotor in an electric motor."

We have to give these proposals some critical thought in my opinion, because magnetic fields and hot jet streams of molten iron consume vast quantities of energy. They are not self-sustaining systems and they would have ceased to function eons ago when their energy source ran out. I think they have the cart pushing the horse in this case and we should really stop and ask them, "Where is all this energy coming from?"

NATURAL EVENTS MUST FOLLOW NATURE'S LAWS

We're proposing that the changes in the length-of-the-day and the angular momentum exchanges with the moon are initiated by earthquakes, and as such they must obey the same laws that the egg obeyed...and we're proposing that the earthquake system derives its energy from the gravitational influences of the sun and the moon and that they add energy to the system...not consume it. We need an explanation for how earthquakes are involved and for that we'll have to go on to the next chapter, but first I would like to reiterate a theme that we have stated throughout this book. The most fundamental Law in all of nature is this, "Only forces cause motion...not heat, not energy...just forces."

IT'S THE LAW!

Nature works its way because it's the law. The length of day phenomenon is a prime example of nature obeying its own laws. The earth's rotational speed, after it is slowed by earthquake activity, is restored, except for a small portion that is lost to heat from viscus forces that create internal friction, because it is the law. The restorative forces that we demonstrated with the egg were re-active. They didn't come into existence until work was performed from an independent external source! The force was known, and the reaction was predictable, easily described, and in full accordance with known principle, ie., Newton's Third Law of Motion. A body in motion tends to remain in motion.

Now we are in position to ask two critical questions. The first question is, "Are the initiating forces," which we've said are associated with earthquakes, "that bring about the change in the length of day predictable?" The second question is, "Will the initiating forces execute their function in accordance with established principle?"

The answers are Yes! and Yes!

a. Stratigraphy is the art of dating a formation by the seasonal deposition of sediments in layers or beds. The implicit assumption being that environmental uniformity exists and that the layered depositions, or the daily growth patterns in the case of coral, can be counted and a chronology determined.

Chapter 21

Earthquake, Earth's Hidden Unrest.

In this chapter we'll be discussing earth's greatest hidden unrest...earthquake, and we'll relate our story as if it was substantiated fact. You can judge for yourself at the conclusion! But first, let's pick up some background.

THE FORCES THAT LENGTHEN THE DAY ARE COMPLEX IN NATURE!

In the last chapter we saw that 370 million years ago, in Devonian times, a day was only 22 hours long. The earth was spinning faster than and we suggested that earthquakes, without explaining how, were responsible for slowing the earth's rate of rotation and causing the days to get progressively longer. Briefly this means that earthquakes must exert some sort of internal force, some sort of momentary shock loading that acts in the proper direction, and with sufficient magnitude, to slow the earth's rate of rotation. We also said that reactive viscus forces acting through the plastic layers of the earth re-coupled the inner earth with the crust and thereby restored the major part of the rotational speed. Now we'll proceed to prove this theory.

PRIMEVAL, PREDICTABLE! Earthquakes...

a.   ...are a primeval force. They have remained unchanged since antiquity.

b.   ...are self sustaining. They are fed by celestial gravitation and do not consume earth bound energy. If they did they would have ceased eons ago!

c.   ...are a force of stupendous magnitude. Their momentary duration is of a type and character that can change the rotational speed of the earth with ease.

d.   ...act parallel to, and generally within 60 degrees either side of the equator, and thereby produce the torque levels that have the magnitude to change time.

e.   ...are intermittent, seasonal, and whose reaction force acts east to west in opposition to the direction of rotation of the earth.

f.   ...act in sufficiently short bursts of energy that they are incapable of completely breaking the viscus ties in the earth's interior.

g.   ...are a force of predictable nature, and this is extremely important, they execute their function in accordance with well established principle.

h.   ...are a force that work predictably as the triggering mechanism for the change in the length of day phenomenon.

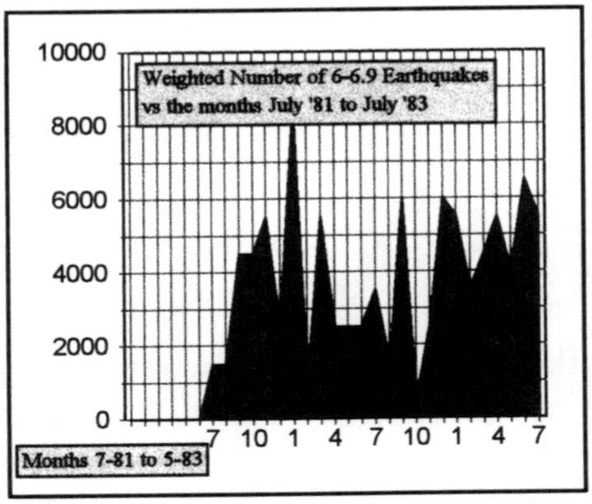

Figure 1. The intermittent and seasonal pattern of the energy in earthquakes of magnitude 6 to 6.9 for the period July 1981 to July 1983, is a near image of the length of day graph of Figure 2. below.

ALTERNATIVE CONCEPTS

Tidal friction?

Tidal friction is a drag put upon the rotational aspects of the earth by the sun and the moon. It is believed to cause ocean tides, and might contribute to some unrecoverable portion of the interior strains within the earth, but it cannot be the force that we're looking for! It clearly has the wrong characteristics. Tidal friction varies somewhat in magnitude due to the relative orbital position of the sun and the moon, but otherwise it is a constant force. The length-of-day data recorded and distributed by The Jet Propulsion Laboratory in Pasadena California, demonstrates an undeniable intermittency and a very distinct monthly and seasonal characteristic. Tidal friction has none of them!

An expanding earth?

It has been suggested that an expanding earth could cause a change in the angular momentum, and affect a change in the length-of-day. Runcorn...

The long ridges that run down the middle of several of the oceans offer some evidence that the earth has expanded ....The mid-Atlantic ridge and the Carlsberg ridge in the Indian Ocean have central valleys that are thought to be cracks that result from a stretching of the crust....Cosmological ideas have been brought into the question. It is conceivable that the universal force of gravity is not constant but has been decreasing, such as to cause the earth gradually to expand.[1]

The expanding earth argument, whereas it affects the earth in the way suggested, is without the proper credentials. An expanding earth does not act intermittently, nor is it seasonal, and the reactive force that it initiates would be in the form of a constant strain, unvarying in magnitude. So both of these considerations, tidal friction and an expanding earth, are obviously incapable of providing the features that characterize the recorded data. So we can accept neither.

On the other hand, examine the Earthquake- per-Month graph illustrated in Figure 1. The data in this graph matches the number of earthquakes of magnitude 6.0 to 6.9, against the month in which they occurred during the two year period from July 1981 to July 1983. This earthquake data displays the intermittent and seasonal pattern that matches our criteria. Now compare this data to the length of day changes shown in Figure 2 and you'll see a match. What we will demonstrate now is that there is a force created in association with earthquakes that acts in the proper direction with sufficient magnitude and duration that they alter the course of time. When we accomplish this, and it is important to us that the force that we identify does not add to the long list of unknowns that already exists, we will have demonstrated, beyond question that earthquakes are responsible!

Our proposal is that the earthquake mechanism is an electro-mechanical process. In every sense of the word we are proposing that earthquakes are earth bound lightning bolts which emanate from the processes associated with the RB-Effect. We also suggest that the length-of-day phenomenon relates to the processes that generate internal electrical ground currents, and by implication the resultant reaction forces. We also suggest that these processes are caused by the Rotational-Bending elements of vibration, fretting, and fatigue, and because they are gravitationally induced, they are self sustaining!

THE FORCE THAT SLOWS THE EARTH! In sequential fashion...

1.   Stress reversals, created continuously within the upper mantle as the earth rotates in the celestial gravitational fields, lead to fatigue and fatigue cracking.

2.   The RB-Effect produces vibration and frictionally generated heat which furthers the cause of fatigue cracking.

3.   Heat and vibration lead to fretting at all mantle boundary surfaces where cracks exist, and water, where available, is squeezed from the rock, or fills in from above.

4.   Electrical currents, which are known to be produced by stress reversals, flow through the silicon rich upper mantle, and follow crack boundaries through the ionized[A] conductive debris that has been laid down by fretting. The strongest electrical currents, enhanced by the presence of water and resident conductive iron and magnesium ions and other conductive ionized debris that litter the paths, flow explosively through suddenly exposed cracks in the earth's mantle.

5.   The direction of (negative) electron flow goes from west to east and is parallel to the direction of the earth's rotation. This flow of electrons requires structural support, and accordingly, produces a reactive force that is in opposition to both the direction of the electron flow, and the direction of rotation of the earth. **It is this reaction force that slows the rate of rotation of the earth!**

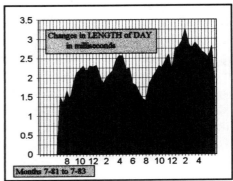

Figure 3. Changes in the length of day, in milliseconds.

6.   The magnitude of the reaction forces, which we can now properly identify as a retrograde force, will develop in direct proportion to the amount of electrical current generated.

7.   Bursts of electrical current, much like lightning, propagate as cracks develop spontaneously. Debris that is laid down in the burst-path forms an enlarged conduct that enhances ensuing discharges. As with atmospheric lightning, it is probable that temperatures along the burst path could approach 50,000 degrees Fahrenheit. These bursts of current are likely to be exceedingly short but with the large quantity of current flow that exist, large quantities of heat must be present.

(If I was to speculate it would be to suggest that ancient burst-paths are modern day aqueducts, filled now with gas or oil, and that volcanoes enter this picture somewhere.)

[A] Ionization of a material such as iron or magnesium, or any other, refers to a chemical process that results in the element having acquired an electrical charge.

We know that low level electrical ground currents abound in the upper mantle,[2] and we know that this current is essentially steady which means that it must be generated by some on-going process, as distinguished, for instance, from the burst-discharge that is associated with the earthquake process. Along these lines I would propose that the generating mechanism for the production of low level ground current is associated with the on-going RB-Effect, and there is an appealing case in favor of these ground currents being the in situ progenitor of the geo-magnetic field.

1.   First, we know without question that magnetic fields are always associated with the flow of electricity. That is what alternators, generators, coils, transformers, and all manner of electrical and magnetic processes are all about.

2.   Secondly, we could look at the vertical component of the geo-magnetic field and recall that "...there is an odd requirement that whenever an electric field is put into motion, or retarded, it must not only set up a magnetic field at right angles to it but it must send out (perpendicular to both) an impalpable electromagnetic wave that travels (outward) through space...."[3] **The earth's magnetic field has such a vertical component.**

3.   Third, there is an 11.5 degree offset of the magnetic axis relative to the earth's rotational axis. The reason for this "offset" is not known, but it is possible that this offset is the result of there being more that one electrical process field. There may be two, or even more, and it is probable that the interaction of these fields of current, acting at different levels within the earth, and acting at different angles relative to one another, produces the offset.

It is known for instance that the magnetic field flows back and forth, from west to east and east to west, on a continual basis. I investigated this phenomenon to see whether some aspect of it would explain the 11.5 degree offset of the axis of the magnetic field, and I got some interesting results that suggest that they are related. See Appendix V.

4.   The reaction forces from the generation of electrical currents, put a compressive load on the upper mantle that leaves a moving trace as the earth turns. These compression forces set up a companion pattern of strain and vibration that creates and dissipates immense quantities of heat as the earth revolves.

We know of such a vibrational pattern, Myeung Hoi Kwon & Randal D. Peters spoke of it in the previous chapter. In a study of Free Earth Oscillations, they wrote...

...we have almost continuously observed long period oscillations of the earth during January to August in 1990. Periods of those vibrations are correlated with more than ten of known long periods of spheroidal and torsional oscillations of the earth **which result from the occurrence of large earthquake.**[4]

In association with the work done by the lengthening-of-the-day forces, there is a loss of energy that is dissipated by vibration and friction in the form of heat, and I indicated its importance in a previous chapter. That importance is traceable now to the verifiable measurement of the moving trace of compression that follows the current path, and its measurement could trace the source of the vibrations that Kwon & Peters addressed above. An additional part of the evidence in support of an electro-mechanical generator, as we've proposed, is also visibly recorded in the growth rings of hardwood trees. This is discussed at length in the next chapter.

Positive current flows westward, but the negative current, ie., the electrons that require reactive support and thus set up the forces that oppose the earth's rate of rotation, flow eastward.

Figure 3 With the hand wrapped around a theoretical wire and the thumb pointing in the direction of the positive current flow, the "north pole" of the associated magnetic field is up, and the reaction forces go east to west!

SUMMARIZING...

It is known that the resistance to electron flow in the upper mantle is high and current generation is comparatively low and self limiting until, as we suggested, fatigue from the RB-Effect develops a wider crack pattern, or water is added, or there is an increase in ionization, any of which would increase the generating volume of electrical current. The steady flow portion of the current would be measurably proportional to the change in resistance of the newly opened flow paths. It was intentional that we said *measurably proportional*, because, as we've stated repeatedly, these currents require a support structure in the earth and this support structure leaves measurable strains and vibrations in its path that would vary with the position of the sun and the moon. The factors affecting current, strain, and vibration can be summarized.

a.   The size of the crack, (length, cross section, etc.)
b.   The resistance to current flow, (i.e., the chemical properties of the path.)
c.   The duration that the crack is open to current flow,

d.   The effectiveness of the sealing process,

e.   The level of "stored" strain in the strata where the crack develops,

f.   The strength of the "generating" strata, and/or the strength of the adjacent strata in relation to its ability to support and transmit the reaction forces.

g.   The degree to which the reaction forces are absorbed through strain.

SHOCKS AND AFTER SHOCKS

It is conceivable that failure to completely seal the fatigue crack is related to after shock potential, as well as to continued low level current flow. Interestingly enough, associating after shocks to crack potential, opens up the opportunity to investigate the orientation of the electrical flow paths by monitoring the associated magnetic field anomaly. It would be a wonderful research project that I might take on some day. (But I have a plan for another book right now!) The earthquake energy level itself is dependant upon many factors, some have not been discussed before, and others are listed above, but the most important ones should be repeated here to firmly establish their association with damage potential. The important factors in damage potential are these...

h.   The level of stored strain in the strata and the strength of the strata.

i.   The degree to which the reaction forces are absorbed through strain or shear.

j.   The amount of current that is absorbed along the flow path

EARTHQUAKES HAVE PECULIAR CHARACTERISTICS:

Earthquakes, regardless of depth of focus, are not known to hit continents, countries, or states or provinces! Earthquakes hit downtown, at the corner of First and Main. From 200 miles below the surface of the earth, earthquakes hit like arrows. Isn't there something quizzical about that? Shock waves can't do that...there is no guidance system! Shock waves dissipate their energy in radial patterns, and they expend their energy somewhat evenly as they propagate from their source.

It is a gift of nature that we all possess a belief system...we use it to filter out the wheat from the chaff. Given the intuitive correctness of this belief system, let me ask you to consider this question! "Does the orthodox view of the earthquake mechanism, i.e., brittle fracture...frictional sliding...shock waves hitting designated targets...with tens of thousands of high-focus, intermediate-focus, and deep-focus events occurring around the world...each with its own causal explanation...each requiring a sieve like structure within the earth...fall within your belief system?" It doesn't fit mine! No shock wave that I have ever seen, or heard tell of outside of earthquakes, has ever done anything but dissipate like an explosion that breaks windows everywhere within a two block radius, or dissipates like ripples on the water. **Why should the shock wave from an earthquake be any different?** No, I don't believe it! Shock waves don't and never did do that. But an earth bound lightning bolt sure could, and it would have no problem doing it!

THAT'S WHAT LIGHTNING BOLTS DO!

Earthquakes are an electro-mechanical phenomenon. They are earth bound lightning bolts that propagate along fatigue cracks! They hit pinpoint at the corner of First and Main from deep below the surface of the earth, because that's what lightning bolts do! In some ways they are like atmospheric lightning. We're generally aware of just three aspects of the discharge characteristics of atmospheric lightning...the high amperage discharge that streaks across the sky, the explosive impact on the ground and the accompanying thunder. But, unlike this common viewpoint, lightning actually discharges in a multi-step sequence which could go from the clouds to the ground, or from the ground to the clouds. Let me describe the process in this fashion. First, and in advance of the main discharge, pathways sheathed by ionized air are formed in the atmosphere by advance low amperage leaders, called scouts, that radiate out from the cloud seeking a path to the ground. Once the pathway is defined the main charge is released in a blinding flash of fury whose temperature can be as high as 50,000 degrees Fahrenheit. Neither the sheath nor the ground can readily absorb the current and the sheath explodes in a thunderous roar and the lightning pierces the ground fusing the soil forming tubular spikes called fulgurites in sandy soils, or it might just shatter some hapless tree. The last step in the sequence follows Newton's Third Law of Motion...For every action there is an equal and opposite reaction...ie., there can **never**, as in never ever, be a single isolated force,[5] and in compliance with this law, the supporting atmosphere rebounds in towering pillars of energy that penetrate the stratosphere in brilliant color.

TO TEST A THEORY

The earth bound lightning bolts that are earthquakes, follow a similar course of ionized sheathes in the mantle and they discharge their energies, most frequently, at the surface of the earth. So whether there is damage at the surface or not, depends on the ability of the ground to absorb the energies. Quartz, or silicon dioxide, (SiO_2) is the commonest rock forming mineral in the crust. In crystal form quartz exhibits piezoelectric properties, in that it responds in a way as to discharge electricity when subjected to a mechanical

206

strain, ie., when it is compressed, and inversely, an input voltage to the crystal induces mechanical strain, ie., it causes the crystal to shrink along one axis and to expand across the other. Thus, depending upon the ground soil characteristics at the point of ground lightning discharge we should expect some kind of piezoelectric performance when the lightning, ie., the earthquake, hits. The soils should contract along one axis and expand across another. I mean cracks should open and faults should move! I think they do!!

ADDITIONAL EVIDENCE:

Let's take a look at what other researchers have found in their investigations so that we can broaden our perspective a bit. Kwon and Peters's approached the question of earthquakes with an instrument designed to produce answers. The instrument they used was a balance, or tiltmeter, that Dr. Randall D. Peters, a Professor in the Department of Physics at the U. S. Military Academy, designed and patented.[6] The meaningful characteristic of the tiltmeter is its measurement capabilities as Dr. Peters describes.

> Many physical phenomena in nature have force changes associated with them. We have studied these changes using a new balance, or tiltmeter.[a] It is responsive to changes in the direction of the acceleration of gravity, being sensitive to variations as small as roughly one nano-radian, ie., 0.000000057 degrees. We have concluded that our balance is responding to free oscillations of the earth which are driven by tidal forces. They are excited in the course of stress relaxation via mechanisms of unknown type. (These tidal forces are not from within the ocean, but from within the rock structure of the earth!)

Stress relaxations, of the type that Kwon and Peters are speaking about here, are identical to those we described in Chapter 5, when we observed that rotation, under simultaneous bending conditions, continually walked internal tension and compression stresses around and around the crust of the revolving earth. Kwon and Peters continue...

> If we assume that the earth is an elastic sphere, then stress release can set it into two fundamental modes of vibration. One type is a torsional oscillation, in which the earth twists relative to another. The other is a spheroidal type...the lowest mode being an oscillation between oblate and prolate spheroid limits. (A mode similar to a water filled balloon pulsing in and out.)

> It is very interesting that the amplitude of the free oscillations we observed varied significantly with time in the lunar synodic period[7].... At the new or full moon, the

207

amplitudes become maximum. (When the earth, moon, and sun are in conjunction.) Conversely, at quadrature (quarter moon), the amplitudes are at there minimum. The short period oscillations were triggered several times during the measurements, and the two largest ones of them were coincident with known earthquakes at Mexico and the Phillippines in July 1990. The Apollo experiments (also) show that moonquakes are definitely related to the lunar synodic cycle.[8] (See Figure 5)

These experiments demonstrate that measurable relationships do exist between the earth, the moon, and earthquakes. They further demonstrate that the relationship is neither hidden nor obscure. The task at hand remains for us to expose that relationship.

ANGULAR MOMENTUM: The hidden culprit.

The physical aspects of the transfer of angular momentum between two perfectly elastic homogenous bodies is well known and is discussed in all physics and mechanics text and hand books. But regarding the transfer of momentum between the earth and the moon, there are no text books to consult. Besides, neither body is perfectly elastic, nor are they homogenous, so the transfer of angular momentum between them is likely to be bumpy and unpredictable relative to consequence. On the other hand to say that all interactions between the earth and the moon would be un-predictable would be misleading. One thing we know for certain is that the exchanged 'energy' must be in proportion to the work that compels the

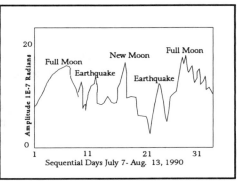

Figure 4 Vibrational oscillations within the Earth correlate directly with phases of the moon, and the occurrence of earthquake. Copied from Kwon & Peters

exchange. That is to say that the earth cannot give up more than it has! We should expect, therefore, that there is some form of angular momentum *potential* stored somewhere within the earth. It could be stored in the form of strain, or in the form of kinetic energy, ie., energy of movement. Both are suitable containers for such storage.

It would be reasonable to expect that the angular momentum *potential* is held in storage until some breakaway threshold is reached, or some initiating event occurs that releases it. But how much potential can be stored...how much can be released at one time...how abrupt a given release may be...what affect an abrupt, or large quantity release could have on either the earth or the moon, is still all a matter of some conjecture. Although it might be reasonable to assume that the abrupt and the high-quantity exchanges could be quite damaging. We should be concerned, too, with where the *potential* is stored, because a discharge from a single storage location would have different consequence than exchanges from several locations. So, accepting this for the moment, lets try to imagine where this *potential* is stored. One place would be in the extraneous rotational speed of the core of the earth, another could be in the elastic strain stored in the upper mantle. A third, and a very likely place is in the equatorial bulge. Some potential may even be stored in the moon! It's not unsolvable, so lets ask ourselves some questions.

1.   What is the probability of the exchange being "bumpy."

2.   What is the probability of there being a substantive exchange and the "strain" of gravitational confinement be of damaging magnitude, like the breaking up of the comet that eventually hit Jupiter in 1996? Could the moon in that case cause some real physical damage to the earth, or to itself? If so what form might that damage take? Could it flip the magnetic field, or destroy it entirely?

3.   Could it induce events that would affect the earth's climate, or bring about floods, or extinction, or a shift of the crust?

We should look at what happens when there is an exchange of momentum between two known bodies so that we can get some sort of a picture of what this means in our mind. An example that I could relate, one that results in a damaging outcome, can be described rather easily. Picture yourself at the Olympics where you have entered the hammer throw competition. You have hold of the handle and are turning in a circle as you transfer your momentum to the hammer at the end of the wire. You turn faster and faster, and the wire pulls harder and harder on your hands as the exchange builds, when all of a sudden...the wire breaks! Now this is far from an authentic example of what happens between the earth and the moon, but in terms of damaging results you know that you're headed for the ground, and who knows where the hammer is going. The feeling that I want you to experience is one of your body reeling out of control, of you trying to get your footing but can't, and the feelings that you have as you realize that it is hopeless! It is not the exchange of momentum that causes alarm, it is the potential for natural events to get out of control. In the case of the earth, the extraneous speed of the core, and the stress that is stored in the mantle in the form of strain, are two forms of storage, because they would normally give up their burden gradually, are the mediating elements between the earth and the moon that prevent natural events from getting out of control. How well they do their job and how fast they respond, is a function of the materials and the interfaces of the strata that bind them.

There is no magic in catastrophe! It is simply a case of natural events getting out of control, and there is a real potential for this with an exchange of momentum between the earth and the moon! An example of natural events getting out of control catastrophically was demonstrated in the case of the wire breaking in the example above, here, where the principle of threshold constraints was involved, we saw the explosiveness of sudden releases of angular momentum. Here, in an example of threshold constraints, the wire held until the fibers were over stressed, and at that point it broke, and the stored strain was released like a rubber band retracting. We know that the wire would not have broken at a lower stress level, i.e., when the hammer was revolving slower for example. If we extend the concept of threshold constraints to a momentum exchange event between the earth and the moon we can readily see the great potential for these events to get out of control naturally, with the result being natural catastrophe. Conjecturing on these points is not without substantial foundation, for instance in regard to the storage of angular momentum in the earth's upper mantle, Sir Harold Jeffreys,[9] an English author, astronomer and geophysicist who wrote *The Earth: Its Origin, History, and Physical Constitution* (1924) *Scientific Inference* (1957) and *Methods of Mathematical Physics* (1946), among others, recognized this very problem...

> ...the earth appears as a triaxial ellipsoid, and is more elliptical than the hydrostatic theory would suggest by about 0.5 percent...the departure from hydrostatic conditions implies the existence of shear stresses within the mantle, that are either statically or dynamically maintained. *Jeffreys* (1962)[10]

If we attribute this 0.5 percent, as Jeffery suggests, to stored momentum strain, latent momentum strain, or momentum *potential*, any of these terms will do, we can see that we are dealing with a very large quantity indeed. This is catastrophe waiting to happen. It also happens to be a measurable quantity, something that we can keep our eyes on.

TO SUMMARIZE: WE HAVE SUGGESTED THESE RELATIONSHIPS.

a.   We've suggested that earthquakes relate to the lengthening of the day.

b.   We've suggested that the inertial and viscus forces, operating in a reactive manner, respond to re-establish a longer day...once the active earthquake forces have slowed the earth and lengthened its day.

c.   We've suggested that the processes of rotational-bending acts to produce fretting, fatigue, fatigue cracking, and the generation of electrical currents in the upper mantle.

d.   We reject the common theme that earthquakes are caused by "...brittle fracture and frictional sliding deep within the earth, and somehow hit downtown at the corner of First and Main from 200 miles away, saying that shock waves don't do that! But, we suggest, an earth bound lightning bolt sure could, and it would have no problem doing it!

e.   We've suggested that earthquakes are an electro-mechanical phenomenon. They are earth bound lightning bolts that propagate along fatigue cracks, and that compressive stresses follow the wake of the sun and the moon about the earth, and "ring earth's bell."

f.   We believe that a crucial role of the earth's core is to moderate the consequence of the release of pent-up strain from stored angular-momentum *potential*.

g.   We've related how Sir Harold Jeffreys has suggested that there is a storage, in the form of strain, of angular momentum *potential* in the equatorial bulge.

h.   And we have demonstrated the explosiveness of sudden releases of angular momentum *potential*.

Can these same processes relate to other mysteries of the earth as well?

a. This balance, is (a)modified Cavendish type pendulum whose deflection is monitored by a linear rotary differential capacitance transducer (LRDCT).

Chapter 22

Means to Ends

Astronomers, geologists, geophysicists, palaeontologists, and other investigators whose concern is the origin and evolution of the earth are handicapped by a shortage of evidence. The events of interest occurred in times so distant that geological records are only borderline reliable, if they exist at all. As a result the theories that have been advanced are largely conjectural. Moreover, because of the scantiness of the evidence, theories differ considerably and therefore are highly controversial.[1]

WHILE SOME THEORIES ARE CONTROVERSIAL, OTHERS ARE NOT

Mountains have downward projecting images called, "cold mantle roots."

Figure 1 Mountain roots.

An essay on continental form would start by saying that continents have plains, hills, mountains, rivers, and lakes, and a down-projecting image of the surface profile called cold mantle roots. These roots are generally oriented somewhat centrally, and extend, in the case of ancient crust, as deep as 150 miles.[2]

A cross section of the continent to expose its detail would reveal a complexity of form that no set of terms could describe because we would be startled into disbelief by what we saw. Almost every particle has been re-cycled. We have to search to find anything original. Even more startling, the entire expanse, top to bottom, side to side, is one huge grave yard! Fossil and un-fossilized, bone and tissue, human and animal. You can find sea shells buried on mountain tops and trees standing upright on the ocean floor and others buried deep and standing upright in coal beds. An aerial view would show the continental plains to be scoured by glacier, or over run with lava.

213

The view would expose some hills fashioned of solid rock, and others of glacier deposited sands and gravel, and still others from eroded mountain debris. Lakes would be seen as ancient marine basins, or general catch-all's for the flowing waters. It would show rivers formed from ground water, or glacial melt, or flowing from lakes or out of mountain fissures. This is our natural world, though hidden from view by the grasses and the trees, but the mountains are different. There is nothing natural about a mountain. Even the most ancient are composed of sedimentary and metamorphic rock, cored with towers of lava, and have at one time or another, been buried deep beneath the surface of the sea. And what about the continents? No one knows how or when they were formed. But if we need to seek an answer, logic tells us that everything is bounded by some type of surface, and experience tells us that everything responds in predictable ways to the elements of time and environment, and these ingredients in themselves, the bounded-surfaces and time, will make a continent, so we can leave it at that.

OTHER PROCESSES:

The mantle roots, were we able to examine them, would show a distinct character. They would be seen as low density rock that penetrates the earth like the hull of a ship that serve to support the continents hydrostatically. There is a companion to the process of root formation called isostasy that explains the manner by which the surface, acting through the mantle roots, achieves (hydrostatic) equilibrium. But we have to be careful here because the term isostasy has been kicked around a bit with the question of debate surrounding the question of whether isostasy refers to the final *condition* of equilibrium, or to the *processes* that work to achieve equilibrium. I use the term isostasy in reference to the *process* that establishes equilibrium, preferring an expression like "...the land has achieved isostatic equilibrium" to refer to the final condition. In either case the *process* of isostasy is best defined by applying Archimedes principle.

> ...a body, immersed or supported, in a medium is buoyed up by a force equal to the weight of the displaced material.

This principle relates to the process of isostasy in a manner better described below, but for now let it suffice to say that the process is one wherein the submerged interface of the supported land mass undergoes a material change that acts either to weight the land mass down or to buoy it up, depending upon the density of the material exchanged. In search for a contemporary example no better one comes to mind than the Himalayas as they have been rising over the past few decades.[3] Lake Titicaca is another good example. In Chapter 17 we saw the Andes rise to new heights taking the lake, which was once a

214

bay at ocean level, to elevations well above the ocean.

There has been much interest shown in the continental root phenomenon and it has been awarded extensive investigation as a result. Our interest in the phenomenon relates to the question of root origins because we believe that the growth areas are the breeding grounds for some earthquakes, and that a demonstrable relationship exists between root growth and the processes of isostasy. So we'll take a look at these processes with an eye towards the RB-Effect and the fretting phenomenon. The process is obviously continuous and apparently not very precise, as the continents are forever rising and falling as the mechanism hunts for a stable condition. It is a little like the balancing act we might see in a circus where the juggler will adjust his position under his charge in a hunt for its center of gravity.

We're not the first to have coupled the process of isostasy with the occurrence of mantle roots. Other authors have advanced the same theory. Their investigations, in the sense, that they are relating the process of isostasy with the occurrence of mantle roots are embracing a management technique called "...a systems approach." A systems approach acknowledges cause and effect which, in an elementary sense, recognizes that when something happens there is a reason for it. Or conversely, if we want something to happen then we must put those processes into effect that will lead to the desired outcome. This takes my thoughts back to our earlier discussions on the Apollo program. The success of the Apollo program, besides the fine people and the superb engineering and scientific efforts that went into it, can be attributed to the organization of the program under the systems approach concept. Systems engineering is an excellent means for organizing work efforts and it has broad application. It worked well for Apollo, and the concept can work equally as well in the sciences. The cause and effect constraints, however, require that the researchers adhere to the fundamental concept that, "...if something happens there is a reason for it." The task is to juggle "cause and effect" in a way that they maintain their dominance over the urge to sidetrack into simpler methods of investigation, and let me tell you, that isn't always easy.

Another term relating to the process of isostasy, which we'll discuss as we go on, was coined by Jochum and McDonough to associate *isostasy* with the growth of mantle roots. It's an interesting term...they call it *underplating*. Underplating is a strange acting process. It can add buoyant material to the underside of a continent thus causing it to rise, or the process can reverse itself and become destructive and cause the mantle roots to erode and allow the continent to subside. Greenland is the best current example of active subsidence although there are others. Unfortunately, the appropriateness of this concept

215

has done nothing to bring about agreement on whether root growth is gradual, or whether the roots are ancient rudiments of a dead process. Hoffman, in a 1990 article in the journal *Nature*,[4] summarized the topic in one question...

> (are) "..mantle roots accumulated progressively (so being thickest beneath the oldest plates) or are they a product of unique conditions existing in the Archaean?" (In the very ancient past.)

It may be the opportunist's role, given the character of the underplating process, to concede to the progressive accumulation side of the debate. It has the advantage of the high ground, being consistent as it is with contemporary observations.

THE SEARCH FOR A UNIFYING THEORY

The theory of Plate tectonics has been described by some as the unifying theory of geophysics. But there is no help here, because plate tectonics is itself a theory looking for a driving force, Bonatti expressed it...

> Although the theory of plate tectonics is well established, the engine that drives the motion of the lithospheric plates continues to defy easy analysis because it is so utterly hidden from view.[5]

We must look elsewhere, and that elsewhere is in the force system associated with the RB-Effect, and in particular fretting. Fretting is a metallurgical term that we have defined earlier, but we should take another look at it. By definition...

> ...fretting occurs between two mating surfaces, it is a heat producing wear phenomenon that is adhesive in nature and is usually accompanied by corrosion that produces a chemical debris in some materials. Vibration is its essential causative factor...[6]

Let me give you an example. You've purchased a brand new pick-up truck and have installed a bed-liner to keep the pick-up bed clean. Now, six months later, you are taking the liner out to clean under it and low-and-behold the bed looks like it has the measles. Everywhere the liner touched the bed the paint is worn down to bare metal and only an unidentifiable residue remains. The condition was caused by fretting, slow vibrational agitation between the liner and the truck bed. Now, with the damaged truck on your hands it is your turn to fret, and interestingly enough it's the same thing, mild agitation!

216

While I was contemplating the responses that I might get from the use of metallurgical terms and principles in the solution of natural events like mantle roots, I was reminded of the mild controversy that developed when the opposition party got hold of the statement that Charles Wilson, then head of General Motors, made when he was before a U.S. Senate committee where he said, "...what was good for our country was good for General Motors and vice versa."[7] The press quickly picked up on the "vice versa" part and turned things around so that now what we were hearing was that, "....what is good for General Motors is good for the country!" The press and the general public got some fun out of the episode for a while, and then it sort of died away. We'll have to wait and see what the opposition party has to say about my metallurgical solutions!

Fretting, to get back to the matter at hand, by definition is a wear phenomenon, created in a low amplitude vibrational environment. It is adhesive in nature, produces heat by friction, and leaves a chemical debris in its path. This makes it a sterling candidate for the principles controlling the mechanism of "underplating," and earthquake too for that matter. Underplating enriches the lower continental and oceanic plate surfaces with a low density chemical debris whose buoyant effect produces upward acting forces that search out hydrostatic equilibrium. The concept of underplating was advanced by Jochum and McDonough in an August 17, 1989 *Nature* article[8] wherein they suggested that root growth occurs mainly by underplating by asthenospheric material[9] (from the Greek asthenēs, meaning weak), with a composition similar to that of mid-ocean or island basalt. It takes a long time for the process of underplating to do its job, but eventually the buildup of debris begins to take on the distinguishable form of mantle roots. Zhou[10], and Grotzinger & Royden[11] in separate papers have gone so far as to suggest a causal relationship between root form and continental flexural rigidity. The lighter weight "wings" of the plains region flex ever so much, they say, as the plating process proceeds selectively in seeking to balance the continent. If the plating process is sensitive to bearing stresses, ie., stresses created in support of other loads, as they say, than it would support our contention that fretting is our culprit, because fretting exists only where there are bearing stresses. This is corroboration from an unexpected source and gives interested researchers a tool where before there was only conjecture. The unifying principle that we are going to suggest now, ie., the principle that bonds the theories of mantle roots, their origin, and the condition of isostatic equilibrium together with underplating, is *fretting*, and we'll call the process "Debris Controlled Hydrostatics."

DEBRIS CONTROLLED HYDROSTATICS

We have already visited India to observe the Himalayan mountains rising ineffably as

217

if from out of the very heart of the foothills. If we could disturb the grandeur of this event for a moment of analysis we could apply the principle of Debris Controlled Hydrostatics to test our theory. For instance, if the Himalayas are rising because of root growth, rather than the theory that the Indian sub-continent is on a north bound collision course, then we might expect to see the central body of the mountain rising, and the hinterlands sloping away radially. We'd want to determine where the downward flexing of the continental plate begins, Zhou, and Grotzinger & Royden, in unknowing support, have already suggested a relationship. This flexure, like the drooping wings of an airplane during landing, would be measurable. Another point, if Debris Controlled Hydrostatics, ie., root growth, is the controlling process, then we should expect the average density of the mountain to decrease with time, since underplating deposits low density material in these instances. Another test, since associated cracks would develop circumferentially and electrical ground currents would follow their course as the mountain rises, we should anticipate that the changing magnetic field intensities in the region would form a "ring-of-fire" that is more concentric to the event than parallel to the coastline. This would confirm a root oriented event rather than a broadsiding event like a continental collision.

THE EARTH IS A REMARKABLE MECHANISM:

In the previous chapter I introduced you to the pendulum type tiltmeter designed and patented by Dr. Randall D. Peters, a Professor in the Department of Physics at the U. S. Military Academy. The principle characteristic of the instrument is its measurement capability. I was given the opportunity to test this instrument on a theory of mine, and it performed marvelously. The test that I conducted related to a suspicion that I had that a wave of energy passes through the earth at regular intervals. I thought of it as a ground swell of vibrational energy, I wanted to find it. I set the instrument on a rigid platform on the porch and connected its output to a strip-chart recorder,[12] then I sat down and waited for my energy wave to come through; confident that the instrument was sensitive enough to sense its passage. At 1:00 P.M. that day the stylus on the strip-chart recorder started to go wild with great sweeping swings of red ink on the greenish paper that was feeding through. Here was my energy wave. I was working on the project with a good friend, Phil Troyer, but I had to wait until he was out of work that evening to show him.

"Hey Phil! What do you think," I yelled as I shoved the strip chart paper in front of him! I must have actually shouted it out I was so excited. Well to make a long story short we sat down and tried to figure out how many things in this world would respond to this kind of energy form and leave a measurable trace. We could come up with three. Gravel

218

roads, the mysterious moving rocks of the Nevada desert, and trees! Well we didn't want to go to Nevada and investigate the moving rocks, but our access to gravel roads was direct enough. The rational behind the gravel road **guess** was that we were disenchanted with the orthodox explanation given for the wash board effect. This explanation has cars and trucks traversing and braking on the road and inputting strains that result in the wash boarding. Well we felt that this vibrational input from cars was just so much talk because we'd seen freshly graded gravel roads turn to washboard all by themselves before they ever saw any traffic. It wasn't a car or truck that input that energy. But associated with this wave was a vibrational energy form that visited us, as I discovered, three times a day just looking for something to mess up. We didn't take the gravel road investigation much beyond the talking stage, but the trees now, that was a different story!

It is well known that trees and other plants respond to external forces, like wind for instance, in a way that would reduce the internal stress loads that forces induce. So, knowing this, Phil and I decided to test a related theory. Here is what we theorized...

The energy wave, in passing through three times a day, would over-stress the trees by causing them to sway in response to the input energy, and the tree's biological response would be to grow wider yearly bands in the direction coincident with the wave. This defense mechanism would give the tree more stock to brace itself against the vibrational forces, and reduce the stress load.

We looked at hundreds and hundreds of tree stumps...studying the growth pattern of the rings...and much to our good fortune we found that the rings do in fact grow thicker along a course parallel to the vibrational wave. (See Figure 2.) Our tests were conducted at approximately 44.5 degrees north latitude, and at this latitude the energy wave came from the west northwest, and as we said, it caused the trees to modify their growth accordingly.[a]

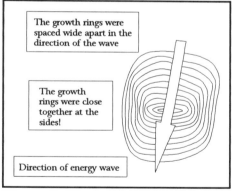

Figure 2. The growth rings on old oak trees were spaced wider apart on those sides coincident with the direction of the energy wave.

We also found that hard woods like oak showed the effect much better than soft wood trees. Soft woods seemed to yield to everything, while hard woods tended to respond only to steady forces. We suspected that the wind would effect an unprotected tree and we didn't want to get fooled by this contingency, so we compared ring patterns from trees that were deep in the woods and protected from strong winds to those that grew unprotected. We found that there was no difference. So we were confident that we were looking at ring growth patterns resulting from the wave form and not ring growth patterns from the wind. Although it was possible to see a wind effect overlaying the other more dominant pattern.

The energy wave that we had recorded was clearly produced from the gravitational effects of the sun and the moon. We've discussed earlier how scientists have long felt that there were tidal effects on the land surfaces as well as in the oceans— Phil and I were confident that this is what we were observing. Now if I could paraphrase Dr. Randall's observation:

> These experiments demonstrate that measurable relationships do exist between the earth and the moon. They further demonstrate that the relationship is neither hidden nor obscure. The task at hand remains to expose that relationship.

It was a good project with some good results and it revealed some obvious opportunities for additional investigation. For instance, earlier in this chapter I mentioned the existence of some trees standing upright in coal beds. Well, there is also a great stand of trees on the bottom of the North Atlantic ocean not too far off the Southern coast of England. It would be an interesting project for someone, (...else, I am not a deep sea diver) to determine the original orientation of the trees by examining the ring growth patterns. It might tell us something about continental movements.

PLATE TECTONICS IS NOT THE ANSWER - IT IS NOT EVEN A QUESTION!

We've been discussing the processes that cause the crust to shift and mountains to form, for mantle roots to grow and erode, and for the forces of hydrostatic equilibrium to preside over elevations. We've been calling them natural events that issue from natural interactions between the earth, the sun, and the moon. No where have we sought the tenants of plate tectonic theory, which postulates a doctrine that puts thermal energies at the helm of floating continents, to answer our inquires. We didn't ask because we didn't believe we'd get an answer.

Mercury, Venus, Earth, and Mars are the four terrestrial planets, but Earth is unique, it is different! It has a mechanism that generates electricity that powers its nerve centers...it has a mechanism that wears down the surface through erosion to sculpture the landscape and bring refreshing soils to the fields...it has a mechanism for regrowth through dynamic shifts of the crust that rebuilds the mountains and the fields and replenishes the ground waters, devastating as the process is to man, animal, and forest...it has a mechanism for the exchange of angular momentum with the moon that was put in place to keep the stresses produced from gravitational interactions, to tolerable limits. Were it all to stop, erosion would make a flat desert of the land, and the waters would be the dominating feature, and the earth would strain for relief from the stresses. Revitalization and regrowth takes place through cataclysmic events. It has been our heritage. It is our future! William Buckland, in the following passage, calls it means to ends...

In the whole machinery...of springs and rivers, ...constructed hills and valleys......and the apparatus that is kept in action for their duration...of never-failing fountains...as to supply the earth by constant evaporation. So also in the adjustment of the relative quantities of sea and land..and the appointment of the atmosphere to be the vehicle of this wonderful and unceasing circulation; in thus separating these waters from their native salt, (which...is...of the highest utility to preserve the purity of the sea...) and transmitting them in genial showers to scatter fertility over the earth...in all these we find such undeniable proofs of a nicely balanced adaption of means to ends...[13]

William Buckland (1830)

a. Plant scientists have always known, though perhaps not why, that transplanted trees have a better chance of survival if they are planted at the same compass point from which the seedling grew. Perhaps now we know the "why."

APPENDIX I. Dr Yen's Centroid & Author's Bending Moment Analysis

The most curious property that we discovered during the many months of study was the role that earth's gravity played in holding the crust together as it underwent the throes of deterioration at the sub-mantle interfaces and during the ultimate shifting phase. This can be best appreciated by looking at the position of the crust's volumetric centroid and realizing that there is virtually no component of the resultant force along the plane of the ecliptic. There is a significant component relative to the rotational axis, (Ref. distance "d" in Figure 1), which plays a significant roll in determining the distance that the crust will move during any one shift; but the lack of a component relative to the normal to the ecliptic means, significant to this analysis, that the bending moments, in the final analysis, are unopposed.

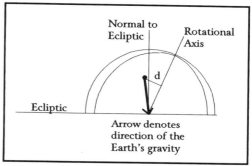

Figure 1 The gravitational influence on the centroid of the oblate spheroid is one as to hold the crust together. There is virtually no component of this influence along the plane of the ecliptic.

TABLE AI-1. Dr. David Yen's centroid data.

T=Thickness of the crust in miles.	Centroidal Distance X, in Miles	Centroidal Distance Y, in Miles	Centroidal Distance Z, in Miles	Volume in Cubic Miles
T=7	0	304.429	1763.99	1.55499E09
T=37	0	106.064	1894.30	4.46322E09
T=87	0	51.3872	1919.93	9.21209E09
T=155	0	30.5881	1917.76	15.4761E09

This being as it is, it was possible to compute the bending moments, as they acted upon the centroid of the earth's crust from the sun and the moon's gravitational fields, without accounting for the influence of earth's gravity on the crust as it had no net bearing on the outcome. The centroid data that Dr. Yen calculated from the general equations, which you'll find in a later part of this Appendix, was based on the data and the drawings that I provided him. The centroid data is also given to you in Figure 1, of Chapter 6, as well Table 1, above.

The reaction forces between the inner surface of the lower crust and the outer surface at the lithospheric interface was assumed to be significant in compression on the interface surfaces **away** from the gravitational pull of the sun and/or the moon, but insignificant in tension on the side facing the sun or the moon. The reactive surface was assumed to be represented (simplistically) by a segment of a sphere with the general equation:

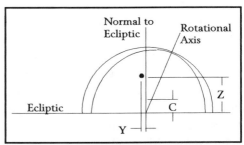

Figure 2. The volumetric centroid, hence the mass center, of the Earth's oblate spheroidal shape of the outer crust above the ecliptic.

1.   Area=$(4\pi r^2)/4$ Units are in square feet (ft^2)

The Bending Moments, M, were calculated for each value of "C", from C=0, at the ecliptic, to C=3959 at the zenith, in increments of 100 miles.

UNIVERSAL LAW OF GRAVITATION: Newton's Law of Gravitation[1] states that two particles of mass m_1 and m_2 are mutually attracted by a force, F, given by the formula:

2.   Force (F) =$G(m_1m_2)/r^2$ Units are in pounds (#)

     Where: G=Universal constant of gravitation.[2]
               r= Distance between the mass center of the two particles.
               m=Mass

TABLE AI-2. Gravitational FORCES that act upon the Earth's Spheroidal Centroid due to influences from the Sun.

	T=7 miles	T=37 miles	T=87 miles	T=155 miles
Force, in lbs.	8.30252E20	2.38305E21	4.91864E21	8.26321E21

224

3. Moment (M) $= F(Z-C) - F(A_T - A_{(T-B)})$

Where:
M = Bending Moment
F = Gravitational Force on Centroid.
Z = Distance to Centroid from Ecliptic
C = Increments of 100 miles, (0, 100, 200, 300, etc.)
A_T = Total reactive Area above the Ecliptic. (The value is the same for identical circumstances below the Ecliptic.)
$A_{(T-B)}$ = Reactive surface in compression above the Ecliptic, less the reactive surface **below** the Area excluded by "C" for each increment of "C".

The bending moment values for the solar influences are given in table 3 below: (Values for the lunar influences are given in Tables 4 and 5)

NOTES REGARDING BENDING MOMENT DATA:

1. Positive figures denote bending to form tension, negative figures denote bending to form compression.

2. These moment values do not go the full 3959 miles to the zenith above the ecliptic, because the numerical values for the bending moments get too small in comparison to the previous number to be taken into consideration

3. A process of integration to solve for the bending moments would be appropriate if a model for the reactive surfaces could be defined for the inner spheroidal shell that would encompass the entire effective surface. However, this would be a monumental task for an initial investigation, and there is scant scientific data to base an inquiry on, or even sufficient scientific data to **begin** such a project. So the simplistic approach was used. See above discussions for comments on "reaction" criteria that pertains to this data.

TABLE AI-3. Representative Solar BENDING MOMENT Values:

Vertical Dist. from Ecliptic, to Zenith in Miles	Bending Moment For T=7 Miles (ft/lbs)	Bending Moment For T=37 Miles (ft/lbs)	Bending Moment For T=87 Miles (ft/lbs)	Bending Moment For T=155 Miles (ft/lbs)
0	+1.25277E27	+5.37277E27	+1.22516E28	+2.16077E28

Vertical Dist. from Ecliptic, to Zenith in Miles	Bending Moment For T=7 Miles (ft/lbs)	Bending Moment For T=37 Miles (ft/lbs)	Bending Moment For T=87 Miles (ft/lbs)	Bending Moment For T=155 Miles (ft/lbs)
100	+1.20819E27	+5.24496E27	+1.19872E28	+2.11623E28
200	+1.14939E27	+5.07573E27	+1.16363E28	+2.05688E28
300	+1.07643E27	+4.86548E27	+1.11996E28	+1.98288E28
400	+9.89414E26	+4.61468E27	+1.06782E28	+1.89439E28
500	+8.88536E26	+4.32377E27	+1.00730E28	+1.79157E28
600	+7.73942E26	+3.99321E27	+9.38488E27	+1.67463E28
700	+6.45790E26	+3.62345E27	+8.61494E27	+1.54369E28
800	+5.04244E26	+3.21498E27	+7.76415E27	+1.39895E28
900	+3.49469E26	+2.76028E27	+6.83354E27	+1.24058E28
1000	+1.81634E26	+2.28384E27	+5.82415E27	+1.06877E28
1100	+9.14159E23	+1.76217E27	+4.73706E27	+8.83704E27
1200	−1.92514E26	+1.20379E27	+3.57338E27	+6.85580E27
1300	−3.98468E26	+6.09233E27	+2.33423E27	+4.74592E27
1400	−6.16760E26	−2.09556E25	+1.02079E27	+2.5947E27
1500	−8.47198E26	−6.68212E26	−3.65757E26	+1.48531E26
1600	−1.08958E27	−1.38569E27	−1.82416E27	−2.33472E27
1700	−1.34371E27	−2.11959E27	−3.35316E27	−4.93805E27
1800	−1.45155E27	−2.88649E27	−4.95143E27	−7.65913E27
1900	−1.29015E27	−3.68603E27	−6.61761E27	−1.04956E28
2000	−1.13983E27	−3.18378E27	−6.27264E27	−9.86724E27
2100	−1.00037E27	−2.78832E27	−5.47330E27	−8.56386E27
2200	−8.71512E26	−2.42343E27	−4.73745E27	−7.36006E27

Vertical Dist. from Ecliptic, to Zenith in Miles	Bending Moment For T=7 Miles (ft/lbs)	Bending Moment For T=37 Miles (ft/lbs)	Bending Moment For T=87 Miles (ft/lbs)	Bending Moment For T=155 Miles (ft/lbs)
2300	−7.53016E26	−2.08837E27	−4.06353E27	−6.27705E27
2400	−6.44616E26	−1.78238E27	−3.89474E27	−5.28789E27
2500	−5.46037E26	−1.50463E27	−2.89474E27	−4.39751E27
2600	−4.56991E26	−1.25430E27	−2.39634E27	−3.60269E27
2700	−3.77178E26	−1.03049E27	−1.95274E27	−2.90003E27
2800	−3.06283E26	−8.32282E26	−1.56196E27	−2.28594E27
2900	−2.43972E26	−6.58683E26	−1.22186E27	−1.75662E27
3000	−1.89892E26	−5.08657E26	−9.30189E26	−1.30802E27
3100	−1.43668E26	−3.81096E26	−6.84547E26	−9.35799E26
3200	−1.04903E26	−2.74816E26	−4.82351E26	−6.35267E26
3300	−7.31640E25	−1.88541E26	−3.20808E26	−4.01321E26
3400	−4.79870E25	−1.20803E26	−1.96865E26	−2.28321E26
3500	−2.88672E25	−7.03171E25	−1.07138E26	−1.09963E26
3600	−1.52194E25	−3.51364E25	−4.77995E25	−3.89258E25
3700	−6.41672E24	−1.33840E25	−1.43763E25	−6.35378E24

TABLE AI-4. Gravitational FORCES that act upon the Earth's Spheroidal Centroid due to influences from the Moon.

	T=7 miles	T=37 miles	T=87 miles	T=155 miles
Force in lbs.	4.64323E18	1.33272E19	2.7507E19	4.62119E19

TABLE AI-5. Representative Lunar BENDING MOMENT Values:

Vertical Dist. from Ecliptic, to Zenith in Miles	Bending Moment For T=7 Miles (ft/lbs)	Bending Moment For T=37 Miles (ft/lbs)	Bending Moment For T=87 Miles (ft/lbs)	Bending Moment For T=155 Miles (ft/lbs)
0	+7.05513E24	+3.00471E25	+6.85167E25	+1.20841E26
100	+6.73681E24	+2.93324E25	+6.70384E25	+1.20841E26
200	+6.42789E24	+2.83859E25	+6.50756E25	+1.15030E26
300	+601985E24	+272101E25	+6.26336E25	+1.10892E26
400	+5.53327E24	+2.58075E25	+5.97176E25	+1.05944E26
500	+4.96912E24	+2.41806E25	+5.63328E25	+1.00194E26
600	+4.32825E24	+2.23319E25	+5.24847E25	+9.36532E25
700	+3.61156E24	+2.02641E25	+4.81789E25	+8.63306E25
800	+2.81997E24	+1.79772E25	+4.34209E25	+7.82358E25
900	+1.95440E24	+1.54815E25	+3.82164E25	+6.93791E25
1000	+1.01578E24	+1.27723E25	+3.25714E25	+597706E25
1100	+5.11241E21	+9.85491E24	+2.64919E25	+4.94210E25
1200	−1.07663E24	+6.73218E24	+1.99840E25	+3.83409E25
1300	−2.22284E24	+3.40712E24	+1.30541E25	2.65415E25
1400	−3.44922E24	−1.17194E23	+5.70873E24	+1.40342E25
1500	−4.73744E24	−3.83763E24	−2.04550E24	+8.30666E23
1600	−6.09347E24	−7.75093E24	−1.02016E25	−1.03569E25
1700	−7.51467E24	−1.18538E25	−1.87525E25	−2.76160E25
1800	−8.1178E24	−1.16427E25	−2.76908E25	−4.28335E25
1900	−7.21513E24	−2.06141E25	−3.70088E25	−5.86962E25
2000	−6.37448E24	−1.78053E25	−3.50796E25	−5.51`823E25

Vertical Dist. from Ecliptic, to Zenith in Miles	Bending Moment For T=7 Miles (ft/lbs)	Bending Moment For T=37 Miles (ft/lbs)	Bending Moment For T=87 Miles (ft/lbs)	Bending Moment For T=155 Miles (ft/lbs)
2100	−5.5945E24	−1.55936E25	−3.06093E25	−4.78932E25
2200	−4.87391E24	−1.35530E25	−2.64941E25	−4.12057E25
2300	−4.21123E24	−1.16792E25	−2.27252E25	−3.51043E25
2400	−3.60500E24	−9.96792E24	−1.92933E25	−2.95724E25
2500	−3.05370E24	−8.41462E24	−1.61888E25	−2.45930E25
2600	−2.55571E24	−7.01464E24	−1.34015E25	−2.01480E25
2700	−2.10936E24	−5.76301E24	−1.09207E25	−1.62183E25
2800	−1.71288E24	−4.65452E24	−8.73522E24	−1.27841E25
2900	−1.36441E24	−3.68376E24	−6.83322E24	−9.82386E24
3000	−1.06196E24	−2.84465E24	−5.20206E24	−7.31508E24
3100	−1.03463E23	−2.13127E24	−3.82832E24	−5.23343E24
3200	−5.86666E23	−1.53691E24	−2.69754E24	−3.55272E24
3300	−4.09168E23	−1.05441E24	−1.79411E24	−2.24438E24
3400	−2.68366E23	−6.76037E23	−1.10096E24	−1.27692E23
3500	−1.61046E23	−3.93247E23	−5.99165E23	−6.14967E23
3600	−8.51433E22	−1.96500E23	−2.67318E23	−2.17692E23
3700	−3.58854E22	−7.48499E22	−8.03992E22	−3.55334E22

The Bending Moments that I have set out in the tables above, (Reference Tables 3 & 5) represent the maximum values for two conditions of Solar orbit corresponding to the Summer and Winter Solstices, and to the corresponding period in the Lunar orbit about the Earth, ie., when the moon would be in a position similar to the sun at the time of Summer and Winter Solstice. It must be noted, as can be imagined given the character of this concept, that since the **Centroid** of the spherical shell **stays fixed** relative to the stars, (ie., it does not rotate with the earth), and it stays fixed in relation to the Earth's Solar orbit and the Moon's orbit, **but moves** relative to the Earth's rotational axis, the gravitational forcing varies continually over time. (See Figure 4. Below)

A COMPLEX BENDING SPECTRUM:

The fact that the Solar and Lunar orbits are on an unrelated schedule, ie., one gravitational influence could be maximizing while the other is at, or approaching a minimum, and vice versa, could make the data base immensely large. Moments, if calculated by integration over the sidereal year, ie, a year relative to a fixed star, would require a continually changing set of input circumstances. Such an integration would yield many unique and transient maximum and minimum bending conditions on the crust, as a function of time, from the Rotational-Bending phenomenon and may thereby

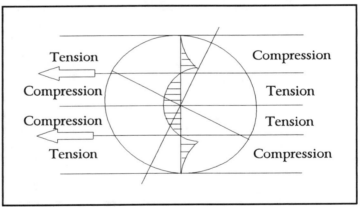

Figure 3. A typical Bending Moment Diagram constructed from the Earth's bending moment data of Tables 3 and 5 above. See also Bending Moment Diagrams generated from computer data in Chapter 6, and within this Appendix.

represent an extraordinary number of unique conditions which well might help in the establishing of predictive models for fatigue, fretting, to produce isostatic changes, as well as earthquake, and other geo-physical phenomenon.

Figure 3, above, represents a bending moment diagram across the full normal axis above and below the ecliptic, sampling data from Table 3. The simple rod of Figure 5 is illustrated as it would be deformed under a similar loading condition. Some might object to the fact that I have chosen to represent the gravitational load as being applied separately to each of the two centroids of the earth's crust, ie., above and below the ecliptic, rather than to apply it to the centroid of the combined image which would put the centroid on the ecliptic.

The rational behind this decision is based on the fact that the crust acts like an independent agent working against the inner lithosphere as the lithosphere is being held taught by the pull of gravity from the sun. Under this scenario the inner earth is a "rock-in-space" against which the crust reacts, like a teeter-tauter reacting against its center support while two playmates are playing. If in this scenario, the teeter-tauter was experiencing the resistance of a mildly resistant agent as if it was in water, for instance, just as the earth's crust experiences a mildly supportive agent in the "plastic layer, it would bend in the exact manner as shown by the simple rod of Figure 5.

Figure 6. below is one of two drawings supplied to Dr. Yen for determining the centroid of the upper shell of the crust. See Figure 7, for additional data.

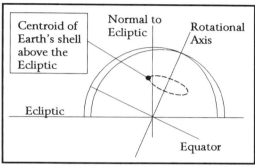

Figure 4. The centroid of the Earth's crust stays fixed in space as the Earth rotates. The dotted line represents the path that the materials of the crust follow in the daily business of rotation.

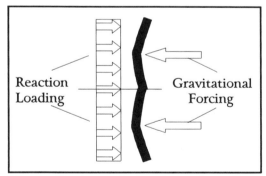

Figure 5. A simple bar being bent by a similar loading pattern as encountered by the Earth's crust due to gravity and the resistance of the plastic layer at the upper lithospheric surface!

231

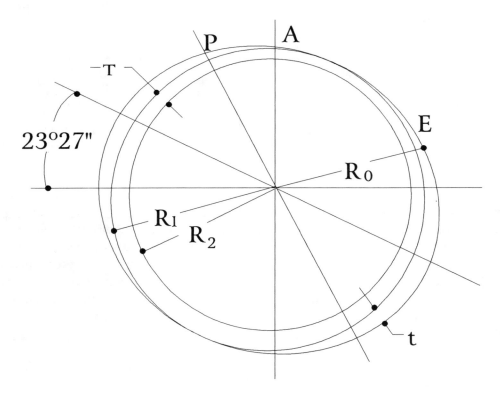

Figure 6. R_1 Is constant at 3949.92 miles.

R_0 Varies at the rate of one part in 298.25 (The surface gradient of the outside crust.).

T Varies per specific input. 7, 37, 87, & 155.

t Varies correspondingly according to the Formula:
$(13.29 - (0.147667 \text{ x } ((\text{angle from horizon, ie., Ecliptic})))$

Figure 7 above represents additional data given Dr. Yen for determining the coordinates of the centroid of the crustal shell above the ecliptic.

APPENDIX II. Spherical Trigonometry

NOTE: All quotes and equations, except where specified, are taken from the text *Engineering Trigonometry*, by Edward M. J. Pease, (Professor of Mathematics and Electrical Engineering, Rhode Island State College) and George P. Wadsworth, (Associate Professor of Mathematics, Massachusetts Institute of Technology.) International Textbook Company, Scranton, Pennsylvania, (1946)

Problems that we think of as being mathematical problems are those that deal with numbers. But actually mathematical problems are more than that, they are problems that deal with physical realities, and as such, they can be verbalized, they can be expressed in written form, and they can be drawn out graphically. Problems are varied, so depending upon the method of solution that we apply, we associate it with a particular branch of mathematics. For instance, algebra introduces equations, and geometry deals with problems that can be described graphically with lines, curves, plane shapes, (circles, triangles, etc.) and shapes with volume, (spheres, cubes, pyramids, etc.).

Trigonometry takes geometry one step further, by applying analytical methods to problems that can be expressed graphically using plane and volumetric shapes that are triangular. Among the disciplines within the field of trigonometry we can identify two that are of interest here; one that deals with triangles that are drawn on a flat surface, or plane trigonometry, and one that deals with triangles drawn on a spherical surface, (such as a globe) which we call spherical trigonometry.

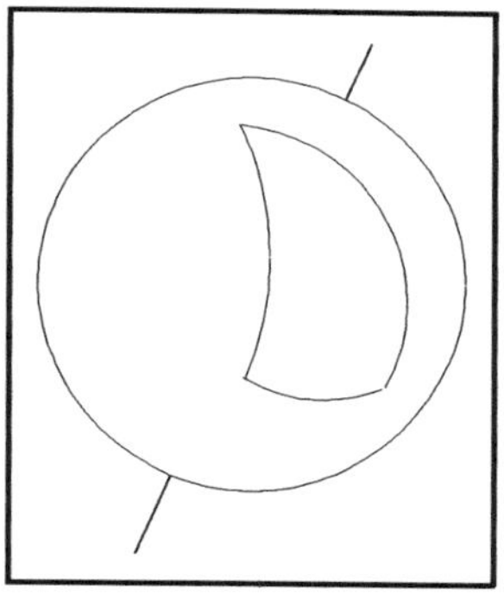

Figure 1 A "spherical triangle" illustrated on a spherical surface!

The problems we're dealing with here, that of solving the triangular relationship on the global surface between Giza and Nasca, and the former location of the North Pole in Alaska, deals with spherical trig. and uses an established set of equations. These equations are given below.

SPHERICAL TRIGONOMETRY,

RIGHT SPHERICAL TRIANGLES. (Chapter 13, Pages 256-279.)

233

By definition:

1. "Spherical trigonometry may be defined as the study of relations involving the sides and angles of spherical triangles and the problems which ultimately necessitate the solution of spherical triangles."

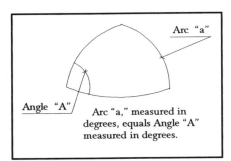

Figure 2. A spherical triangle made from the intersection of three great circles.

2. "A spherical triangle is that geometric configuration on the surface of a sphere bounded by arcs of *three great circles*. These arcs are the *sides* of the triangle."

3. "An angle of a spherical triangle is the opening between two sides, and this *spherical angle* has the same measure as the *plane angle* between the tangents of the sides at their intersection."

4. "The *face angle*, "a", of Fig. 2, has the same measure, in degrees, as the length of the opposite *arc* "A" when measured in degrees. Similar statements may be made of the other *face angles* and *arcs* within the spherical triangle of Fig. 2."

5. "In a spherical triangle the *sum of the angles* may have any value from 180° to 540°". (In contrast the sum of the angles in a plane triangle is 180°, no more, no less.)

6. "In a spherical triangle the *sum of the sides*, in degrees, must be in the range from 0° to 360°."

7. "Triangles formed on the surface of the earth are referred to as terrestrial triangles."

8. "The following ten formulas are useful in solving a right spherical triangle."

a) cos A=sin B cos a
b) cos c=cos a cos b
c) sin b=tan a cot A
d) cos A=tan b cot c
e) sin a= sin c sin A

f) cos c= cot A cot B
g) sin a= tan b cot B
h) cos B= tan a cot c
I) sin b= sin c sin B
j) cos B= sin A cos b

OBLIQUE SPHERICAL TRIANGLES. (Chapter 14, Pages 280-312)

234

By definition:

8. **Law of Sines.** "In any spherical triangle, the sines of the angles form proportions with the sines of the opposite sides;" hence:

    a) (sin a / sine A)=(sin b / sin B)
    b) (sin a / sine A)=(sin c / sin C)
    c) (sin b / sine B)=(sin c / sin C)

9. "In any spherical triangle having *sides* a, b, c and angles A, B C, the following relations exist:"

Law of Cosines for *Sides* is:

    a) cos a= cos b cos c + sin b sin c cos A
    b) cos b= cos c cos a + sin c sin a cos B
    c) cos c= cos a cos b + sin a sin b cos C

10.) "In any spherical triangle having *angles* A, B C, and sides a, b, c the following relations exist:"

Law of Cosines for *Angles* is:

    a) cos A= –cos B cos C + sin B sin C cos a
    b) cos B= –cos C cos A + sin C sin A cos b
    c) cos C= –cos A cos B + sin A sin B cos c

11.) **Table AII-1. Functions of Angles in any Quadrant in Terms of Angles in the First Quadrant.**[1]

	– α	90° ± α	180° ± α	270° ± α	360°± α
sin ...	– sin α	+ cos α	± sin α	– cos α	± sin α
cos ...	+cos α	± sin α	– cos α	± sin α	+ cos α

1. From Burington, *Handbook of Mathematical Tables and Formulas*, Handbook Publishers, Inc. Sandusky, Ohio, 1955, Pg. 17

Appendix III. Solution to the Nasca, Giza, Alaska relationship [1]

It has been our objective to present major evidences in support of an opening observation that the earth's crust moves great distances catastrophically, and that it moves with a conspicuous measure of regularity. We've brought the reader along on this adventure so that they too could discover the energetic system that we are all a part of! It is clearly not one that asserts itself slowly year by year, but it is one that acts, on occasion, rather dynamically and instantaneously. To prove this we have chosen to present circumstance upon circumstance, evidence upon evidence, to demonstrate that the principle is never compromised. That it meets with agreement from every sector that we investigated.

Part III, dealt with evidences left by the Ancients that tell us that the North Pole during ancient time was in Alaska. These evidences, also disclosed the existence of an ancient cultural relationship that is repeated with precision in the design of the Great Pyramid of Giza. The evidences tell us that the equator passed through both Nasca and Giza in ancient times and that the corner points of a triangle that delineates a path from Nasca, Peru in the West, to Giza, Egypt in the East, and to Alaska in the far North that forms a construction that I call the *Terrestrial Triangle,* and this *triangle* forms an identical Double, ie., with identical corner angles, with the Great Pyramid of Giza. A coincidence?

The calculations in Figure 1. show that the base angle of the Great Pyramid is 51°52' or 51.87°.[2] We will now look at the base angle of the Terrestrial Triangle for comparison. (See angle C & A of Figures 2 & 3). The comparison will illustrate that there is a cognitive link between the Terrestrial and Pyramidal triangles. The analysis will start with the determination of the distance between Nasca and Giza, (Arc CA) which for practical purposes is the same today as it was in ancient times.

We can calculate the current distance

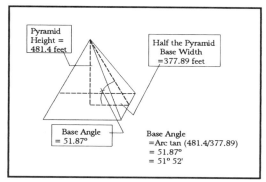

Figure 1. The Great Pyramid of Giza, illustrating the calculation of the base angle to be 51.87°, or 51° 52'. (See also foot note 2, below)

237

between Nasca, Peru and Giza, Egypt, (Arc CA) using spherical trigonometry.

SOLUTION

1. Arc BC is a meridional line from the North Pole to Nasca $(90° + 15°) = 105°$.

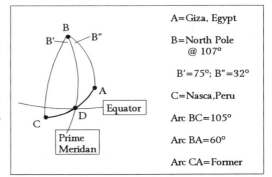

2. Arc AB is a meridional line from the North Pole to Giza this is 60° because Giza is situated at 30° North latitude.

3. Giza is located at 31° East longitude.

4. Nasca is located at 75° West longitude.

5. Angle B, therefore is $(31° + 75°) = 106°$.

6. Using equation 9b, from Appendix I,

Figure 2. The triangular relationship between Nasca, Giza, and the North Pole. It is illustrated here to assist calculation of the "great circle" distance between Nasca and Giza, (Arc CA)

A) cos b (in quadrant II) = cos 60 cos 105 + sin 60 sin 105 cos 106

Rewriting this equation to insert equivalent first quadrant functions:

B) sin α = cos 60 sin 15 + sin 60 cos 15 sin 16

C) sin α = (0.5 x 0.2588) + (0.866 x 0.9660 x 0.2756)

D) sin α = 0.35998

E) α = 21.099°

Converting this to an equivalent angle in quadrant II: (See Appendix IIb)

F) Arc CA = b = (90° + 21.099°) = 111.099°

Now we must redraw the *spherical* Terrestrial Triangle to form a *plane* triangular figure so that we can make a direct comparison with the base angle of the Great Pyramid. Once this is done we can calculate the value of the base angle of this new plane triangle.

Figures 3 and 4 above illustrate the relationships that we're trying to establish with this analysis. The triangle of Figure 3, joins Nasca, Giza, and Alaska as they are today. From this we're able to calculate the angular distance between Nasca, and Giza. The triangle of Figure 4 is the Terrestrial Triangle of the Ancients. A cultural triad as it were, and the Great Pyramid's *Double* laid out on the surface of the earth.[3]

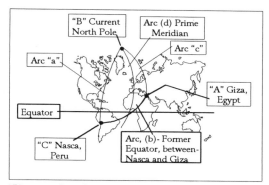

Figure 3. Current triangular relationship between Nasca, Peru; Giza, Egypt; and the North Pole.

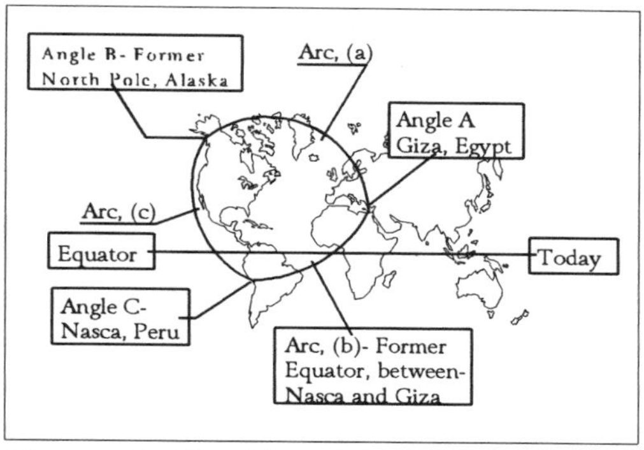

Figure 4. The *Terrestrial Triangle* of the Ancients whose base angles, "C & A", prove to be the same as the base angles of the Great Pyramid.

The calculations above, (See Figure 1) show the base angle of the Great Pyramid to be 51.87°. Figure 5 shows the *Terrestrial Triangle* converted to a plane triangle with the apexes linking Nasca, Giza, and the North Pole in Alaska. The base angle of the *plane Terrestrial Triangle* is shown to be 51.88°. A difference, relative to the Great Pyramid, of only 0.01 degrees, (51.88°– 51.87°=0.01°)

This difference, (0.01°) one-hundredth-of-one-degree, is no difference at all. They are identical. The Ancients, come from a time before history, from a time when some historians would deny them the knowledge

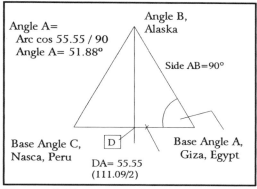

Figure 5 Plane triangle representation of the Terrestrial Triangle of the Ancients

even of the early mariners. So how did they travel? And why did they "build" this globe encircling Terrestrial Triangle? Is there a message here? What ever the answers, the Ancients have confirmed for us that the North Pole was in Alaska during that ancient time. But what does this say of the Pyramid? Does it stand as a colossal megalithic record telling us that Giza and Nasca were, at one time, on the equator? Else what would have been the purpose of the exactness of the base angles? And what of the Sphinx? Might it have been built in that more ancient time as well?

Given the truth to these interpretations, are we not witness to the most extraordinary coincidence in the history of the world! That coincidence being that the Giza complex, than as now, faced the Cardinal Points. Through two shifts of the earth's crust, Giza has maintained its orientation. The Sphinx, had it been built when Alaska was at the North Pole, and Giza was on the tropical equator, would have faced East. Than two shifts of the crust took the North Pole first from Alaska to Hudson Bay, and then moved it to its current position in the Arctic Ocean. These shifts would now account for the change in the climate of this sub-Mediterranean region, a change that would have taken it from a tropical climate to dry desert. Our way has been to present circumstance upon circumstance, evidence upon evidence, to demonstrate that the earth's crust moves great distances catastrophically, that it moves dynamically, and that it moves with a conspicuous measure of regularity. We think that this accounting is one such set of circumstance and evidence.

1. Note the interesting fact that the three localities that we're investigating end in an "a", Nasca, Giza, and Alaska, thus giving us *a sort of triad,* and "Alaska starts with an "A". Alpha, α, the first letter of the Greek alphabet, from which the English "a" is derived, means the beginning; the first principle from which all things proceed. (From An Illustrated Encyclopedia of Traditional Symbols, by J. C. Cooper, Thames and Hudson, Ltd, London, (1978) Is this mere coincidence?

2. It would also have been possible to calculated the base angle of the Great Pyramid directly from the known perimeter to height relationship of 2π. This would have yielded us the following result: Tan $\alpha = (1 / (2\pi / 8) = 1.2732$ $\alpha = 51.85°$, where α=the base angle of the Great Pyramid. (Compare with $51.87°$ above.) However, we chose use of the actual dimensions of the Pyramid for the calculations above, rather than the 2π relationship, because we felt that the dimensions would be more familiar to the casual reader.

3. Le Plongeon, as we stated earlier, makes this observation in question form of the associations between the Egyptians and the peoples dwelling in the "Lands of the West." "May we not assume that the identity of traditions indicates that at some epoch, more or less remote, intimate relations and communications (ie., cultural) must have existed between the inhabitants of the valley of the Nile and the peoples dwelling in the "Lands of the West"?

APPENDIX IV. The Thickness of the Crust has no Bearing on the Final Outcome.

The following is quoted from Chapter 8, *Thirty Degrees, No More, No Less.*

> The biggest surprise that we encountered during our investigations, as I mentioned in an earlier chapter, however, was that the thickness of the crust had no consequence to the final outcome.
>
> We were working on some of the mathematical solutions, and the last piece of data that we had to derive were the differential forces that acted upon the mass centers of the crust, when all of a sudden we discovered that wasn't necessary. We discovered that it didn't matter how thick the crust was when the ice began its movements, because the differential forces acting to restrain the crust from above and below the ecliptic, were always going to be the same anyway. The crust could be 30 miles thick, or two hundred and thirty, it didn't matter. In fact all the forces acting during a crustal displacement, those from the ice, and now the restraining forces, were going to be the same regardless.
>
> TABLE AIV-1. Differential forces, $(F_1 - F_2)$ for both Solar and Lunar influences, for various thicknesses of the crust.

Thickness of the Crust	Differential Solar Forces	Differential Lunar Forces
7 Miles	1.087E16	2.36E16
37 Miles	1.087E16	2.36E16
155 Miles	1.087E16	2.36E16

What I would like to do is to show you the origin of the data in Table 1. This will take us back to Chapter 8, *A Continent Without a Home.* Dr Yen, who was a professor in the math department at Michigan State University, had written the equations for the crustal shape and had solved the equations for the values that I've reproduced in Figure 1, below.

I had realized that the gravitational influences from the sun and the moon had a bending influence upon the crust of the earth and that they acted upon the centroids of the crustal segments above and below the ecliptic. I also realized that their magnitudes would be different, one from the other, because the centroids were at different distances from the gravitational sources. So I used this "Yen data" to calculate their magnitudes, see Appendix 1, and I looked at the difference between their respective magnitudes. I did this because they were the controlling influence on the movements of the crust.

Well much to my surprise, as I have stated earlier, there was no difference between the differential forces based on thickness. The inevitable conclusion was that the ongoing working of the crust was going to produce a weakened layer at some point within the upper mantle which would be the eventual point of failure, but it was going to be independent of thickness. That is not to say that the gravitational influences might not always work within certain limits in the first place, just as we know that mountains seem to grow 5-6 miles high, and that is all, and that oceans are no more deep than mountains are high. There seems to be a limit to height, length, and breath that we do not understand yet. So it is quite reasonable to think that gravity would seek its own limits, and that the stored angular momentum potential might also seek its own limits, just as we have seen with the distance of crustal movements seeks its own limits, ie., *Thirty Degrees, No More No Less!*

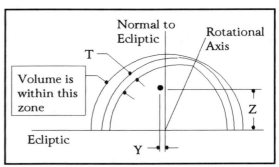

Figure 1. The Earth's crustal shell above the Ecliptic.

@T=7 miles
 Y=304.4., Z=1763.9, V=1.5E9 cu mi
@T=37 miles
 Y=106.1., Z=1894.3, V=4.5E9 cu mi
@T=87 miles
 Y= 51.4., Z=1919.9, V=9.2E9 cu mi
@T=155 miles
 Y= 30.6., Z=1917.8, V=15E9 cu mi

We have to learn to accept the fact that there is more to this earth than can be explained by the radiant heat from the sun, so until that occurs we have no hope of learning why there are limits to such things as height, length, and breath.

APPENDIX V. The 11.5° Offset of the Geo-magnetic Axis.

The analysis of the 11.5 degree offset of the axis of the geo-magnetic field, relative to the earth's rotational axis is going to be more speculation than scientific fact, but in as much as there is no other explanation, scientific or otherwise, a speculative view may be worth some consideration. There are some well established facts that we might start with...

A compass needle will be vertical to the earth's surface at the dip pole as it is called. This point is north of the Prince of Wales Island at 75° N. and 100° W. In the Southern Hemisphere the dip pole is at 67° S and 143° East.

The Northern *axis* of the geo-magnetic pole is at 78.5° N. and 69° W., and the Southern axis is at 78.5° S. and 111° East.

Records compiled for the entire earth reveal that changes in the magnetic field are regional rather than global.

As long ago as the seventeenth century it was known that the magnetic field exhibits continual change in declination, inclination and intensity. These changes are detectable through historical records only and are called *secular changes*. We can do a fair job of defining the earth's magnetic field by equating its characteristics to those of a bi-pole magnet, and from this establish the limits of its field, and than work back and define its central axis. When we do this we find the axis offset 11.5° from the earth's rotational axis.

DOES THE MAGNETIC FIELD ORIGINATE IN THE CORE?

There is a theory that suggests that electromagnetic currents are generated within the liquid portion of the core, and it is further suggested that the energy to drive this system comes from convection, ie., heat transferred within the surrounding mass. But it is known that materials loose their magnetic properties above a temperature called the Curie temperature which is unique to each material. For iron, based on

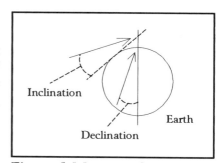

Figure 1 Magnetic Orientation

some estimates, this temperature would be reached somewhere around 16 miles below the surface of the earth. So, based on this, and what we are otherwise told about temperatures at the core of the earth, it is highly unlikely that the core has much, if anything, to do with the generation of the magnetic field.

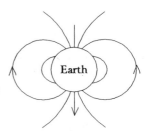

The theory that suggests that the magnetic field is generated in or near the core is highly improbable from another point of view as well. If the energy to drive this system comes from convection, as it is suggested, than wouldn't this infer the existence of a reservoir of heat to supply the system? And given the age of the earth and the length of time that this system has been in operation, wouldn't the reservoir have to be immense? And wouldn't it have to have the improbable characteristic of being able to transfer heat at a rate equal to, or greater than, the rate at which the magnetic field is consuming it? And what can we say of the probable condition of this reservoir after the heat has migrated from its boundaries, wouldn't this have cooled the boundaries down and form thereby a crust or thermal barrier? Supplying heat to an ongoing process is not an easy task for a thermal system to accomplish, particularly since rock ranks just about dead last in its ability to transfer heat in the first place.

Figure 2 Magnetic lines of force, drawn as though the earth was a bar magnetic.

We have suggested that the magnetic field originates from electrical ground currents, but it would be well to consider some published works on the conductivity of the upper mantle so that the reader does not assume that the prospect of ground currents are a matter of speculation.

A team of scientists, B. Ronald Frost, William S. Fyfe, Kazue Tazaki & Tammy Chan, in an article in the journal *Nature*, titled "Grain-boundary graphite in rocks and implications for high electrical conductivity in the lower crust," wrote...

> Here we show that a fine film of graphite is present on the grain boundaries in three rocks from the Laramie Anorthosite Complex...We maintain that in all of the rocks the grain boundary graphite precipitated from a CO_2 - rich fluid during cooling[1]

> Our observation that grain-boundary graphite may occur in many rocks in the lower crust greatly enlarges the number of rock types that can produce high-conductivity anomalies...to the petrologist it obviates the necessity, when accounting for high-conductivity anomalies, of considering interlocking surfaces

of brine in the lower crust, a situation for which evidence is largely lacking.

In a 28 January 1993 *Nature* article on the reversibility of the earth's magnetic field, "About turn for reversals," Catherine Constable, writes:

> ...the earth's magnetic field during reversals tends to sweep down a line through the Americas, or else along the antipodal line through East Asia and Australasia.

> ...if true, it suggests that the earth's magnetic field...is somehow controlled by the overlying mantle...(and)...the fact that the same paths were repeated time and again (further) suggests that some form of mantle control is exercised...

The character of the geo-magnetic field, because it has all of the characteristics of a bar magnetic, is often drawn as I have shown it in Figure 2. In Chapter 21 we suggested the existence of a mechanism for the generation of electrical currents,[2] where "...mantle control is exercised..." and that yielded a magnetic field that was not dependant upon the bar magnet scenario. It is associated with the on-going stress reversals associated with the Rotational-Bending that is forever alive in the upper mantle. Our arguments went like this...

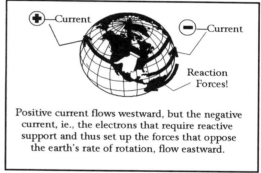

Positive current flows westward, but the negative current, ie., the electrons that require reactive support and thus set up the forces that oppose the earth's rate of rotation, flow eastward.

Figure 3 With the hand wrapped and the thumb pointing toward positive current flow, the "north pole" of the magnetic field is up, and the reaction forces go east to west!

a.   First, there are always magnetic fields associated with the flow of electricity. That is what alternators, generators, coils, transformers, and all manner of electrical and magnetic induction processes are all about.

b.   Secondly, we could look at the vertical component of the geo-magnetic field and recall that "...there is an odd requirement that whenever an electric field is put into motion, or retarded, it must not only set up a magnetic field at right angles to it but it must send out (perpendicular to both) an impalpable electromagnetic wave that travels (outward) through space...."[3] The earth's magnetic field has such a vertical component.

What we are proposing is that there are two electrical fields that run within the mantle that work at some angle and depth to one another, and that it is the difference in depth and angle that are responsible for the 11.5 degree offset of the magnetic axis relative to the earth's rotational axis. There are too many unknowns to generate any meaningful mathematical equations to prove the concept, however, it is possible to keep this scenario in mind whenever investigating magnetic anomalies to see whether the field data will support it in any demonstrable way.

Figure 4 illustrates the concept that we are proposing of two interacting electrical fields. One field is at radius R1 from the center of the earth, and the other is at radius R2. We are further proposing that fields, R1 & R2, act at some angle, one relative to the other and that it is this difference in depth and angle that are responsible for the 11.5 degree offset of the magnetic axis.

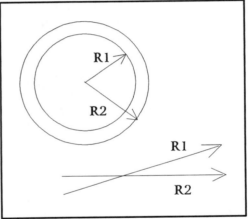

Figure 4 We are proposing two electrical fields, One at radius R1 from the center of the earth, and the other at radius R2. We are further proposing that fields, R1 & R2, act at some angle, one relative to the other.

Notes and References

Introduction to Part 1, *From Apollo to Monadnock*

1.   The term "Plastic Zone" was coined by Don L. Anderson, in "The Plastic Layer of the Earth's Mantle," *Scientific American*, July 1962, No 1, Pg. 52-9

2.   Richard W. Noone, 5/5/2000, Ice: The Ultimate Disaster, Harmony Books, New York, 1986.

Chapter 1, *Living and Non-Living Creatures*

1.   Joseph V. Kopp, Teilhard de Chardin, *A New Synthesis of Evolution*, Deus Books, Paulist Press (Paulist Fathers) Glen Rock, New Jersey, 1964. Pages 28-30. Imprimatur: Francis Cardinal Spellman, Archbishop of New York.

2.   Augustus Le Plongeon, *Queen Moo and the Egyptian Sphinx*, published in New York by Augustus Le Plongeon, 1896, Pg. 40

Chapter 2, *The Book*

1.   Ivars Peterson, American Physical Society meeting, Washington, D. C., "Lightning treatment of waste," *Science News*, Vol. 147, May 6, 1995, Pg. 282

2.   Janet Raloff, "Managing water pollutants in soil with electric currents." *Science News*, Vol. 148, September 9, 1995, Pg. 168

Chapter 3, *From Apollo to Monadnock*

1.   Michigan State was a Land Grant College and ROTC was a requirement for male freshmen. Uniforms were issued and there were classes in military drill, and weapons, etc,. There was a valuable side benefit to this training when in 1952 General Douglas MacArthur came to Lansing and the MSU-ROTC units marched in review and later stood in rank to listen to him speak from a podium on the Capitol steps. He had with him, and displayed to the surprise of everyone, the black bullet proof car that Hitler used on "State Occasions."

2.   Charles H. Hapgood, *Earth's Shifting Crust*, Pantheon Books, 1958

3.   Mount Monadnock, meaning a rocky mass that resists erosion and stands in isolated level areas, is a peak in southwestern New Hampshire.

Chapter 4, *Rivers of Molten Rock*

1. Machines of this type use guide pins to align the die halves, but the speed and size of the operation, and the severity of the shock played against it. A proportioning valve could have been used, but its characteristics weren't well suited.

2. Charles H. Hapgood, *Earth's Shifting Crust*, Pantheon Books, 1958, Pg. 314

3. L. Don Leet, Sheldon Judson, Marvin E. Kauffman, *Physical Geology*, Fifth Edition, Prentice-Hall, Inc., 1978 Chapter 7, Pg. 175-210

4. Ibid.

5. Ibid., Chapter 8, Pg. 211-39

6. Ken C. Macdonald, News and Views, "A slow but restless ridge," *Nature*, Vol. **348**, 8 Nov. 1990, Pg. 108

7. Note that the author of this passage stated that the crust was **on** the Northern California shoreline not subducted **under it** as required of plate tectonic theory.

8. Since this geologist's visit to Freeport's Grasberg Mine in Irian Jaya, rock of very ancient origin has been discovered in the Alps and in the Andes.

9. Bernard Elgey Leake, "Finding space for granite intrusions," *Nature*, Vol. **343**, *News and Views,* 1 February 1990, Pg. 413

10. Appenzeller, Tim, "In the Earth but Not of it." *Discover*, January 1997, Pg. 19

11. Raymond Jeanloz & Thorne Lay, "The Core-Mantle Boundary," *Scientific American*, May 1993, Pg. 48-55

Chapter 5, *The R. R. Moore Machine*

1. *Metals Handbook*®Desk Edition, Copyright©1985 by the American Society for Metals, Library of Congress Catalog Card Number: 84-71465.

2. L. Don Leet, Sheldon Judson, & Marvin E. Kauffman, *Physical Geology*, Fifth Edition, Prentice-Hall, Inc., Pg. 169 & 472

3. Don L. Anderson, "The Plastic Layer of the Earth's Mantle," *Scientific American*, Vol. 207 No. 1, Pg. 52-9, July 1962

Chapter 6, *A Continent Without a Home*

1. Sushel Unninayar & Kenneth H. Bergman, *Modeling the Earth System in the Mission to Planet Earth Era*, NASA July 1993, Pg. 48

2. Ibid.

3. Ibid.

4. Charles H. Hapgood, *Maps of the Ancient Sea Kings*, Chilton Book Publishers, New York, 1966

5. The Force units would be in pounds (#) when the units of G, the universal constant of gravitation, and r, the distance between the mass center of the two particles, and m, the mass are appropriately selected in the English pound, foot, second units.

6. The Principle of Isostasy refers to a system where by the elevations of the land masses are controlled by deep earth processes.

7. James Hutton, *Theory of the Earth*, Royal Society Edinburgh, 1788, (Per R. J. Chorley, A. J. Dunn, & R. P. Beckinsale, *The History of the Study of Landforms*, John Wiley & Sons Inc. 1964

Introduction to Part 2, *Evidences of Catastrophe*

1. Chorley, R. J. & Dunn, A. J., The History of the Study of Landforms, Methuen & Co. LTD. (1964), Pg. 102

2. Ibid., Pg. 112

Chapter 7, *Fire, Water, Earth and Air*

1. Lao-tze, Chinese philosopher c 604 B.C., (Yin is woman, Yang is man.)

2. Paracelsus, Greek philosopher c 500 B.C.

3. Empedocles, Greek philosopher c 490 B.C.

4. From "Drift-Wood," *Table-Talk,* by Henry Wadsworth Longfellow, (1857)

5. Plato, Greek philosopher c 427-347 B.C. *The Republic*, Book 2, Section 5

6. Richard Heinberg, *Memories and Visions of Paradise*, Quest Books, 1989, Pg. 180

7. Ibid., Pg. 102

8. (Per Richard Heinberg) Ovid, *The Metamorphoses*, Book II, trans. Horace Gregory (New York, 1960), Pg. 38

9. Hesoid (Per Richard Heinberg) *Theogony*, trans. By H. G. Evelyn-White Cambridge, Mass.: Harvard University Press, 1914, Pg. 693ff

10. Le Plongeon, Augustus, M.D., *Queen Moo and the Egyptian Sphinx*, Published by the Author, New York, (1900)

11. Ibid., Heinberg, Pg. 107

12. Graham Hancock, *Fingerprints of the Gods,* Crown Publishers, Inc. N, Y, 1995

13. Barry Fell, *America B.C.,* Pocket Books, New York, 1976, Pg. 3

14. Barry Fell, *Saga America,* Times Books, New York, 1983, Pg. 15

15. (Per Richard Heinberg) *Memories and Visions of Paradise*, Quest Books, USA, 1989, Pg. 180

16. Fluvial erosion is erosion brought on by the action of rivers and the like.

17. James Hutton, *Theory of the Earth*, Royal Society Edinburgh, 1788, (Per R. J. Chorley, A. J. Dunn, & R. P. Beckinsale, *The History of the Study of Landforms*, John Wiley & Sons Inc. 1964

18. Ibid., James Hutton, *Theory of the Earth*, Pg. 547

19. Ibid., Pg. 564

20. Ibid., Pg. 218

21. Charles C. Lyell, *Principles of Geology*, 1st Edition Vol. 3, 1833, Pg. 7

22. Ibid., Pg. 6

23. W. D. Conybeare, Letter on Mr. Lyell's *Principles of Geology* (Per R. J. Chorley, A. J. Dunn, & R. P. Beckinsale, *The History of the Study of Landforms*, John Wiley & Sons Inc. 1964, Pg. 151)

Chapter 8, *Thirty Degrees, No More-No Less*

1. Charles H. Hapgood, *Earth's Shifting Crust*, Pantheon Books, Inc. New York. 1958, Pg. 277

2. Ibid., Pg. 284

3. This general theme, and the visitation on this continent by early Europeans, is the subject of two books by Barry Fell, *Saga America*, Times Books Inc. New York 1980, and *America BC*, Pocket Books, Inc. 1976

4. Graham Hancock, *Finger Prints of the Gods*, Crown Publishers, Inc. New York. 1995, Pg. 1-32

5. Sushel Unninayar and Kenneth H. Bergman, *Modeling the Earth System in the Mission to Planet Earth Era*, Prepared for NASA, July 1993, Pg. 3

6. Ibid., Pg. 3

7. Alexandra Witze, "Some Like it Hot," *Earth*, February 1996, Pg. 18

8. Ibid.

9. Immanuel Velikovsky, *Earth in Upheaval*. Buccaneer Books, Cutchogue, New York. 1955, Pg. 88-9

10. Ibid., Pg. 67

11. This accounting was related to me by his cousin Beth Hapgood. Fred Hapgood, Charles's son, later told me that Charles eventually did get his Ph.D. But he never received the recognition he sought for his work during his lifetime.

12. Ibid., Charles H. Hapgood, Pg. 210

13. Whether the crust shifts from the Arctic, to say Alaska, and than back to the Arctic again has no impact on the ancient cultural data, as the Ancients only spoke to the final condition, and not to the processes. But I strongly believe that the "Bobbing Scenario" is probably the correct one.

14. Ibid., Charles H. Hapgood, Pg. 273

15. Ibid., Pg. 275

16. Ibid., Pg. 368

17. Ibid., Pg. 367

18. Broad, William J. "Earth's Core, a Planet Within the Planet, Is Spun by Twin Streams of Molten Iron," The New York Times, Tue, Dec. 17, 1996, Pg. C1

Introduction to Part 3, *The Pampa Jumana-Colorada*

1.   Count Goblet d'Alviella, *The Migration of Symbols*, University Books, New York, 1956, Pg. 96

2.   The Concise Columbia Encyclopedia, Columbia University Press, Electronic Edition. 1995

3.   Ibid.

4.   Grolier Electronic Publishing, Inc. 1995

5.   Alfred, Lord Tennyson recounts this tale in his poem "The Lotus-Eaters." (1832)

6.   J. C. Cooper, *An Encyclopaedia of Traditional Symbols*, Thames and Hudson, Ltd. 1978, Pg. 100-101

7.   Ibid., Pg. 178

8.   The American Heritage Dictionary®Dictionary of the English Language, Third Edition copyright © 1992 by Houghton Mifflin Company, Electronic Version.

9.   Ibid., J. C. Cooper, *An illustrated Encyclopaedia of Traditional Symbols,* Pg. 178

10.   Faulkner, R. O. *The Ancient Egyptian Pyramid Texts*, Aris & Phillips-Warminster-England, Oxford University Press, 1969, Pg. 198

Chapter 9, *The Story Begins*

1.   R. O. Faulkner, *The Ancient Egyptian Pyramid Texts*, Aris & Phillips-Warminster-England, 1969, Pg. 9

2.   The American Heritage Dictionary®Dictionary of the English Language, Third Edition copyright © 1992 by Houghton Mifflin Company.

3.   Robert Bauval and Adrian Gilbert, The Orion Mystery, Crown Paperbacks, New York, 1994, Pg.173

4.   The Concise Columbia Encyclopedia, Columbia University Press. Copyright ©1995

5.   Richard W. Noone, *5/5/2000 Ice: The Ultimate Disaster*, Harmony Books, New York 1986, Pg. 28

6. Pi, or "π" is both transcendental and "irrational." Irrational meaning that it cannot be expressed as an integer or as a ratio between two integers. Computers as late as 1995, had calculated "π" to 100,000 decimal places, according to the Columbia Encyclopedia, See ref. 5.

7. The American Heritage Dictionary®Dictionary of the English Language, Third Edition copyright © 1992 by Houghton Mifflin Company, Electronic Version.

8. Ibid.

9. The results of this research is the subject of an entire works by Robert Bauval and Adrian Gilbert, titled, *The Orion Mystery*, Crown Trade Paperbacks, New York.

10. Bauval, Robert & Gilbert, Adrian, *The Orion Mystery*, Crown Trade Paperbacks, New York, 1994.

11. Ibid., Pg. 193-94

12. Ibid., Pg. 174

13. Ibid.

14. Ibid.

15. Ibid.

16. Edward Bacon, *Archaeology, Discovery in the Sixties*, Praeger Publishers, New York, 1971, Pg. 235

Chapter 10, *A Rope of Many Hues.*

1. R. J. Campbell, *The Super-rational*, Pg. 756. G. A. Gaskell, *Dictionary of All Scriptures and Myths*, The Julian Press, Inc. New York. 1960.

2. Faulkner, R. O. *The Ancient Egyptian Pyramid Texts*, Aris & Phillips, Warminster, England, Oxford University Press, 1969

3. Robert Bauval and Adrian Gilbert, *The Orion Mystery*, Crown Trade Paperbacks, New York, 1994, Pg. 57-8

4. Ibid., Pg 62-3.

5. Ibid., Faulkner, R. O. *The Ancient Egyptian Pyramid Texts*, Pg. viii. (Introduction)

6.   Adrian G. Gilbert and Maurice M. Cotterell, *The Mayan Prophecies*, Element Books, Inc. Rockport, Maine, 1995.

7.   Ibid., Chapter 4.

8.   Translated by, Dennis Tedlock, *Popol Vuh*, Simon & Schuster, New York, 1985.

Chapter 11, *Alone on the Equator*

1.   Faulkner, R. O. *The Ancient Egyptian Pyramid Texts*, Aris & Phillips-Warminster-England, Oxford University Press, 1969. *Utter.* 535, § 1288

2.   E. A. Wallis Budge, *The Gods of the Egyptians*, Volume II, Dover Publications, Inc. New York

3.   Grolier Electronic Publishing, Inc., Copyright 1995.

4.   The Concise Columbia Encyclopedia, Columbia University Press. Copyright© 1995

5.   Ibid.

6.   Faulkner, R. O., *The Ancient Egyptian Pyramid Texts*, Aris & Phillips - Warminster - England, Oxford University Press, 1969.

7.   The passages of the Texts are organized by units called Utterances, these in turn are sub-divided into articles.

8.   Ibid. §1461, Pg. 223-25

9.   Hawkins, Gerald S., *Beyond Stonehenge*, Harper & Row, Publishers, New York, London, 1973, Pg. 102-103

10.   Ibid.

11.   Ibid.

Chapter 12. *It is No Other*

1.   Faulkner, R. O. *The Ancient Egyptian Pyramid Texts*, Aris & Phillips-Warminster-England, Oxford University Press, 1969, Pg. 198

2.   Four was a sacred number to many Ancient Civilizations. The Raven was the *creator* in the myths of Alaska, where it beat its wings four times over each creation

to give it life. To the Egyptians and the Mayans, the vault of heaven was supported by four pillars, whose care was assigned to four personages. The Chinese designated their country Sse-yo, or the land of four mountains. (Per Le Plongeon, Queen Moo and the Egyptian Sphinx.)

3. Budge, E. A. Wallis, *The Gods of the Egyptians*, Dover Publications, Inc. New York, Volume II, Pg. 88

4. Quoted from *Religion*, Pg. 422, by Budge.

5. Ibid., Budge, Pg. 88

6. Bauval, Robert & Gilbert, Adrian, The Orion Mystery, Crown Trade Paperbacks, New York, 1994, Pg. 93-4

7. The name "Nut" is a version of the name of the Egyptian God Tefnut.

8. By some accounts the body of Osiris was spread all over the world!

9. Bayley, Harold, The lost Language of Symbolism, Vol. One, Ernst Benn Limited, London, 1957, Pg. 168

10. I think that we could call these Godly powers!

11. O Osiris the King, take the water, ie., the semen which characterizes the role of union.

Chapter 13, *Thoth*

1. God responds to Moses, when asked of His name, replies, I Am That I Am. EXODUS 3:14. (See also reference 16, on page 175, in Chapter 18.)

2. Faulkner, R. O. *The Ancient Egyptian Pyramid Texts*, Aris & Phillips-Warminster-England, Oxford University Press, 1969, Pg. 198

3. This image is often identified as a spider monkey, however, as suggested by August Le Plongeon in *Queen Moo and the Egyptian Sphinx*, as well as the repeated references in the *Texts* to the "Wings of Thoth, it is more probable that Thoth is a cynocephalus monkey, a variety of flying monkey or "flying Lemur."

4. J. C. Cooper, *An Illustrated Encyclopedia of Traditional Symbols*, Thames and Hudson, Ltd, London. 1987, Pg. 96

5. Ibid.

6.   Ibid., Pg. 196

7.   Richard W. Noone, *5/5/2000 Ice: The Ultimate Disaster*, Harmony Books, New York, 1986, Pg. 92

8.   Peter Tompkins, *Secrets of the Great Pyramid*, Harper & Row, New York, 1971

9.   Ibid., J. C. Cooper, *An Illustrated Encyclopedia of Traditional Symbols*, Pg. 116

10.   Ibid., Richard W. Noone, *5/5/2000 Ice: The Ultimate Disaster*, Pg. 122

Chapter 14, *In the Land of Spreading Darkness*

1.   Another interesting characteristic is that as the circle converts to a triangle, even though the areas remain the same, the number of degrees included within the figures changes from 360 degrees in the circle to 180 degrees in the triangle. At the same time the included boundaries change from 2π for the circumference of the circle, to just over 4π for the perimeter of the triangle.

2.   Count Goblet d'Alviella, *The Migration of Symbols*, University Books, New York, 1956, Pg. 96

3.   There have been many estimates on the length of the precessional cycle since it was "first" discovered by Hipparchus in about 120 B.C. but they vary all over the map, so to speak, Graham Hancock in *Fingerprints of the Gods*, for instance, cites the official "modern" value at 25,776 years, ref. Pg. 259. We will use 25928 years as the actual figure.

4.   It is interesting that hand-held calculators gave a value for this equation of 103711.8, while computers with math co-processors yield values of 103712.2. It was not at all clear which value is correct because **all** hand held calculators that I tested agreed on the former value, while **all** computers agreed on the latter.

5.   A legend is "A story handed down by tradition from earlier times and popularly accepted as historical." A myth on the other hand is "A traditional story, usually concerning some superhuman being, and is imaginary of factitious."

6.   Ibid., Count Goblet d'Alviella, Pg. 128

7.   The Concise Columbia Encyclopedia, Electronic Version, Columbia University Press, 1995.

8.   Encyclopedic Dictionary of Physics, Edited by J. Thewlis, Pergamon Press, Oxford & London, 1962

9.   Concise Columbia Electronic Encyclopedia, Electronic Version, Columbia University Press, 1994

10.   The obliquity of the earth's axis changes somewhat over time, for instance, it has changed from 24° 08' 30" to the current value of 23° 27' over the last 6500 years according to J. Laskar, *Astronomy and Astrophysics*, Vol. 157, 1986, Pg. 68

11.   Katharine Berry Judson, *Myths and Legends of Alaska*, Tsetsaut Legends, "The Meteor," A. C. McClurg & Co., 1911, Pg. 113

12.   According to L. Don Leet, Sheldon Judson, Marvin E. Kauffman, *Physical Geology*, Fifth Edition, Prentice-Hall, Inc., 1978, Pg. 324, the hypothesis that advances this theory is called the Orbital Hypothesis, or the *Milankovitch Hypophysis* after the Yugoslavian astronomer who developed the theory.

Chapter 15, *The Whole of Manifestation*

1.   Count Goblet d'Alviella, *The Migration of Symbols*, University Books, New York, 1956, Pg. 155

2.   Ibid., Pg. 3

3.   The American Heritage®Dictionary of the English Language, Third Edition copyright© 1992 by Houghton Mifflin Company. Electronic version licensed from InfoSoft International, Inc.

4.   Ibid.

5.   The Ancients identified with the stars of the constellations of the Zodiac, but I have found no records that name them in accordance with modern terminology. I use the modern names for lack of any other definition.

6.   Tying knots in a rope and sending the rope by way of a courier to its destination was one way the Ancients would sent messages.

7.   Per Faulkner.

8.   J. Laskar & P. Robutel, "The Chaotic Obliquity of the Planets," *Nature*, Vol. **361**, 18 February 1993, Pg. 608-12

9.   We know that the obliquity of the earth's axis changes somewhat over time, for instance, it has changed from 24° 08' 30" to the current value of 23° 27' over the last 6500 years according to J. Laskar, *Astronomy and Astrophysics*, Vol. 157, (1986), Pg. 68

Chapter 17, *In Perfect Alignment*

1. My use of the term topsy turvy, may seem casual here, but it takes on purposeful significance in the next chapter.

2. United States Geological Survey, National Earthquake Information Center, "Epic Retrieval Software for the Global Hypocenter Data Base," CD-ROM. June 1992

3. J. W. Gregory, *Contributions to the Physical Geography of British East Africa, Geographical Journal*, IV (1894), Pg. 290

4. Immanuel Velikovsky, *Earth in Upheaval*. Buccaneer Books, Cutchogue, New York. 1955, Pg. 89

5. J. W. Gregory, *The Great Rift Valley*, Pg. 5, 236. (Quoted from Velikovsky, *Earth in Upheaval*, Pg. 91)

6. Graham Hancock, *Fingerprints of the Gods*, Crown Publishers, Inc. New York, Pg. 64-5

7. Ibid., Velikovsky, Pg. 81-3

8. Hapgood, Charles H, Earth's Shifting Crust, Pantheon Books, 1958, Pg. 225

9. Sir. Archibald Geikie, *Text Book of Geology*, 3rd edition. New York and London, Macmillan, 1893, Pg. 288 (From Hapgood, *Earth's Shifting Crust*, Pg. 225)

10. Ibid., Hapgood, Pg. 227

11. Frank C. Hibben, *The Lost Americans*, New York, Crowell, 1946, Pg. 168

12. Ibid., Velikovsky, Pg. 46-52

13. Ibid., Pg. 52

14. William H. Hobbs, *Earth Features and Their Meaning*, New York, Macmillan, 1935. (From Hapgood, *Earth's Shifting Crust*)

15. Ibid.

16. Irian Jaya is an Indonesia island province on the Western half of New Guinea.

17. Since this geologist's visit to Freeport's Grasberg Mine in Irian Jaya, other rock of very ancient origin have been discovered in the Alps.

18. Edward Bacon, *Archaeology, Discovery in the Sixties*, Praeger Publishers, New York, 1971, Pg. 235

Chapter 18, *The Gods, Gemini, and the Great Pyramid*

1. According to Budge, the ennead consists of five gods and four goddesses. The five male gods of the Plateau and of Egypt are... Atum, Shu, Gēb, Osiris, and Seth, and the four goddesses are, Tefēnet, Nūt, Isis, and Nephthys! (From, Budge, E. A. Wallis, *The Gods of the Egyptians*, Dover Publications, Inc. New York, Volume I, page 114.)[A]

2. Peter Tompkins, *Secrets of the Great Pyramid*. Harper & Row, New York, 1971

3. Reference Chapter 9, *The Story Begins!*

4. Le Plongeon tells us that the number ten was held "most sacred" by all civilized nations of antiquity. (Augustus Le Plongeon, M.D., *Queen Moo and the Egyptian Sphinx*, Published by the Author, New York, (1900), Introduction, Pg. *XX*)

5. J. C. Cooper, *An Illustrated Encyclopedia of Traditional Symbols*, Thames and Hudson, 1995, Pg. 118-19

6. Does his raise the question that perhaps the idiom the "correct triangle" might have been just as appropriate here? And could the term "right triangle" have been

---

[A] (Copied from Chapter 13, *Thoth*) However, there is a tenth god, both on the Plateau and in the Egyptian Text, so whether an ennead, today meaning nine, should really mean ten, is a matter that has not been addressed before. But there is a point that should be made, and that is that the Great Pyramid images ten triangular forms. Eight triangles are obvious from the Pyramids construction, because each of the four sides of the Pyramid are divided by an indentation that runs from the apex of the Pyramid to the base.[10] The ninth and the tenth triangles are only visible from above. The pyramidal shaped top of the Pyramid is not in place, and this exposes a square form that can be divided into two triangles. That this is the intent of the Ancients is clear from the following passage where Atum is named twice! (Atum is the ninth and Thoth, the embodiment of all, is the tenth.)

{§. 1655} O you Great Ennead which is on Ōn, (namely) Atum, Shu, Tefēnet, Gēb, Nūt, Osiris, Isis, Seth, and Nephthys; O you children of Atum...!

O you Great Ennead...on Ōn, (namely) **Atum**...O you children of **Atum**...! So Atum is named twice, both here and on the Great Pyramid of Giza!

a clue that was embedded in our language but has languished for centuries for lack of recognition? Before we laugh it off as preposterous, somebody aught to research the history of our having named a triangle with a 90° angle in it, a right triangle! And where did the term "right angle" come from in reference to a 90 degree angle?

7. J. C. Cooper, *An Illustrated Encyclopedia of Traditional Symbols*, Pg. 113

8. The date of the issue is 14 September 1962

9. ie., G. Patrick Flanagan

10. Every researcher of the Pyramid, and the Pyramid Texts, wants to be the person who will "come from the West" with the ultimate code, and I include myself here. I'd be fun!

11. Richard Noone, *5/5/200, Ice: the Ultimate Disaster*, Harmony Books, New York, 1968, Pg. 88

12. Ibid., Pg. 13

13. R. O. Faulkner, *The ancient Egyptian Pyramid Texts*, Oxford University Press. Aris & Phillips-Warminster-England, 1969, Pg. 191

14. Augustus Le Plongeon, M.D., *Queen Moo and the Egyptian Sphinx*, Published by the Author, New York, (1900) Pg 77-8

15. Budge, E. A. Wallis, *The Gods of the Egyptians*, Dover Publications, Inc. New York, Volume I, Pg. 17

16. Harold Bayley, *The Lost Language of Symbolism*, Vol. One, Ernst Benn Limited, London, 1957, Pg. 168

17. The American Heritage Dictionary of the English Language, Third edition, copyright 1992 by Houghton Mifflin Company. Electronic version licensed from InfoSoft International, Inc.

18. Grolier Electronic Publishing, Inc. Copyright 1995.

Chapter 19, *And The Sphinx Faced East*

1. Richard W. Noone, *5/5/200, Ice the Ultimate Disaster*, Harmony Books, New York, 1986, Pg. 225

2.	The terrestrial axis refers to the position of the crust and is not intended to imply a shift of the earth's rotational axis.

3.	Ibid., Richard W. Noone, Pg. 4

4.	See Chapter 6, *A Continent Without a Home,* in this book.

5.	Count Goblet d'Alviella, *The Migration of Symbols*, University Books, New York, 1956

6.	Ibid., Pg. xiv (Introduction)

7.	Could the "Holy Mountain" have come into significance because the Terrestrial Triangle, which took on the bearing of a mountain, linked the religious centers of the Ancient world?

8.	Ibid., Count Goblet d'Alviella xviii (Introduction)

9.	Ibid., Pg. 43

10.	Graham Hancock, *Fingerprints of the Gods*, Crown Publishers, Inc., New York, 1995, Pg. 345

11.	Ibid., Pg. 345

12.	John Michell, *The New View Over Atlantis*, Thames and Hudson, Inc. New York, 1983, Pg. 23

13.	Ibid., Pg. 23

14.	Ibid., Pg. 62

15.	Ibid., Pg. 102

16.	Gerald S. Hawkins, *Beyond Stonehenge,* Harper & Row, Publishers, Inc. New York, Pg. 93

17.	Ibid.

18.	Ibid., Pg. 103

19.	Ibid., Pg. 104

20.	Ibid., Pg. 117

21. Ibid.

22. Here the figure, which I identify as a leopard, is referred to as a dog .

23. Ibid., Gerald S. Hawkins, *Beyond Stonehenge*, Pg 147

24. Ibid., 149

Introduction to Part 4, *Earth's Hidden Unrest*

1. Taken from Chorley, R. A., Dunn, A. J. & Beckinsale, R. P. *The History of The Study of Landforms*. John Wiley & Sons, Inc., Pg. 99

2. Ibid., Pg. 99

3. Unninayar, Susel & Bergman, Kenneth H. *Modeling the Earth System in the Mission to Planet Earth Era*, NASA, July 1993, Pg. 11

4. Buckland, W. *Vindiciae Geologicae* (Oxford) 1820, Pg. 12-13. (Per R. J. Chorley, A. J. Dunn & R. P. Beckinsale, The History of The Study of Landforms, John Wiley & Sons, Inc. 1964, Pg. 109

Chapter 20, *370 Million Year Old Coral*

1. Green, Harry W. II, "Solving the Paradox of Deep Earthquakes," *Scientific American*, September 1994, Pg. 64.

2. Frohlich, Cliff, "Deep Earthquakes," *Scientific American*, January 1989, Pg. 48

3. Ibid.

4. Ibid., Green, Harry W. II, "Solving the Paradox of Deep Earthquakes," Pg. 64

5. United States Geological Survey, National Earthquake Information Center, "Epic Retrieval Software for the Global Hypocenter Data Base," CD-ROM. June 1992

6. Ibid., Frohlich, Cliff, "Deep Earthquakes," Pg. 54

7. Kwon, Myeung Hoi, & Peters, Randal D., "The study of Eigenmode Types and Source Non-linearity in the Free Earth Oscillations," *Journal of Korea Physics Society*, 1995

8. S. K. Runcorn, "Corals as Paleontological Clocks", *Scientific American*, Vol. 215, No. 4, Pg. 26-33. October 1966. (offprint 871), Pg. 583

9. Ibid.

10. Ibid.

11. Derek Howse, *Greenwich Time and the Discovery of the Longitude* Oxford University Press, New York, 1980

12. John Wahr, "Getting to the core," *Nature* Vol. **345**, News and Views, 7 June 1990, Pg. 476

13. An interesting article on the accurate measurement of time can be found in the July 1993 issue of *Scientific American*, entitled, "Accurate Measurement of Time," by Wayne M. Itano and Norman F. Ramsey.

14. The primary "length-of-day" data is from R. S. Gross, *A Combination of Earth Orientation Measurements*: SPACE94, COMB94, and POLE94, Jet Propulsion Laboratory, California Institute of Technology, Pasadena, California. Data is on 3.5 inch floppy disk. Similar data is discussed and reproduced in Sushel Unninayar & Kenneth H. Bergman's, *Modeling the Earth System in the Mission to Planet Earth Era*, NASA, July 1993, Pg. 60

15. Frank D. Stacy, *Physics of the Earth*, John Wiley & Sons, 1969, Pg. 34-6

16. S. K. Runcorn letter to the author dated February 3, 1994.

17. In a 7 June 1990 *Nature* "News and Views" article (Vol. **345**. Pg. 476) John Wahr put the change in the length of day at 4-5 milliseconds over a period of a few decades.

18. Ibid., S. K. Runcorn, "Corals as Paleontological Clocks, Pg. 586

19. Ibid., John Wahr, "Getting to the Core."

20. Tippens, Paul E., *Physics*, Forth Edition, Macmillan/McGraw-Hill, New York 1991, Pg. 41

21. The earth's inner core is known to rotate faster than the crust.

22. "Earth's Core, a Planet Within the Planet, Is Spun by Twin Streams of Molten Iron," *The New York Times*, William J. Broad, Tuesday, Dec. 17, 1996, Pg. C1

23. Tim Appenzeller, "In the Earth but Not of it." *Discover*, Jan. 1997, Pg. 19

Chapter 21, *Earth's Hidden Unrest*

1. S. K. Runcorn, "Corals as Paleontological Clocks," *Scientific American*, Vol. 215, No. 4, Pg. 26-33, October 1966. (offprint 871), Pg. 587

2. There are many articles on the general subject of electrical currents within the earth's mantle, some of these are: From the journal *Nature*, S. Karato, "The Role of Hydrogen in the Electrical Conductivity of the Upper Mantle;" B. J. Wood & J. Nell, "High-Temperature Electrical Conductivity of the Lower-Mantle Phase (Mg, Fe)0."

3. *Anti-Gravity & the United Field*. Adventures Unlimited Press. Stelle, Illinois. Edited by David Hatcher Childress, 1992, Pg. 23

4. Kwon, Myeung Hoi, & Peters, Randal D., The study of Eigenmode Types and Source Non-linearity in the Free Earth Oscillations, Journal of Korea Physics Society, 1995

5. Paul E. Tippens, *Physics*, Forth Edition, Macmillan/McGraw-Hill, New York 1991, Pg. 41

6. "Tiltmeters and Angle Measuring Equipment," *Encyclopedia of Scientific Instrumentation*, Dr. Randall D. Peters

7. The lunar synodic period is the period of time that it takes the moon to orbit the earth and return to a point of conjunction with its starting reference.

8. D. R. Lammlein, G. V. Latham, J. Dorman, Y. Nakamura, and M. Ewing, Reviews of Geophysics and Space Physics 12, 1 (1974)

9. Sir Harold Jeffreys, astronomer, geophysicist, author; *The Earth: Its Origin, History, and Physical Constitution* (1924), *Scientific Inference* (1957), and *Methods of Mathematical Physics* (1946).

10. Frank D. Stacy, *Physics of the Earth*, John Wiley & Sons, 1969, Pg. 26-7

Chapter 22, Means to Ends

1. Runcorn, S. K. "Corals as Paleontological Clocks." *Scientific American*, Vol 215, No. 4, Pg. 26-33. October 1966. (offprint 871), Pg. 587, 589

2. Shen-su Sun, "Growth of lithospheric mantle," *Nature* Vol. **340**, 17 August 1989, Pg. 509

3. Douglas W. Burbank, "Causes of recent Himalayan uplift deduced from deposited patterns in the Ganges basin," *Nature*, Vol. **357**, 25 June 1992, Pg. 680-82

264

4.   Hoffman, Paul F. "Old and young mantle roots," *Nature* Vol. **347**, 6 September 1990, Pg. 19-20

5.   Enrico Bonatti, "The Earth's Mantle below the Oceans," *Scientific American*, March 1994, Pg. 44-51

6.   *Metals Handbook®Desk* Edition, Copyright © 1985 by the American Society for Metals, Library of Congress catalog card number: 84-71465

7.   As reported in the *New York Times*, 24 Feb. 1953

8.   Jochum, K. P., McDonough, W. F., Palme, H. & Spettel, B. "Compositional constraints on the continental lithospheric mantle from trace elements in spinel peridotite xenoliths," *Nature* Vol. **340**, Pg. 548-550 (1989)

9.   L. Don Leet, Sheldon Judson, & Marvin E. Kuffman, *Physical Geology*, fifth Edition. Prentice-Hall. 1978, Pg. 8

10.   Zhou, Q -Y. Et al. *Nature,* Vol. **347**, Pg. 76-80 (1990)

11.   Grotzinger, J. & Royden, L. "Elastic strength of the Slave craton at 1.9 Gyr and implications for the thermal evolution of the continents," *Nature* Vol. **347**, Pg. 64-66 (1990)

12.   A strip-chart recorder is an instrument with continuously running paper and an inked stylus that renders the input data. They are similar to the apparatus used to record earthquake waves and cardio-vascular responses, etc.

13.   Buckland, W. *Vindiciae Geologicae* (Oxford) 1820, Pg. 12-1

Appendix I

1.   Newton's Principles of the Law of Gravitation are based on experimental evidence and cannot be derived mathematically. Their *universality* has been challenged by Einstein's theory of relativity, but in applications where system velocities are small compared to the speed of light, they have yet to be disproved.

2.   There has been some debate over whether the gravitational constant is actually "constant". It has been argued that it has varied with time in this solar system, and may vary from point to point throughout space.

Appendix V

1.   B. Ronald Frost, William S. Fyfe, Kazue Tazaki & Tammy Chan, "Grain-

boundary graphite in rocks and implications for high electrical conductivity in the lower crust," *Nature*, Vol 340, July 13, 1989, Pg. 134

2.   Catherine Constable, "About turn for reversals," *Nature*, Vol 361, 28 January 1993, Pg. 305-306

3.   (Edited by David Hatcher Childress), *Anti-Gravity & the United Field*. Adventures Unlimited Press. Stelle, Illinois. 1992, Pg. 23

NOTES

Index

[A] The Tree of Knowledge, The Tree of Life, The Cosmic Tree, The Whole of Manifestation, by what ever name...a tree!

MY RESEARCH PROJECTS OF INTEREST

- Associating after shocks to crack potential. Reference page 205.
- Debris Controlled Hydrostatics, Reference pages 217-18.
- Investigating Ōn and The Zodiac
- Measuring latent momentum strain, or momentum *potential*. Reference page 211.
- Rotational-Bending, (the RB-Effect), Reference pages 30, 36-9, 41, 67-8, 144, 148, 151, 215-16
- The angle and differential rotational speed of the earth's core and the exchange of angular momentum with the moon. Reference page 71, 209-11
- The ring of fire surrounding the Himalayas. Reference page 217
- Tree rings and gravel roads. Reference pages 204-219

NOTES